Sleep, Dreams, and Arousal

THE CENTURY PSYCHOLOGY SERIES

Richard M. Elliot, Gardner Lindzey
& Kenneth MacCorquodale
Editors—

Sleep, Dreams, and Arousal

Edward J. Murray

SYRACUSE UNIVERSITY

New York

APPLETON-CENTURY-CROFTS

Division of Meredith Publishing Company

ACKNOWLEDGMENTS

Acknowledgment is gratefully made to the following publishers and authors who have granted permission to use tables and figures from copyrighted publications.

p. 35   *Figure 1*. American Psychological Association, Washington, D.C. Murray, E. J., Williams, H. L. & Lubin, A. *J. exp. Psychol.*, **56**, 272.

p. 47   *Figure 2*. The University of Texas. Emmons, W. H. & Simon, C. W. The non-recall of material presented during sleep. *Amer. J. Psychol.*, 1956, **69**, 76-81.

p. 48   *Table 1*. Lindsley, D. B. Psychological phenomena and the electroencephalogram. *Electro. clin. Neurophysiol.*, 1952, **4**, 443-456.

p. 50   *Figure 3*. American Association for the Advancement of Science, Washington, D.C. Lester, D. Continuous measurement of the depth of sleep. *Science*, 1958, **127**, 1340-1341.

p. 73   *Figure 4*. Elsevier Publishing Company, Amsterdam. Dement, W. & Kleitman, N. Cyclic variations in EEG during sleep and the relation to eye movements, body motility, and dreaming. *Electro. clin. Neurophysiol.*, 1957, **9**, 673-690.

p. 125   *Figure 6*. The Williams & Wilkins Company, Baltimore, Md. von Economo, C. Sleep as a problem of localization. *J. nerv. ment. Dis.*, 1930, **71**, 249-259.

p. 127   *Figure 7*. McGraw-Hill, New York. Morgan, C. T. & Stellar, E. *Physiological psychology*, 364, 1950.

p. 143   *Figure 9*. The Ronald Press Company, New York. Miller, N. E. Experimental studies in conflict. From J. McV. Hunt, ed., *Personality and the behavior disorders*, 434, 1944.

p. 153   *Figure 10.* American Psychological Association, Washington, D.C. Simon, C. W. & Emmons, W. H. Responses to material presented during various levels of sleep. *J. exp. Psychol.*, 1956, **51**, 89-97.

p. 162   *Figure 11.* American Psychological Association, Washington, D.C. Webb, W. B. Antecedents of sleep, *J. exp. Psychol.*, 1957, **53**, 162-166.

p. 172   *Figure 12.* American Psychological Association, Washington, D.C. Williams, H. L., Lubin, A. & Goodnow, J. Impaired performance with acute sleep loss. *Psychol. Monogr.*, 1959, **73**, 16, No. 14 (Whole No. 484).

p. 177   *Figure 13.* American Association for the Advancement of Science, Washington, D.C. Lindsley, O. R. Operant behavior during sleep: a measure of depth of sleep. *Science*, 1957, **126**, 1290-1291.

p. 182   *Table III.* American Psychological Association, Inc., Lancaster, Penna. Wilkinson, R. T. Interaction of lack of sleep with knowledge of results, repeated testing, and individual differences. *J. exp. Psychol.*, 1961, **62**, 263-271.

p. 190   *Figure 14.* The Journal Press, Provincetown, Mass. Murray, Schein, Erikson, Hill & Cohen. The effects of sleep deprivation on social behavior. *J. soc. Psychol.*, 1959, **49**, 229-236.

p. 191   *Figure 15.* The Journal Press, Provincetown, Mass. Murray, Schein, Erikson, Hill & Cohen. The effects of sleep deprivation on social behavior. *J. soc. Psychol.*, 1959, **49**, 229-236.

p. 228   *Table V.* American Medical Association, Chicago, Illinois. Morris, G. O., Williams, H. L. & Lubin, A. Misperception and disorientation during sleep deprivation. *Arch. gen. Psychiat.*, 1960, **2**, 247-254.

p. 229   *Figure 16.* American Medical Association, Chicago, Illinois. Morris, G. O., Williams, H. L. & Lubin, A. Misperception and disorientation during sleep deprivation. *Arch. gen. Psychiat.* 1960, **2**, 247-254.

p. 236   *Figure 17.* American Psychological Association, Washington, D.C. Murray, E. J., Williams, H. L. & Lubin, A. *J. exp. Psychol.*, **56**, 272.

p. 238   *Figure 18.* American Psychological Association, Washington, D.C. Murray, E. J. *J. abnorm. soc. Psychol.*, **59**, 97.

p. 272   *Table VI.* The British Psychological Society, London. Anthony, J. An experimental approach to the psychopathology of childhood: sleep disturbances. *Brit. J. med. Psychol.*, 1959, **32**, 19-37.

p. 293   *Table VII.* Harper & Row, New York. Louttit, C. M. *Clinical psychology of exceptional children*, 21. Copyright © 1936, 1947, 1957, Harper & Brothers. Reprinted with the permission of Harper & Row, Publishers.

p. 295   *Figure 20.* Harper & Row, New York. Gesell, A., M.D. *The embryology of behavior*, 155. Copyright 1945 by Arnold Gesell. Reprinted with the permission of Harper & Row, Publishers.

p. 297   *Figure 21.* The University of Chicago Press, Chicago, Illinois. Kleitman, N. *Sleep and wakefulness*, 367, 1959.

p. 317   *Figure XV.* Harper & Row, New York. Sears, R. L., Maccoby, Eleanor E. & Levin, H. Patterns of Child Rearing, 295. Copyright 1957 by Row, Peterson & Company. Reprinted with the permission of Harper & Row, Publishers.

p. 322   *Figure 22.* The American Psychological Association, Inc., Lancaster, Penna. Williams, C. D. The elimination of tantrum behavior by extinction procedures. *J. abnorm. soc. psychol.*, 1959, **59**, 269.

To my Father, Mother, and Brother

Preface

A book on as esoteric a group of topics as sleep, dreams, and arousal requires some explanation. To begin with, this work reflects a long-standing interest on my part in the problems of motivation—an interest kindled by three very fine teachers, William N. Schoenfeld at Columbia, Sigmund Koch at Duke, and Neal E. Miller at Yale. The question of motivation is, after all, at the center of the inquiry into human nature. In whatever area of empirical research I have been engaged—animal behavior, psychotherapy, or family dynamics—I have found myself drawn towards the motivational problems.

In the years from 1956 to 1958, I had the good fortune to be assigned as a psychology officer to the Division of Neuropsychiatry at the Walter Reed Army Institute of Research in Washington, D. C. There I was able to participate in an ongoing, interdisciplinary research project on the physiological, psychological, and social effects of prolonged sleep deprivation. I would like to express my appreciation for the intellectual stimulation provided by this fine group of scientists, especially to Harold L. Williams, Ardie Lubin, Jacqueline Goodnow, Margaret Thaler Singer, Gary Morris, Seymour Fisher, John Armington, George Crampton, William Biersdorf, Melvin Cohen, and Stanley Pliscoff, with whom I worked most closely on sleep deprivation, and also to David McK. Rioch, Walle Nauta, Joseph Brady, Robert Galambos, and Murray Sidman, from whom I learned a great deal. The excitement about relating the reticular activating and limbic-midbrain systems to behavior, the interdisciplinary effort to obtain complementary data, and the long nights staying awake to observe the subjects made a lasting impression on me. Whatever small value my theoretical ruminations have depends entirely on the hard empirical facts won by these people and others like them around the world.

From the outset, I viewed the phenomena of sleep deprivation as relevant to the problem of motivation—to the consternation of my colleagues at Walter Reed who had little use for the concept of motivation. Later, when I arrived at Syracuse University, I began a systematic analysis of the sleep motive. The problem became more complex as I wrestled with the relationship between sleep deprivation and arousal. About this time, the breakthrough on dream research was producing exciting results and my interest in dreams was further increased by my association with Calvin Hall at Syracuse. I came to the conclusion that the interrelationships of the phenomena of sleep, dreams, and arousal were of considerable theoretical significance. Furthermore, I felt that the complexities involved required a book-length motivational analysis.

The work on the book was greatly aided by a research leave granted by Syracuse University for the spring semester in 1961. I would like to thank the faculty research committee, the Board of Trustees, and Vice-President Frank Piskor for making this time available for reading and writing. I am particularly appreciative of the trust placed in me, since it was unusual to grant a research leave to such a junior faculty member.

In the spring of 1962, I offered an advanced graduate seminar on the Psychopathology of Sleep. I profited greatly by the literature surveys and reports made by the members of the seminar. I would like to acknowledge the contributions of Betty Lou Arfmann, Joyce Bedrava Ebmeyer, David Geisinger, Michael Grund, Peter Haimes, Estelle Kushner, Lawrence Perlmutter, Judith Monblatt Ross, and Sharon Workman. I would like especially to thank Carol Lucas, whose fine report on excessive sleeping is directly cited in the chapter on the pathology of sleep, and Raleigh Huizinga, whose search of the Cross-Cultural Area Files at the University of Michigan is drawn upon extensively in the chapter on the socialization of sleep.

The survey data presented in Chapter Nine were obtained

from undergraduate classes at Syracuse University. I appreciate the cooperation of these students. The statistical calculations were made by James Donohue, Arthur Seagull, and John Shafer.

Some of the ideas in this book have been presented earlier. I want to thank Donald Lindsley and Elliot Rodnick for inviting me to present a public lecture at the University of California at Los Angeles on "Sleep and Motivation" in the summer of 1962 and to the psychology graduate students there for their lively, critical comments. Donald Lindsley also invited me to present a similar paper at the VIIth International Congress of Psychology in 1963 at Washington, D. C. (see Murray, 1964 c). Due to my illness at the time, the paper was read by Ardie Lubin, to whom I am grateful. I wish to express my appreciation to Arthur Shapiro and Allan Rechtschaffen for making it possible for me to participate in the conference of the Association for the Psychophysiological Study of Sleep in the spring of 1963 at the Downstate Medical Center, Brooklyn, New York.

I would like to thank a number of people who read parts of the manuscript and made useful suggestions. These include Daniel Berlyne, William Dement, Hiram Evans, Edward Evarts, Dean Foster, Calvin Hall, Rául Hernández-Peón, Jerome Kagan, Martin Kohn, Irwin Kremen, Richard Lazarus, Donald Lindsley, Elliot Luby, Robert Malmo, George Mandler, Wallace McAllister, Robert Nichols, Frederick Sherman, Walter Surwillo, Herman Weiss, and Harold Williams. I am particularly grateful to Walle Nauta and Warren Roberts for help with the physiological material. I want to pay special tribute to Allan Rechtschaffen for a detailed critique of the chapter on dreams and to Victor Laties for a similar analysis of the chapters on personality and psychopathology. Robert Wilkinson was particularly helpful on the learning chapter and David Bélanger on the chapter on arousal. David Bélanger also had several students test and confirm some of the implications of this theoretical analysis in the area of heat and cold. I was pleased that Donald Hebb, David McClelland, William Estes, and Judson Brown gave me the benefit of their evaluations and criticisms of the implications I drew for their theoretical positions. The editors of the Century Psychology Series—Gardner Lindzey and

Kenneth MacCorquodale—read the entire book and made many valuable suggestions. Finally, I want to thank William Claiborn, Robert Deysach, Peter Hemingway, David Streiner, and John Shafer for proofreading the manuscript.

Anyone writing in the area of sleep owes a special debt to Nathaniel Kleitman (see Murray, 1964 d). His books became my constant companions. This work would not have been possible without Nathaniel Kleitman's lifelong devotion to the area of sleep and wakefulness.

E.J.M.

Contents

3

4

5

6

7

8

9

List of Tables

8

9

List of Figures

2

3

4

5

6

7

9

CHAPTER 1

The Motivational Context

In recent years there has been a good deal of empirical research on the topic of sleep and the related phenomena of dreams and arousal. Neurophysiologists, biochemists, psychiatrists, and social scientists, as well as psychologists, have made fascinating discoveries about the state of sleep, the occurrence of dreams, the effects of sleep deprivation, the relation of arousal to performance, and the socialization of sleep behavior. Nevertheless, the area has remained a disorganized collection of isolated facts with little impact on the main body of psychological thought. Sleep and related phenomena have little theoretical status in general conceptions of behavior. This is due, in part, to the fact that sleep phenomena have not been conceptualized in any systematic fashion. The purpose of this book is to make a motivational analysis of sleep and related processes.

More specifically, the major thesis of this presentation is that a motive to sleep may be assumed. The advantage of this hypothesis is that the findings in the area can be integrated into the conceptual networks provided by a number of general theories of behavior. A motivational variable is assumed by theorists to have certain relationships with goal-seeking behavior, deprivation, learning, cognitive processes, task performance, socialization procedures, and so on. Certain relationships with biological functioning and neural mechanisms can also be anticipated.

Thus, the wide array of discrete empirical findings about the disposition to sleep can be organized into a meaningful pattern.

THE CONCEPT OF MOTIVATION

Just what is a motive? There is no shortage of definitions—motivation has been described by various theorists as a driving force, a goad to action, a goal-directed disposition, a conscious urge, and a source of energy. We will define motivation as an *intervening variable* with certain properties (Koch, 1941). An intervening variable is often introduced in scientific work to account for certain kinds of observations. For example, in physics the intervening variable of *resistance* was introduced by Ohm to account for the flow of electric current through a wire. If a battery of a given voltage is hooked up to a circuit, a certain amount of current flows through the wire. However, if a different kind of wire is used the current may be increased or decreased. Another factor is involved which Ohm called *resistance*. Ohm's Law states that the amount of current in a circuit equals the voltage divided by the resistance. Both voltage and current may be measured directly, but resistance is inferred. Resistance is an intervening variable.

The intervening variable of motivation is introduced in psychology to account for the variability of behavior with respect to a goal. For example, at one time a person will eat food but at another time he will not. Food can be used as a reward for learning a response at one time but not another. In another situation a person, given a choice between food and water, will sometimes select one and sometimes the other. This variability persists even where the attractiveness, or incentive value, of a goal is held constant. Furthermore, there is also variability between individuals and between species in the attractiveness of a given goal. The degree of familiarity with a goal and the learning of responses to get to a goal are important factors in behavior, but even they do not account for all the variability. Clearly, some additional factor is involved and this has been called the intervening variable of motivation.

In the examples given above the strength of the hunger motive accounts for the variability in behavior. Several properties may be ascribed to the hunger motive in relation to behavior. Given a hunger motive, food will be eaten, a response will be learned if food is given as a reward, the probability of the occurrence of a previously learned response will increase, verbal reports of a hunger experience may be given, and so on. On the other hand, providing enough food to produce satiation will eliminate the hunger motive and the behavioral effects just mentioned.

There is some reason to believe that the intervening variable of motivation may be found to be the same as the operation of a neural mechanism. For example, an area at the base of the brain—the hypothalamus—contains two mechanisms relevant to hunger. One tiny area, when stimulated electrically, produces an increase in the kinds of behavior associated with a hunger motive. Another area produces satiation. In order to identify a neural mechanism with an intervening variable, the two must be shown to have the same functional properties. This seems to be the case in hunger and it may be true for other motives as well.

While the intervening variable of motivation is not directly observable, it may be tied to certain measurable antecedent conditions. These may be of an organismic nature such as blood sugar level, hormone production, or age. Antecedents may also be environmental conditions such as availability of food, ambient temperature, or monotony of stimulation. A number of psychologists have asked why it is not possible simply to relate the individual antecedent conditions to various behavioral outcomes and thus dispense with the intervening variable of motivation. There are several good reasons, however, for retaining the concept of motivation.

To begin with, the complexity of all the possible relationships between antecedent conditions and behavioral consequences would require an incredibly voluminous and detailed handbook for their tabulation alone. Hunger, for instance, can be increased by total or partial food deprivation, by a very cold environment, by injections of insulin, by increasing anxiety, by providing an incentive, and so on. On the other hand, behavioral consequences may include general activity, learning, performance, heart rate, verbal report, etc. Miller (1959) has shown how introducing a limited number of intervening variables may simplify and organize this vast array of possible relationships.

The second reason for retaining the concept of motivation is that central, integrating neural mechanisms have been discovered for several motives. For example, sexual behavior is dependent not only on an intact motor response system but also on a triggering or motivating mechanism in the hypothalamus. This central mechanism is necessary for mammalian sexual behavior while the traditional antecedent condition of sexual hormone level is not. The hypothalamic mechanism is sensitive to a whole host of antecedent conditions—recovery from sexual fatigue, memories mediated by the cortex, and stimuli from the sex object, as well as hormone level. No single antecedent condition is absolutely essential but the central integrating mechanism is necessary for normal sexual behavior.

Finally, the concept of an intervening motivational variable is particularly useful in accounting for the variability of adult human behavior where the antecedent conditions date back to early childhood and cannot be measured. A motive can be inferred from one set of behavioral measures and used to predict behavior in a wide variety of other situations. For example, an achievement motive may be inferred on the basis of verbal responses in a fantasy test and predictions made about performance in various tasks, choices between social goals, and the effectiveness of different rewards.

THEORIES OF MOTIVATION

While a great many psychologists agree on the need for a concept of motivation, there is considerable disagreement on the precise properties to be attributed to this intervening variable. Madsen (1961) found a score of important theories of motivation in his review of this area, even though he excluded the psychoanalytic theories. We will make no attempt to present the many systems here but rather we will discuss some of the major concepts and issues.

One of the prevailing ideas in the field of motivation is that motives arise from specific tissue needs. This model seems adequate in explaining something as simple as the eating of hydra by the tiny microstoma (Lashley, 1938). The microstoma acquires its weapons—small, poisonous stinging cells arranged around the surface of its body—from the hydra. The consumption of hydra is inversely proportional to the concentration of the stinging cells on the body surface of the microstoma. This model has been extended to include mammalian hunger and thirst as well as sex, pain, and other motives. According to this view a motive is a simple, reflexive reaction to an internal state of homeostatic imbalance. Thus a motive is a somewhat more elaborate version of homeostatic mechanisms like the shivering reflex or the carotid sinus reflex.

This view has been challenged on a number of grounds. For example, Miller and Dollard (1941), McClelland et al. (1953), Wenger et al. (1956), Morgan (1957), and others have pointed out that tissue needs and psychological motives are not perfectly correlated. Homeostatic imbalance does not always give rise to a motive and a motive may lead to a nonhomeostatic condition. Reward does not seem to be dependent on the reduction of tissue needs. Then, too, a whole new class of nonhomeostatic motives has been discovered—or rediscovered—in the last decade. There are motives for intrinsically rewarding activity, manipulation, and curiosity. White (1959) has summarized this evidence and suggested a general motive for effectance that has a good deal of survival value but is not dependent on homeostatic imbalance. Beach (1956) has also pointed out that sexual motivation serves no physiological need for the individual, although it serves species survival.

The entire question of the relation between motives and homeostasis has been opened for discussion in recent years (Murray, 1964 b). Several theorists (Murray, 1938; Miller, 1959) have suggested that motives consist of evolved neural mechanisms with certain behavioral effects. The behaviors mediated by these neural motivational mechanisms typically have homeostatic consequences but are not simple homeostatic reflexes. The neural mechanisms may be sensitive to homeostatic imbalance but they are also controlled by environmental stimuli, learning, and endogenous rhythms.

The intervening variable of motivation is viewed by most psychologists today as an energizing process (Madsen, 1961). The very term "motive" came from the Latin *movere*, meaning "to move" (Brownlow et al., 1941). Environmental stimuli set the stage for behavior but an internal source of energy is also required. Motives provide that energy—literally providing power for muscular movement or lowering stimulus thresholds or providing a noxious state of tension. The motivated organism is, therefore, active, alert, and tense.

The energizing concept appears in various theories as *libido* (Freud, 1949), *tension* (Lewin, 1938), *energy* (Freeman, 1948), *activation* (Duffy, 1951, 1957), *arousal* (Malmo, 1959), and so on. The most influential term has been *drive*. Woodworth introduced the term *drive* to psychology in 1918, to refer to the energizing factor as opposed to the directional factor in behavior. He said drive was like the physical energy required to make a train move, while habit was like the tracks that steer the train. While later writers referred to a number of different "drives," Woodworth used the singular "drive" as a nonspecific energy source that is present in all behavior.

The concept of general drive has been elaborated most creatively by Clark L. Hull (1943) and his followers (Spence, 1956; Brown, 1961). Hull thought of drive as the energy derived from various motivating conditions but his most important contribution was to define its mathematical relationship with behavior. Hull assumed that drive multiplies habit to produce overt behavior. Furthermore, drive energy from any source contributes to a common pool that multiplies all habits indiscriminately. The actual emergence of particular responses depends on the strength of various habits, the environmental stimuli present, the compatibility of various responses, inhibitory factors, and so on. While variables such as drive stimulus and incentive were added as ancillary concepts, Hull's chief motivational concept was the general energizer, drive.

A more recent development of the energizing concept is the introduction of the idea of internal arousal. Malmo (1959) sees this concept as integrating the Hullian general drive, Duffy's idea of behavioral activation, and the important physiological discoveries concerning the reticular activating system. Malmo does not assume that motives necessarily lead to an increase in overt activity or performance. Instead, a motive involves an internal arousal affecting muscular tension, autonomic functioning, and brain potentials, all under the control of the reticular activating system. At moderate levels internal arousal may facilitate overt behavior but at extreme levels it may be inhibitory.

The energizing concept of motivation has not been without its critics, and alternative views have been presented. The main alternative is that motivation is an intervening variable that directs behavior toward certain goals. Energy might be involved but it is a delimited expenditure of energy determined by the requirements of attaining the goal. The concept of goal-direction can be seen clearly in the classical instinct theories of William James and William McDougall as well as the modern ethologists and comparative psychologists like Tinbergen (1951) and Beach (1956). Actually, nearly all motivational theorists, including Freud and Hull, have some sort of goal-directing factor in their motivation theories as a secondary concept (Madsen, 1961).

In McDougall's (1960) classical theory, for example, an instinct was defined as a propensity which, in the presence of an appropriate stimulus, results in goal-directed striving. An interesting feature of McDougall's theory is that there is a characteristic emotion associated with each instinct. There are many difficulties with the instinct theory (Murray, 1964 b), but an important heritage is the idea that a motive involves goal-directed striving.

Today, one form which the directional theory of motivation takes is in definitions of motives as internal stimuli (Miller and Dollard, 1941; Guthrie, 1952; Wenger et al., 1956; and Estes, 1958). In some of these theories, motives are simply assumed to have the functional properties of stimuli and various behavioral consequences are deduced. In other versions, the stimuli are identified as visceral or neural. Evidence for the stimulus point of view includes the fact that a motive can serve as a cue for behavior (Hull, 1933; Leeper, 1935; Amsel, 1949; Levine, 1953). The stimulus theorists explain the elicitation of behavior, general activity, and internal arousal on the basis of learned and unlearned connections between internal motivational stimuli and responses rather than on the basis of general energization.

The nature of reward and satiation constitutes still another modern controversy. General drive theorists, and some of the drive stimulus theorists, assume that reward and satiation consist of eliminating the noxious drive state or drive stimulus. Reward involves partial drive reduction and satiation involves a drastic drive reduction. In this view, all motivation is aversive; there is no positive goal-seeking except as a means to eliminate the noxious goad. There are many difficulties with this theory and alternative proposals have been suggested (Miller, 1963).

Among others, Hebb (1958) proposed that an organism seeks an optimal level of stimulation and arousal. When stimulation is too great, a stimulus reduction is sought. When stimulation is too low, a stimulus increase is sought.

On a simple descriptive level intrinsically rewarding activities, sexual behavior, and the ingestion of certain substances such as saccharine, appear to involve the subjective experience of pleasure. Recent discoveries of rewarding and punishing areas in the brain (Olds and Milner, 1954; Delgado, Roberts, and Miller, 1954) also suggest the operation of pleasure and pain. Several theorists (McClelland et al., 1953; Young, 1961) have revived hedonistic theory as an important explanatory system. In the formulation by McClelland and his associates certain stimuli innately evoke an affective arousal reaction of a pleasurable or painful nature. Motivation consists of the learned expectations of a goal to arouse positive or negative emotions.

Social motivation has always been a difficult problem for psychology. Traditionally, social motives have been thought to be based on biological motives and derived from them by one mechanism or another. However, the studies on the "contact comfort" of a maternal object (Harlow, 1958, 1962) and the effects of maternal deprivation (Yarrow, 1961) suggest an independent affectional need. This author has suggested (Murray,

1964 a) that this motive is basic to personality development and change. This author has also reviewed (1964 b) alternatives to the derived motive theories. Biological motives of several types may be channelized in certain ways toward certain goals. The relationship between biological motives, social motives, and social channelizing remains a major problem for motivation theory.

At the present time, the field of motivation is in a period of creative flux. Old theories are being challenged and new concepts proposed. Part of the reason for this period of change and growth is the examination of motives other than the traditional trio of hunger, thirst, and pain. Murray (1938), Miller (1959), and Allport (1961) have stressed the importance of studying a wide variety of motives. The research on motives, such as sex, affection, and effectance has broadened our perspective enormously. A close examination of still other types of motivation, such as the motive to sleep, should have implications for motivational theory.

As we examine the motive to sleep, we will keep in mind some of the basic issues in the field of motivation. What is the relationship between homeostatic need and behavioral motivation? Can a motive be best construed as a goal-directed tendency, an internal stimulus, or a general energizer? What is the relationship between motivation and arousal? How do biological motives become socialized?

THEORIES OF SLEEP

Since most of the scientists interested in sleep have been physiologists, most of the theoretical accounts of the phenomenon have been physiological in nature. Kleitman (1939) has reviewed these theories and used Pieron's classification of them as partial or complete. The partial theories account for the onset and offset of sleep, while the complete theories also attempt to account for the necessity of sleep.

The partial theories postulate some sort of neural or humoral process that serves as the mechanism for the production of sleep. These range from the ancient idea that sleep results from a congestion or anemia of the brain, to functional neural blocks, to the accumulation of some kind of fatigue product, and to endocrine periodicities. There are ancient and modern versions of these theories. Pieron's idea of a hypnotoxin is one of the best known. Pavlov's theory of sleep as an irradiation of focal inhibition to the entire cortex is another well-known formulation. They all are partial in that they deal only with the onset and termination of sleep.

The most general biological conception of sleep is Kleitman's (1939) Evolutionary Theory. Kleitman believes that the usual way of stating the problem—why must we interrupt wakefulness to go to sleep—is incorrect. Instead, he assumes that the phylogenetically most fundamental state is sleep, with wakefulness being an addition of activities above and beyond this basal level of existence. Thus sleep is viewed as a passive state that occurs when the processes underlying wakefulness are not operating.

In simpler organisms, wakefulness is a transitory thing depending on immediately present stimuli from the environment and internal organs. This results in a polyphasic alternation of activity and inactivity. Kleitman calls this primitive reactive activity "wakefulness of necessity" and points out that it characterizes simple organisms, newborn infants, and decorticated animals. As one goes up the evolutionary scale, it may be observed that wakefulness may be increasingly prolonged and the polyphasic pattern changed to a monophasic one. This is dependent on the development of the cortex, both phylogenetically and ontogenetically. Kleitman calls this "wakefulness of choice" and suggests that it is not dependent on immediate needs. However, such wakefulness is dependent upon internal and external afferent stimulation interacting with acquired information in the developed cortex.

In his recent formulation, Kleitman (1961) modified his theory to take the recent studies on the dream stage of sleep into account. He now talks of subcortically controlled primitive sleep and primitive wakefulness, as well as advanced sleep and advanced wakefulness dependent on cortical function. However, the basic idea that sleep is a basal state occurring in the absence of other factors is retained.

Thus Kleitman sees prolonged wakefulness as a great evolutionary achievement. The fact that we can stay awake for 16 hours a day is the pinnacle of this evolutionary process. We have no quarrel with the evolutionary aspects of this theory nor with the great importance of wakefulness. But the view of sleep as an entirely passive state is not convincing to us. Through evolution man has been able to free his eating behavior from the offerings of the immediate environment, his sexual behavior from seasonal variations, and his eliminative behavior from reflexive expression. Yet the hunger, sexual, and eliminative needs still exist. In the case of sleep, the question is why do we ever go back to sleep?

The return to sleep is explained by Kleitman as due to reduced afferent stimulation that deprives the cortex of its necessary raw material. Bremer and others also have such a "stimulus deficiency" theory (Lindsley, 1960). The sleep state is achieved by retiring to a quiet place, closing the eyes, and relaxing the muscles. But why this relaxation? Kleitman's answer is neuromuscular fatigue. Actually, this hints at an active function for sleep. However, fatigue is seen by Kleitman as simply one operation that reduces stimulation. The establishment of a diurnal rhythm is attributed to the alternation of night and day and the cultural learning to adapt to this.

In opposition to Kleitman's position, many biological scientists view sleep as a positive function necessary for the continuance of life. Various anabolic, restorative processes are assumed to operate more efficiently during sleep. The leading exponent of this theory is Hess (1957), who assumes that sleep is a parasympathetic function that provides for rest and restoration. This is a positive function and not simply the result of the exhaustion of the sympathetically dominated wakeful activities. Thus sleep is an active, not a passive phenomenon. Similarly, Davis (1950) sees sleep as a homeostatic protective mechanism for the cortex.

As mentioned earlier, these are theories by physiologists

to account for the biological changes and functions of sleep. Psychologists are interested in these problems, of course, but are concerned primarily with the behavioral phenomena associated with this variable. How can a psychologist conceptualize sleep? Descriptively it can be classified as a particular form of response with a characteristic level of activity and reactivity, or for the more introspectively inclined, as a particular state of consciousness. On a theoretical level, however, the question is whether it is a reflex, a goal response, or a learned habit—the three main categories of behavioral variables. Apparently, no one thinks of sleep as a reflex. A few think it may be a habit. Most psychologists, however, conceive of sleep phenomena as determined by some sort of motivational system.   ∿√

The most systematic early statement of sleep as due to a motivational variable was made by Claparede (1905). English summaries of this position are available (Claparede, 1911; Camp, 1907; Kleitman, 1939). Claparede believed that "sleep is not purely negative or passive, not the result of an arrest of function: it is a positive function, an act of a reflex order, an instinct" (translation by Camp, 1907, p. 19). The instinct is thought to have developed through evolution just as other instincts have. Sleep is not produced by the accumulation of fatigue products, but occurs on an instinctive basis to *prevent* the consequences of prolonged fatigue. Fatigue itself cannot explain sleep since we frequently go to sleep when not fatigued. Camp adds a case of neurotic narcolepsy as an example of the lack of dependence of sleep on fatigue.

It is clear that Claparede is using instinct here in a fashion analogous to the modern use of the concept of motivation. The similarity is even more marked when we consider how he explains the onset of sleep. Sleep is seen as a loss of interest in the world. The onset of sleep is determined by the relative strength of the sleep instinct and all the other instincts operating. Thus the more powerful instinct of self-preservation can prevent the onset of sleep. We wake up when the sleep instinct has been satisfied or when other instincts predominate. This analysis is comparable to modern theories of conflict (Miller, 1944).

Claparede also brings a habit factor into his theory. He

distinguishes between purely mechanical reflexes and instincts which are "plastic, adaptable, and modifiable by habit" (Claparede, 1911). The particular time and conditions for going to sleep and waking up are subject to learning. This is consistent with nearly all modern theories of learning and motivation.

Most of the other instinct theorists around the turn of the century also thought of the sleep tendency as a positive instinct. Perhaps the earliest was Freud who in 1900 described the "wish to sleep" as a withdrawal function (Freud, 1961; Jekels, 1945). McDougall (1960) listed sleep as one of the minor instincts. He saw an analogy between sleep and hibernation; he was impressed by the fact that everyone has the power to sleep and can cultivate it.

The modern-day instinct theorists—the ethologists—consider the tendency to sleep as an instinct. For example, Thorpe (1956) lists sleep along with nutrition, fighting, body care, and social relations as an independent instinct. Tinbergen (1951) gives three reasons for classifying sleep as due to an instinct: 1) it has a controlling mechanism in the brain; 2) it is the goal of a specific kind of appetitive behavior; and 3) it can act as a displacement activity for other blocked instincts.

This last point needs clarification. Displacement for the ethologists refers to the kind of thing that happens when an animal is, say, faced with a superior enemy. His fighting instinct is aroused but he cannot fight, so he may show displacement activities such as eating. The ethologists say that only true instinctive goal acts are utilized as displacement activities. The sleeping attitude (head under wing) in the European oystercatcher and European avocet has been observed as an outlet of the fighting instinct when blocked. Tinbergen mentions yawning in mild conflict situations and sleeping in combat as human analogies.

Most of the major behavior theorists have included the disposition to sleep as a primary motive. These include Tolman (1932), Hull (1943), Hebb (1950), and Skinner (1953). Guthrie and Edwards (1949) say that "sleep has all the earmarks of a drive." They also mention an incident in a British World War I retreat when wounded men were unable to get continuous sleep for days. When the retreat finally stopped, the observer heard only snores, instead of the usual groans, from the wards. Miller and Dollard (1941) mention fatigue as an important drive and the tendency to sleep would be analogous to this (Miller, personal communication).

Many elementary psychology textbooks list a primary "drive" to sleep, including Ruch (1953), Munn (1956), Morgan (1956), and Smith and Smith (1958). Morgan says that "Sleep is typical of physiological drives in about every way except that it involves passive resting of the body rather than an active striving." In his classic book on motivation, Young (1936) lists the demand for sleep after sleep deprivation as a basic drive.

Personality and social theorists and textbook writers also frequently count the disposition to sleep as a physiological motive. They include Allport (1937), Klineberg (1940), Sullivan (1953), Young (1956) and Shaffer and Shoben (1956). Sullivan says that sleep has the same relation to the tension of needing sleep as the satisfaction of the need for sugar has to the need for sugar.

This list of references is not meant to be an appeal to authority. Just because most psychological writers have listed sleep as a motive does not make it so. Rather, this section has shown the historical development of the idea of sleep as a motivational variable and some of the reasons why it makes psychological sense. There are other views, however.

Sleep may also be viewed as a habit, without motivational properties. The person most closely associated with this theory is Hollingworth (1927). Hollingworth viewed sleep as an organic response, representing a vestigial and unnecessary adjustment from our evolutionary past. It is a vague instinct crystallized into a fixed habit. Hollingworth thought it might be eliminated through several generations of selection. The ascetic religious leaders St. Francis of Assisi and St. Teresa, and the Methodists Fletcher and Wesley had similar views and tried to live without sleep but were unsuccessful. The famous subject who volunteered for a prolonged sleep deprivation study for Katz and Landis (1935) also believed sleep was a habit that could be broken. He developed delusions of persecution when he was unable to break this habit.

Recent evidence that sleep deprivation does not lead to physiological activation has led some behavioral scientists to doubt that sleep is a motivational variable. For example, Ax and Luby (1961) believe that the term "sleep deprivation" has led to an unfortunate analogy with alerted states associated with the deprivation of food and water. They believe that the term "prolonged wakefulness" would eliminate this semantic confusion. However, they do not provide an alternate theoretical analysis of the role of prolonged wakefulness in behavior. Hebb (1949) has also taken the position that sleep is "an extreme case of lack of motivation" (p. 223). Many other psychologists would agree with this; they are the psychological equivalent of the physiologists who think of sleep as an absence of functioning.

THE ANALYSIS OF THE SLEEP MOTIVE

The theoretical analysis of the sleep motive will begin with the assumption that sleep shares the basic characteristics of other primary, physiological motives. It serves a biological function, it operates through physiological mechanisms, and its deprivation motivates learning and performance. Its deprivation also poses a biological, behavioral, and personality adjustment problem. Through the influence of cultural and social learning, the sleep motive is shaped and developed and may become involved in psychopathology.

While the emphasis will be on showing that sleep has the essential features of a motive, the reader should be alert for important differences between this motive and others. After all, one reason for writing this book is to broaden the base of motivational phenomena on which our general conceptions rest. Thus the peculiarities of sleep may be of importance in assessing the adequacy of current concepts of motivation.

A note on terminology is in order. The terms *sleep motive* or *the motive to sleep* are used throughout in a general sense to refer to the entire gamut of phenomena in this area. It really should be read as "the disposition to sleep, serving a biological need, controlled by physiological mechanisms, with a specific goal response, and with specified relationships to deprivation and other motivating conditions." This is the general sense of the word as used by several theorists. Thus, Miller (1959) uses *motivation* to encompass the facts of deprivation, satiation, and reward—all parts of the whole. Similarly, Morgan (1957) uses the terms *need, drive, incentive, want,* and *reward* to refer to the components, while reserving the term *motive* for broad, general use. Thus, the term *sleep motive* is analogous to the hunger motive, the sex motive, the curiosity motive, the achievement motive, and so forth.

The actual act of sleeping is referred to as sleeping behavior, the sleep response, being asleep, the sleeping state, or most simply as sleep. This is viewed as the goal act or consummatory response of the sleep motive. It is analogous to eating and digesting in the case of the hunger motive, copulating and ejaculating in the case of the sex motive, and exploring, manipulating, or viewing in the case of the effectance motive.

Other responses that become involved with sleep may be viewed as instrumental or operant. These include going to bed, paying for a hotel room, and falling asleep. They are analogous to approaching the food tray, bar-pressing, etc., in the case of hunger. There is a gray area here: it is not clear if closing one's eyes and relaxing are instrumental for sleep or whether they are part of the consummatory response. The same problem exists with other motives, however, as in the problem of whether the goal act in the case of hunger is putting the food in the mouth, chewing and swallowing, or the digestive process. There is a gradation and it is probably influenced by learning.

Another problem is that generally speaking there is no particular goal object for sleep. There may be innate tendencies in some species to seek a particular environment in order to sleep; in man, for example, the bed becomes an important subgoal. But nothing like food is concerned and nothing like a sex object is absolutely necessary. This is true of many motives, however: pain has no particular goal object although the goal is to get away from the noxious stimulus. So too, activity and effectance motives have no object, but the goal is to make certain coordinated movements.

The terms *sleep deprivation* and *sleep loss* refer to the main operation by which the sleep motive varies in strength. Thus one speaks of a greater or lesser degree of sleep motivation. Other operations—drugs, heat, or monotony—may also be said to affect the strength of the sleep motive. Subjectively, this may be experienced as "sleepiness" or the "desire to sleep." Whenever this is meant there should be an explicit or implicit reference to the *strength* of the sleep motive.

Quite distinct from the psychological or behavioral impetus to sleep is the physiological "need for sleep." This refers to those conditions on a purely physiological level that require sleep.

We should say a few words about the scope of a motivational analysis. What kinds of data are relevant? It is our belief that psychology as a whole, as well as motivation theory, has suffered from too great a narrowing of interest to one or another source of data. Some motivation theorists base their work entirely on animal experiments, while others deal exclusively with human motivation. Some of those concerned with animals center their arguments on physiological data, others on learning phenomena. Some of those dealing with human behavior stress human laboratory experiments, others clinical data, still others cross-cultural observations. This splintering seems unfortunate to us. We believe that data from all of these sources are necessary and complementary. Therefore, the scope of our analysis of the motive to sleep will be as broad as possible.

The plan of the book is to examine the phenomenon of sleep in a variety of contexts, each time asking whether the motive to sleep has the characteristics usually attributed to other motives in that particular context. Most of the chapters begin with a section on the appropriate characteristics of other motives in a given context. Following this is an analysis of sleep behavior in those terms, with a final summary and evaluation of the adequacy of viewing the disposition to sleep as a motivating variable. In some instances the organization was altered for purposes of clarity. The review of the characteristics of motives other than sleep is not meant to be original, so that readily available secondary sources are usually cited. In some instances, where little systematic work has been done, a detailed review of the literature was required.

In the two chapters following, the overall biological nature and function of sleep are discussed. The first of these chapters is devoted to the biological need for sleep in general and the second to the functions of dreams in particular. The main question here is whether sleep serves some function in biological survival analogous to eating and other motivated activities. This material will also be relevant to the questions of the relationship between homeostasis and motivation.

The next chapter will be devoted to the physiological mechanisms for the onset and offset of sleep, for dreams, and for arousal and wakefulness. The differences and similarities between the mechanisms for sleep and those for other motives will be examined closely. The relationship between mechanisms for sleep and those for arousal will be of particular theoretical interest.

The chapter on learning and performance in relation to sleep motivation deals with a number of complex issues. Before dealing with the empirical studies, the issues of relevant and irrelevant performance, conflict, and the occurrence of learning during sleep will be discussed. The issues discussed in this chapter are relevant to the general question of the relationship between motivation and behavior.

Following is a chapter devoted specifically to the question of arousal during sleep deprivation. A number of measures of arousal are considered. Clearly, this material is of importance in the theoretical question of the relationship between arousal and motivation as well as the status of the energizing concept of motivation.

The next three chapters deal with human relations with respect to the sleep motive. One chapter is devoted to personality adjustment during sleep deprivation, another to the psychopathology of sleep, and another to the socialization of sleep behavior. In each case, the sleep motive will be compared with other motives. The material will be relevant to the question of how a physiological motive is related to personal and social processes.

Finally, we will devote a chapter to evaluating and integrating all of the material in this analysis of the sleep motive. The biological functions of sleep and the question of homeostasis will be discussed. The motivational concepts of energization and direction will be evaluated in the context of the sleep motive. Implications for socialization and social motivation will also be drawn.

CHAPTER 2

The Biological Need for Sleep

The basic motives assumed by most psychologists are thought to be innate mechanisms with some probable biological survival value. Hunger usually serves the metabolic needs of the body, innate fears have individual survival value, and the sexual motive insures the survival of the species. The purpose of this chapter is to see if sleep serves the organism in a comparable fashion.

An important distinction should be drawn between the physiological function of a drive and its mechanism of control. The two might be quite separate. For example, the old idea that sleep occurs when the products of fatigue build up has been discredited. It is not the way sleep is turned on and off. Nevertheless, the elimination of fatigue products may still be one of the functions performed during sleep. Of late, physiologists have concentrated on the mechanisms of physiological control of sleep. These are, of course, of great importance and will be covered in a later chapter. But the functions of sleep are also of interest in a motivational analysis. This is the topic for the present chapter.

Many psychologists will feel that a consideration of the need for sleep is irrelevant. The old idea that biological needs and psychological motives stand in a one-to-one relation to each other has gone by the boards. So, too, has the idea that reinforcement consists of simple need reduction (Murray, 1964 b). We are not maintaining that the need for sleep is the same as the motive to sleep. However, most psychologists believe that the primary motives serve some biological function even if the connection is partial and inefficient at times. Thus, to discuss the motivation to sleep without at least some consideration of its biological functions leaves an incomplete picture.

It must be admitted, however, that the logic of a motivational analysis does not require the demonstration of a biological need. Motives may be entirely defined on a behavioral level and evaluated in terms of their effects on learning, performance, and personality. As we shall see, the functions of sleep are not clearly understood. But the fact that problems on this level are not solved need not deter the rest of the theoretical development.

In the present chapter we will first examine, briefly, the functions of other basic psychological motives in order to have a basis for comparison. The general survival functions of sleep will be discussed. Following this, several specific functions will be studied. Then the possibility of dreams playing an important role will be discussed. Finally, an attempt to summarize and evaluate the biological functions of sleep will be made as they compare with those of the better-known motives. Advantage will be taken of this discussion to present some descriptive material about the physiological and biological nature of sleep that will be useful for later chapters.

BODILY NEEDS AND MOTIVATION

The body can be viewed as a complex energy system. Each individual cell is a mechanism for transforming energy into activities such as contracting, secreting, conducting, and reproducing. The required energy is obtained by cellular metabolism —the breaking down, transferring, and building up of various chemical compounds. The materials that are needed for metabolic functions—phosphate and carbon compounds, amino acids, water, oxygen, vitamins etc.—are obtained from the environment. The raw materials gotten from the environment are broken down by digestion and intermediary metabolism to a form usable by the cells (Morgan and Stellar, 1950).

The familiar biological motives ordinarily function to provide the raw materials needed for metabolism. Hunger results in acquiring most of the raw materials needed for the various chemical reactions. Specific subhungers—for meat, butter, etc.—insure the supply of many particular items such as amino acids or vitamins. Thirst provides the necessary water. The urge to breathe results in an oxygen supply.

Metabolism also requires a special set of conditions in the internal environment in order for the chemical reactions to continue. Temperature must not vary more than a few degrees for any length of time, the acidity-alkalinity balance must be approximately even, and proper water content and salt concentration in the extracellular fluids must be maintained. It is thought that life began in tropical, salt seas where all these conditions are met for unicellular organisms. But as fish invaded fresh water and organisms crawled on land, mechanisms had to be developed to maintain the individual cells artificially in a tropical sea environment. These are the numerous and complex internal homeostatic mechanisms (Young, 1961).

The homeostatic equilibrium necessary for proper metabolism is also associated with several important motives. The motive to avoid temperature extremes maintains the tropical sea temperature in most mammals. Activity in the cold and inactivity in the heat similarly help maintain body temperature. The taste preference for various concentrations of salt water depends on the internal concentration and helps maintain it. Other motives, or instincts, such as migration, hoarding, hibernation, nest building, and so forth, may also contribute to homeostatic equilibrium (Morgan and Stellar, 1950; Young, 1961).

There is still another requirement of metabolic processes. The chemical reactions and the digestive process result in waste products of various kinds. If these are permitted to be retained in the system, metabolism would be disrupted. For example, if too much acid accumulated in the blood, the pH level would be disturbed. The excess acid is excreted through the kidneys and the lungs. The motives for breathing out, micturating, and defecating play a role in eliminating waste products. Fatigue is also a motive related to the waste products of metabolism. Muscular fatigue may arise when the chemical by-products of the contraction process (CO_2, lactic acid, etc.) must be eliminated. Sensory and neural fatigue would operate in an analogous fashion (Bartley and Chute, 1947).

Pain can be, at least distantly, related to metabolism in that it leads to the avoidance of injury involving a loss of body fluids, destruction of organs necessary for metabolism, and the invasion of harmful organisms.

In spite of the impressive array of evidence for the metabolic and homeostatic basis of many motives, this does not explain all mammalian or human motivations. First of all, the bodily requirements of the organism do not always result in a behavioral motive. Pilots at high altitudes are completely unaware of a lack of oxygen in the air and can die without a motive being aroused. A person will breathe in the deadly poison carbon monoxide without a behavioral change (Miller and Dollard, 1941). Substances such as saccharine, which are not nutritious, may be rewarding and drive-reducing (Miller, 1961). Water and salt intake may be nonhomeostatic under certain circumstances (Falk, 1961). This is not to say that many motives are not homeostatic, but that the concept is not all-inclusive.

Several motives have to do with species' survival rather than homeostasis in a single individual. These include sex, maternal, and retrieving motives that may be regulated by hormones, among other things, but have little to do with metabolism (Young, 1961). At one time these motives were thought to be homeostatic in the sense that the build-up of substances, e.g., seminal fluid, creates tension and demands discharge. However, the enormous role played by stimulus and neural factors outshadows the contribution of tension (Beach, 1949, 1956).

In recent years there has been an interest in intrinsically motivating conditions, i.e., those not based on internal physiological needs. They include motives for activity, manipulation, curiosity, varied stimulation, and behavioral competence. These motives may have some adaptive features, of course, and thus serve long-range metabolic purposes, but they are in no way immediately dependent on metabolism or homeostasis (White, 1959). Similarly, Festinger (1954) postulates an innate biological motive to hold correct opinions about the world. In commenting on

Festinger's paper, Nissen reports that the chimpanzee also appears motivated to have correct information about the world. The ethologists have described many biological motives that are determined almost exclusively by environmental configurations (Tinbergen, 1951).

The recent work on affectional needs in monkeys (Harlow, 1958; Harlow and Zimmerman, 1959; Harlow, 1962) adds another nonhomeostatic motive to our list. Affection used to be thought of as a social drive, perhaps acquired by conditioning on the basis of hunger or sex; Harlow's studies show it is independent of these physiological motives. Considering the dependence of the infant on the mother for survival, the adaptive value of an innate biological motive for contact comfort is obvious. Imprinting in ducks and other fowl may be a similar phenomenon (Moltz, 1960). On the human level, maternal deprivation has profound effects on subsequent personality development (Yarrow, 1961). Other social motives, such as cooperation and competition, may also be rooted in biology (Allee, 1958).

The entire issue is far from closed, but a few points can be made. The appropriate frame of reference for evaluating biological motives is the adaptiveness and survival value of the function in question. Behavioral motives may reflect metabolic needs and operate as a behavioral extension of internal homeostatic mechanisms. Innate motives may also be built into the organism to increase the probability of survival without immediate reference to metabolic needs (Murray, 1964 b). In many cases, the exact function fulfilled by a definitely innate biological motive is not clear. In our present state of ignorance, a pragmatic approach must be taken.

One methodological point may be of importance later on. Biological scientists have many ways of studying the needs of the organism, but one of the most direct and conceptually relevant is to simply deprive the organism of the substance or function and watch the result. The overall survival value of food and water is clearly demonstrated by the fact that death results from the total deprivation of these substances. So, too, the heat cramps following salt depletion, the beriberi or scurvy associated with vitamin deficiencies, and the nutritional edema after a protein-free diet illustrate the functions of those substances (Wohl and Goodhart, 1955). To some extent the more complex motives can be studied this way too. The cognitive disruption during sensory deprivation shows the importance of stimuli in normal brain functioning. The asocial character resulting from maternal deprivation suggests the importance of affection in emotional development. The deprivation procedure may be useful in the case of sleep.

SURVIVAL VALUE OF SLEEP

Survival often involves adapting to the rhythms of nature. Organisms scratching out an existence on this globe of ours face the periodic changes imposed by the excursion of the earth around the sun and its effect on seasonal change, by the phasic appearance of the moon with the ebbing and flowing of the tides, by the rotation of the earth on its axis producing the alternation of day and night, and by less well-known fluctuations of rainfall, barometric pressure, and cosmic radiation.

One of the results of evolution is to provide each species with means of adapting to nature's periodicities in a way suited to the species' particular survival problems. Sometimes these are innate rhythms; sometimes flexible modes of sensing and adapting. The main mode of adaptation is increasing or decreasing activity of some sort—ranging from metabolism to migration. Cycles of quiescence and activity in response to the diurnal rotation of the earth are widespread—these are the primitive forerunners of what we call sleep and wakefulness.

There are basic similarities in the metabolic rhythms of algae, flowering plants, certain invertebrates, and vertebrates, as measured by oxygen consumption, that appear to depend on an internal biological clock. Some of these cycles are remarkably persistent and persevering—transplanting certain crabs in a darkened chamber from the east coast to the west coast does not affect daily or monthly rhythms. Even tissue slices from a rhythmic organism continue to show cycles of oxygen consumption (Brown, 1957; Stephens, 1957).

On the other hand, a great many biological rhythms are

sensitive to temperature, light, and other aspects of the environment. Oysters, some crabs, and other organisms with a tidal rhythm, may adapt to different tidal patterns. The oxygen consumption of the potato plant, grown under "constant" conditions, was found to vary on a daily basis with the amount of high-energy background radiation (Brown, 1957; Stephens, 1957).

The survival value of these rhythms is clear. The plant, for instance, releases oxygen when the sun is out, but releases CO_2 during the night. The fiddler crab has a tidal rhythm because it feeds only at low tide. The rhythms seem to be determined primarily by internal mechanisms but frequently can be influenced or "reset" by an environmental pacemaker (Brown, 1957; Fingerman, 1957).

The study of sleep patterns in higher organisms was pioneered by Szymanski (summarized in Kleitman, 1939; Reed, 1947; Hediger, 1955), who measured the periods of activity and rest in a variety of fish, birds, and mammals. His most important discovery was that some species rested several times during the day (polyphasic), while others had one long period of rest (monophasic), which could occur during the night (diurnal animals) or during the day (nocturnal animals).

Rats, rabbits, puppies, and human infants are polyphasic. Cattle are said to graze on and off all during the night and thus may be considered polyphasic. The cat tends toward a diurnal pattern with one long rest period during the night and several in the day (catnaps?). Most birds, monkeys, and higher mammals are monophasic diurnal. Elephants lie down for several hours around midnight. Many fish sleep during the night, although it is difficult to tell when they are asleep. It is also difficult to tell when snakes sleep, but according to some observations they are monophasic with a waking period of a few hours around noon. Owls, bats, and other creatures are nocturnal (Adrian, 1937; Hediger, 1955; Heinroth and Heinroth, 1958).

As in the lower organisms, the activity-rest cycles of mammals are endogenous, but may be modified by the environment to some extent. Richter (1922-23) showed that the general level of activity in the rat could be lowered by high temperature or light, although the cycles persisted. The light-dark cycles tend to persist in a dark environment but they become random in continuous light. After several weeks in a reversed light-dark environment, the rat's activity cycle will adjust (Browman, 1955). Feeding schedules influence the distribution of activity, but even here cycles persist. An attempt to change temperature, heart rate, muscular activity, and bladder rhythms in a variety of small mammals by exposure to cold has been reported by Folk (1957). While general level of activity was changed, the periodicities were hardly affected.

An observation of considerable significance for several issues to be discussed later in this book is that most animals have a special kind of rest in addition to sleep—this is a semi-wakeful, dozing state. Cattle chewing the cud seem to be in a dreamy, half-asleep state (Hediger, 1955). Primitive man may also show this and in certain Oriental civilizations it is highly cultivated. Objective evidence indicates that the Yoga trance is similar to a drowsy state (Behanan, 1960). Progressive relaxation may be comparable (Jacobson, 1929). Nevertheless, this is a state with which most of the modern world is unfamiliar.

Kleitman (1963) made several attempts to modify the diurnal rhythm in man with partial success. Subjects could not adjust to a 12-hour or 48-hour day very well—a 24-hour rhythm persisted in measures of body temperature. Some, but not all, subjects can adjust to a cycle slightly different from the usual one—a 21- or 28-hour day. Since the difficulty may have been due to the strong light-dark influence and since there were reports of successful reversals in the Arctic darkness, Kleitman and his assistant spent a month in Mammoth Cave, Kentucky, living a 28-hour day. Artificial light was on for 19 hours and total darkness prevailed for 9 hours. Kleitman was unable to adapt but the assistant did. Possibly the age difference and the over-learning of sleep habits account for the divergent results.

Difficulties in shifting the diurnal cycle in several social situations have also been described by Kleitman (1939). For example, world travelers in ocean ships or airplanes have progressive difficulty as they cross the longitudes. Westbound travelers get sleepy early in the evening, but eastbound individuals want to stay up late. Most people have some difficulty adjusting.

Occupations involving frequent changes of shift—nursing, the Navy, etc.—may involve hardships. About two weeks are needed for a complete diurnal readjustment for most people—nurses often change shift that frequently!

Intrigued by travelers' reports of prolonged wakefulness during the summer months in communities above the Arctic Circle, Kleitman and his daughter (Kleitman and Kleitman, 1953) went to Tromso, Norway and interviewed the citizens. According to these investigators the reports were untrue—the inhabitants deviated only slightly from the 24-hour rhythm. They stayed up about an hour later in the summer, but got up at the usual time, sleeping about 7 hours. The extra hour of winter sleep may have been due to the lack of social activities. However, it should be pointed out that Kleitman was studying an organized community. On polar expeditions, men not subjected to community pressures show variable sleep patterns depending on the length of the day and night (Lewis, 1961).

All these studies show a great many individual variations. Kleitman (1952) divides people into two types—the "morning" type who wakes up refreshed, reaches a temperature and performance peak around noon, and tapers off the rest of the day; and the "evening" type who is sleepy in the morning, reaches a peak in late afternoon, and hates to go to bed. Of course, there are several in-between varieties. There may be a genetic basis for this—Sheldon's somatotonics tend to be morning types and the cerebrotonics evening ones.

All of this testifies to the strong persistence of the diurnal pattern. It can be modified, of course, with appropriate environmental change, but it is a powerful, long-lasting influence on behavior. Is it innate or learned? Probably both. Stephens (1957) comes to this conclusion on the basis of studies with a wide variety of animals. He suggests a classification of cycles based on their dependence and independence of the environment. We would expect that the greatest modifiability would be found in the higher mammals, and especially in man. Man can change both to meet different environmental conditions and to resist the effects of environmental control.

Sleep patterns may also be affected by seasonal and temperature changes. In man, for example, sleep motility is greater in the summer than in the winter (Renshaw, 1933; Kleitman, 1939). Kleitman believes that this is due to an avoidance of unwarmed areas of the bed during winter. Cold-blooded animals, such as snakes and reptiles, are completely at the mercy of external temperature. They are called "poikilothermic" and have no internal temperature-regulating mechanism. When the temperature drops, they become inactive and enter a "cold stupor." Homeothermic animals, such as birds, mammals, and man, control their own body temperature by increasing heat production, seeking warm quarters, growing fur, migrating, etc. To the extent that cold stupor represents an extreme state of sleep—a debatable point—temperature and season have an effect.

In this connection, the most interesting animals are those that hibernate. They seem to have a primitive temperature regulatory mechanism which ceases to function at a low temperature. They then change from homeothermic to poikilothermic regulation and enter a cold stupor. This is adaptive because metabolism is slowed down and food requirements are lowered. The stupor is not absolute—hibernating animals wake up if their temperature reaches the freezing point (Suomalainen, 1961). Some of these animals awake in a periodic fashion that suggests a continuance of the diurnal rhythm even in deep hibernation (Folk, 1957). Of particular interest is Suomalainen's finding that hibernation is controlled by a neurosecretory substance from the supraoptic nucleus of the anterior hypothalamus. As we shall see in the next chapter, this is the same general area of the hypothalamus that controls normal sleep. Thus there are important similarities between sleep and hibernation with respect to loss of reactivity, lowered metabolism, and hypothalamic regulation.

All this material suggests that sleep, or some forerunner of it, is universal in organismic life. There is every reason to believe that it serves some adaptive purpose. In some cases the function is clear—the plant releasing CO_2, the feeding of the tidal animal, the monophasic diurnal pattern of birds and mammals highly dependent on vision, the nocturnal pattern of the night hunter, the hibernation of the rodent in the cold, food-scarce winter, and so forth. However, these examples do not answer why sleep itself occurs, but merely how activity is distributed during the 24-hour period to fit in with the adaptive capacities of the particular species.

The simplest answer is that the alternation of active and rest periods provides for a general homeostatic regulation of energy expenditure. The animals that are not adapted to hunt, seek food, water, during particular environmental phases (night, day, winter) must pass the time as economically as possible since no new raw materials for metabolism are forthcoming. This is most dramatic in the hibernating rodent, but the reverse can be seen in the desert rat that burrows in the sand and sleeps during the day because it cannot survive in the sun. The normal diurnal sleep of small bats and hummingbirds is close to a hibernating state because of enormous metabolic needs. Normal mammalian sleep may have this general function of conserving energy (Suomalainen, 1961, and discussion following).

Does sleep involve a more positive function, in addition to the simple conservation of energy? Most observers have felt that it permits some sort of restoration, but the arguments are usually based on indirect evidence. Hess gives a good statement of this idea:

> The more differentiated an organism, the more it depends on conscious elaboration of, and appropriate reaction to, signals from the external world in its struggle for survival. During sleep these capacities are depressed and the individual is left defenseless. The fact that all highly organized creatures accept this risk for a considerable part of their life suggests that sleep must have a vital function. We consider it a reparative process which obviously cannot take place in the highest centers while they are active (Hess, 1954, p. 117).

Actually, the animal is not completely defenseless. As Hediger (1955) points out, the animal never completely lets go of the task of avoiding enemies. For example, Hediger observed that while elephants sleep blissfully in spite of the bumps and turnings of their fellow pachyderms, they wake up immediately whenever a man approaches. Were it not for this, Hediger says, hunting and capturing wild animals would be child's play. Hess' point is still substantially correct, nevertheless, since the animal is at least relatively more vulnerable when asleep.

Is sleep then a vital function? One way of testing this—as with food and water—is to deprive the organism of sleep and see what happens. First of all, if sleep loss is prolonged enough it leads to death. This has been shown in all the reported studies (see Kleitman, 1939, for a review of early studies). Licklider and Bunch (1946) found that all rats died in 3 to 14 days when placed on a treadmill that did not allow normal sleep. Nauta (1946) produced insomnia by destroying the sleep area in the anterior hypothalamus—all the rats died after three days. Mott (1924) mentions that the Chinese used sleep loss as a torture, with all victims dying in five to seven days. Kleitman (1963) reports that total insomnia is unknown as a clinical entity, in spite of occasional unverified reports in the news media.

In addition to the extreme question of life and death, sleep also seems to be important in our general feeling of well-being and efficiency. Some years ago, Barry and Bousfield (1935) demonstrated a relationship between euphoria and the duration of sleep. Euphoria means a subjective positive feeling or simply "feeling good." Euphoria is often contrasted with fatigue (both mental and muscular) or depression. Barry and Bousfield developed an eleven-point scale of euphoria and administered it to several hundred college students. They found a positive relationship between euphoria ratings and the number of hours of sleep on the previous night as reported by the students. The optimum duration of sleep was 8 to 8-¾ hours. Subsequent studies showed that euphoria is also related to the regularity of sleeping and the quality of sleep (Bousfield, 1938; Bousfield, 1940).

A number of people have taken the position that sleep performs no important restorative function because we are usually more tired and less efficient in the morning than later on in the day. In fact, we may be less efficient upon rising than upon retiring the night before. Kleitman (1963, chapter 16) has reviewed studies demonstrating this effect and concludes that they refute the ideas that during sleep metabolic waste products are removed or the battery is recharged. Kleitman maintains that if sleep serves a restorative function we should be most alert and efficient early in the morning. However, the fact that we are most efficient in the middle of the day is due to the diurnal rhythm of metabolic functioning. Kleitman shows a close relationship between efficiency in performance and body temperature. The body needs to be stoked and fired up after sleeping but this does not mean that the over-all efficiency during the day is unrelated to the sleep the night before. The problem is analogous to the baseball pitcher who does best after several days' rest but who still needs a period of warming-up before the game.

In a later chapter, Kleitman (1963, chapter 30) reports a number of studies that support the idea that overall efficiency is facilitated by sleep. In one study reported, Viaud deliberately avoided the early morning period of lowered efficiency and tested subjects in the afternoon. He related afternoon performance to the number of hours of sleep obtained by subjects the previous night. He found a nearly linear increase in performance when the duration of sleep increased from one to six hours. An asymptote was reached after about 8 to 10 hours of sleep. Thus, afternoon performance is positively related to the duration of sleep the night before. Sleep must facilitate some process important in overall efficiency of functioning.

Granted that sleep plays a vital role in biological survival, just what is this role? Speculations have ranged widely (see Kleitman, 1939, for a summary). Three main physiological functions have been proposed. First, sleep may aid in restoring some kind of metabolic balance. Second, sleep may be important in the recovery from muscular fatigue. Third, sleep may aid in neural reorganization or the recovery from neural fatigue. These will be taken up separately in the following three sections.

METABOLIC FUNCTIONS

The logical place to start a search for the functions of sleep is in the area of metabolism, since so many other basic physiological motives are based on metabolic needs. We will first consider some of the general changes in the internal functions of the body during sleep, then examine metabolic changes during sleep, and finally look at the effects of sleep deprivation.

To begin with, a number of physiological changes occur during sleep that are simply the result of muscular relaxation: heart rate decreases, while respiration becomes deeper, slower, and more regular. Blood pressure is lowered, resulting in a seepage of fluids back into the circulatory system. This in turn results in a decrease in the concentration of many chemical constituents of the blood, so that they are of secondary importance. Blood flow to the brain is increased (Kleitman, 1963; Sokoloff, 1956). The increased cerebral blood flow may be due to the heightened CO_2 tension in the arterial blood, which in turn is dependent on the respiratory depression (Kety, 1961). These changes, while of interest in themselves, tell us little of the basic functions of sleep.

During sleep, digestion continues undiminished but general metabolism slows down. Heat production decreases and with it body temperature (Kleitman, 1963; Bartley and Chute, 1947). Hibernating animals also show a dramatic drop in metabolism, heat production, and temperature. Bats and hummingbirds, which have very high metabolic rates when active, show a great drop in metabolic rate and temperature whenever they become inactive or lack food. As mentioned earlier, for these animals daily sleep is almost hibernation (Suomalainen, 1961).

While general body metabolism falls during sleep, brain metabolism does not. This latter has been measured by cerebral oxygen consumption (Sokoloff, 1956; Kety, 1961). The lack of a decrease in brain metabolism fits in with neurophysiological evidence, to be discussed later, that the brain does not become inactive during sleep, but that the activity is distributed differently. It also differentiates sleep from diabetic coma, insulin coma, anesthesia, and other artificial states involving loss of consciousness. The fact that overall cerebral metabolism and electrical activity do not decrease during sleep does not preclude the possibility that certain parts rest while others are active (Sokoloff, 1954; Kety, 1961).

The decrease in general body metabolism during sleep suggests that sleep functions to permit metabolic restoration. Kleitman cites several theorists, especially Salmon and Barbara, who believe that catabolic processes predominate during wakefulness, while restorative anabolic processes compensate during the night. Presumably, this would be under the control of endocrine glands such as the pituitary, thyroid, adrenals, and gonads. Closely associated with this is Hess' theory that sleep is a parasympathetic phenomenon controlled by the autonomic nervous system.

Kleitman (1939) objects to seeing sleep as a period of metabolic adjustment, although he grants the evidence of metabolic change. The same anabolic functions *could* take place during wakefulness. Kleitman prefers to think of the metabolic changes as a consequence of the sleeping posture. It is true that a lower temperature can be produced by the prone position or muscle relaxation independent of sleep. While the positional changes may be necessary, however, they do not preclude the possibility that their function is to permit anabolic metabolism to occur.

Some of these questions may be answered by studying the effects of sleep deprivation on bodily processes. Few experiments have been done on this and most of those have shown negative results (Kleitman, 1963). It is amazing how well the circulatory and other systems hold up in moderate sleep deprivation. However, recent studies have begun to show that there are some metabolic effects.

In the Walter Reed studies, to be mentioned several times again, Murray, Williams, and Lubin (1958) measured oral temperature in 15 subjects undergoing 98 hours of sleep deprivation. The temperature showed an overall decrease but the diurnal rhythm was maintained, as is shown in Fig. 1. Ratings of fatigue and sleepiness were inversely correlated with body temperature. Kleitman and Jackson (1950) related performance efficiency to the continuing diurnal temperature rhythm during sleep loss. If temperature is taken as a measure of metabolic rate, then our data suggest that there is increasing difficulty in maintaining metabolism, although other factors obviously have influence.

What is the nature of the metabolic difficulty during sleep loss? It appears to be related to very basic processes in energy metabolism involving phosphates. In all living organisms, the transformation of energy from all food sources—carbohydrates, fats, alcohol, and protein—into muscular, nervous, and all other cellular activities, depends upon a single chemical "carrier"—

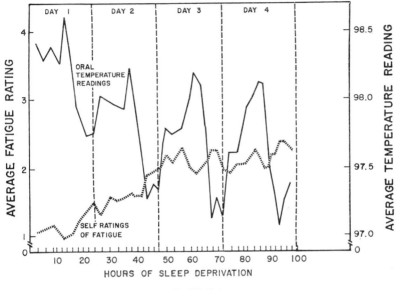

FIGURE 1

adenosine triphosphate (ATP). It has been called the universal currency of living energy. As the energy from food substances is transformed into cellular action, ATP is broken down into the simpler adenosine diphosphate (ADP). This process has been compared with a battery in which ATP represents the charged battery and ADP the battery after discharge. Ordinarily the battery is recharged by combining adenylic acid (AMP) with ADP to reform the ATP. This is called phosphorylation and is closely linked or coupled with oxidation in the cells.

Energy is stored for future use by combining ATP with creatine to form phosphocreatine—the storage item. During activity ATP is released from the phosphocreatine for energy.

During rest the phosphocreatine is resynthesized. During intense, prolonged activity the available supply of stored energy is used up and the organism must find means of creating enough ATP to meet the immediate demands (Brody, 1945; Morgan and Stellar, 1950; Luby et al., 1960).

Sleep deprivation makes an enormous demand on the energy reserves of the body. This has been just recently studied by Luby, Frohman, Grisell, Ax, and Lenzo (1960) and Luby, Frohman, Grisell, Lenzo, and Gottlieb (1960). Two subjects were deprived of sleep for five and ten days. The typical psychological effects of sleep deprivation, with marked personality and performance changes, were observed after four or five days. The initial biochemical effect of the deprivation, as determined on day four, was that of a stressor similar to insulin. Energy production was increased as indicated by the increased specific activity of ATP, ADP, and AMP. The evidence suggested, however, that the AMP was synthesized by an emergency process from three substances not ordinarily called upon—adenine, ribose, and inorganic phosphate. Thus the initial effect was to bring emergency metabolic energy mechanisms into play.

After the fourth day, these emergency mechanisms were exhausted and the specific activities of ATP, ADP, and AMP fell. The emergency production of AMP had failed by this time. Along with the biochemical failure, the personality and performance deterioration became more marked. After a period of recovery sleep, the energy systems returned to normal. Luby et al. suggest that the function of sleep is the restitution of these systems of energy transfer. It should be emphasized, however, that these are the first studies to show a logical connection between sleep and metabolic function. Research along these lines in the next few years could very well settle the question of the function of sleep.

Another recent study (Metz, Schaff, and Grivel, 1960), shows that the closely related endocrine system also reacts to sleep loss as a stress. During a night without sleep the urinary excretion of adrenalin was increased significantly, and noradrenalin showed the same trend. During tasks the next day, the secretions were further raised. During recovery sleep, that night, the excretions of adrenalin and noradrenalin dropped markedly, although not quite to the baseline level for normal sleep.

Along this line, Kline (1958) reports that several of his patients were able to get along very well on 3 or 4 hours of sleep per night for over a year with the aid of the "psychic energizer" iproniazid. Kline tried it himself for a while with pleasant results. He wonders what the world would do with a "daily increase of six or eight billion man hours of time." Iproniazid operates by inhibiting monoamine oxidase in such a way as to enhance the action of serotonin and norepinephrine in the brain. Thus iproniazid probably promotes more efficient brain metabolism and this may be what reduces the need for sleep (Featherstone and Simon, 1959).

For some time sleep has been thought to favor growth processes (Jacobson, 1929). Several studies suggest that the greatest amount of growth takes place in children during the winter months, when they also sleep more soundly (see summary in Renshaw et al., 1933). Reference can also be made to the common observation that sleep needs are greatest during the early years of rapid growth in children (Despert, 1949-50) and least during old age when growth and regeneration are minimal (Ginzberg, 1955). A case has been reported of a senile dog (Sagal, 1958) which responded to artificial sleep therapy with general and sexual rejuvenation! Hibernating animals may also increase their overall life span (H. Matthews in discussion following Suomalainen, 1961). It is ironic to think that the fountain of youth may consist in "living" as little as possible.

The possible involvement of sleep with growth processes is also shown in a sleep-deprivation study with young rats (Lick-lider and Bunch, 1946). Fifty-two 30-day old rats were kept awake for 20 of the 24 hours each day for several months. Before the sleep deprivation they showed no difference in weight in comparison with control animals. During the experimental period both groups continued to show growth but the wakeful animals fell further and further behind in weight, in spite of the fact that food and water were always available. Food intake was not measured and could have influenced the relative weight loss in this experiment. After about 40 days of this regime, the experimental animals almost ceased growing and several of them died. The animals were kept awake on a water treadmill that required constant movement. However, the activity itself did not account for the results, because an exercise control group running the same mileage each day in a couple or hours showed no stunting of growth. The prolongation of mild activity and continuous wakefulness seemed to be the critical factors.

In a more recent study, Webb and Agnew (1962) found that exhaustion time in a water wheel apparatus is related to age. Rats ranging in age from 60 to 220 days were placed in a continuously revolving water wheel until they fell exhausted into the water three times in a fifteen-minute period. Exhaustion time was inversely related to age. The oldest rats reached the exhaustion criterion in about three days and the youngest rats had not reached it in nine. Webb and Agnew observed a weight loss and a decrease in food intake. However, the 60-day-old group, which was in a growth phase similar to Licklider and Bunch's 30-day-olds, actually doubled their food intake from the first to the second day while continuing to show a weight loss. Furthermore, there was no correlation between food intake and exhaustion time. Webb and Agnew conclude that the exhaustion was due to sleep deprivation.

The Licklider and Bunch and Webb and Agnew studies suggest that sleep deprivation interferes with metabolism and energy resources. The effect is explained by neither exercise nor reduced food intake. Younger rats can maintain activity for a longer time but at the expense of normal growth. Older rats presumably have a reduced capacity for growth and recuperation so they show the exhaustion more rapidly. Normal sleep, then, may provide the conditions for the metabolic processes underlying growth and recuperation.

Jacobson (1929) also mentions the possibility that recuperation and the fight against disease are facilitated by sleep. This may be indirect or may have something to do with metabolic changes in sleep. People who go without sleep are said to be run-down and have a lowered resistance. In going through reports of sleep-deprivation experiments, this author was struck by the frequent mention of one or more subjects with colds (Gilbert and Patrick, 1897; Laslett, 1924; Weiskotten, 1925; Freeman, 1932). The writer has never noticed so many references to minor ailments in psychological studies on other problems. On the other hand, some disease processes may be more harmful during sleep so one should not conclude that sleep is always beneficial (Robin, 1958).

All this could mean that not enough energy is available for the basic processes of growth, repair, and recuperation when the organism is awake and active. During sleep the energy needs for muscular, neural, and similar activities are reduced and these other processes may proceed. This is not absolute, of course, since these processes can probably go on during wakefulness, too. But over the long haul, sleep can be seen as facilitating the basic generative powers of the body.

MUSCULAR RELAXATION FUNCTIONS

Typically, when an organism becomes sleepy it closes its eyes, relaxes its muscles, and lies down. This is not universally true since birds sleep while balanced on a perch, but even in this case the larger pectoral and head muscles are relaxed. Some birds have an ingenious locking device involving ratchet-like bumps on the tendon of the leg. When the toes are curled around the perch and the muscles relaxed, the ratchet takes hold and permits relaxed sleep. Other birds sleep on one leg, then another. Seabirds can sleep on the surface of the water (Heinroth and Heinroth, 1958). Fish sleep while floating; this author has frequently observed his goldfish at night motionless and suspended in mid-tank. Whales, dolphins, and porpoises sleep at night at the surface of the water, breathing through their blow-holes (Kellogg, 1961). It has long been observed that horses sleep while standing up. But careful observation has shown that sound sleep is achieved only when the horse is lying down (Kleitman, 1939).

In a delightful book, Love (1958) has described the sleeping habits of homeless vagrants in New York City. Many of them sleep in a sitting position in such places as subway cars, all-night movies, railroad stations, and hotel lobbies for months at a time. This would seem to preclude muscular relaxation. However, this sleep is often not very relaxed or entirely satisfying. The men expressed a desire for sleeping in a prone position every so often. One subway sleeper would get a hotel room on occasion and sleep for 22 of the 24 hours. In general, one may conclude that sleep requires some degree of muscular relaxation, although this is relative, with some degree of sleep possible in less than total tension reduction.

People move around during sleep with as many as 20 to 45 position changes per night. Each person has a dozen or so favorite positions and tends to use them every night (Johnson, Swan, and Weigand, 1930). The function of this movement is probably to prevent cramping or circulation difficulties. The muscular relaxation that goes on in sleep is far from complete. Probably one set of muscles is rested and then another. The changes in position help accomplish this. Recently, evidence has been gathered showing that the level of sleep during the night is not constant nor does it decrease and increase throughout the night in one smooth curve as earlier writers assumed. It waxes and wanes with six or so periods of aroused sleep. These periods of aroused sleep are associated with major bodily movements followed by eye movements, brain waves indicative of a drowsy state, and dreams (Aserinsky and Kleitman, 1955 a; Dement and Kleitman, 1957 a). Kleitman (1957) interprets this as a residual of the primitive wakefulness of necessity cycle. The daytime analog would be cat-naps. We will discuss these phenomena further, later on.

Kleitman and his associates have found that the "depth" of sleep is related to body movements (Kleitman et al., 1933; Mullin et al., 1937). Body movements during the night are inversely related to depth of sleep as determined by the intensity of an auditory stimulus necessary to awaken a person. It is relatively easy to awaken a person just after a muscular movement but the threshold goes up as time elapses until the next movement is approached. The soundest sleep is in between movements and the greater the time between two movements, the sounder the sleep. There are more movements as the night progresses, so that to some extent the old curves are correct in that sleep is at its greatest depth early in the sleep period. But a long period of immobility is sometimes observed in the early morning and this is associated with dreaming. Kleitman believes, however, that motility is the critical factor in depth of sleep.

Eye movements have always been of interest in relation to sleep. Sleep is usually accompanied by a closing of the eyes, but this is not always necessary—people can literally fall asleep with their eyes open (Miles, 1929). However, a relaxation of the musculature of the eyes is a concomitant of sleep onset. The eyeballs roll slowly from side to side, are often unsynchronized, and are a more sensitive indication of sleep onset than the EEG change. When quiet sleep is attained the eye movements stop, with the eyes tending to be pointed upward and divergent. The slow movements reappear abruptly following a body movement (Kleitman, 1939; Dement, 1961 b). Rapid eye movements are accompanied by other indications of arousal (Dement, 1961 b).

Snoring is a well-known phenomenon produced by a relaxation of the muscles of the pharynx (Fischgold and Schwartz, 1961). Normally, snoring begins about 1½ hours after going to bed at the end of the first sleep cycle. It occurs at all sleep stages but especially during the less aroused ones. It tends to be interrupted by gross bodily movements and rarely appears during the periods of rapid eye movements. During daytime naps or sleep induced by Nembutal, snoring appears earlier, within 45 minutes. The occurrence of snoring at the beginning of spontaneous daytime sleep is a harbinger of sounder sleep while a lack of snoring is typically followed by very superficial sleep. The experimenters were struck by the fact that none of the sleepers was aware that he had been snoring even though he was sometimes awakened by the sound. Contrary to the popular belief that snoring occurs only while the sleeper is lying on his back, the authors report observing individuals snoring while lying on their sides.

Respiration becomes more regular during sleep, although it can be changed by various internal and external events. Breathing during sleep becomes a more thoracic than abdominal movement. This is probably due to a relaxation of the abdominal muscles (Kleitman, 1939).

Thus muscular relaxation plays a prominent role in sleeping behavior. But is not this degree of muscular relaxation possible without sleep? It would seem plausible that a person could rest his muscles simply by lying in a prone position. The only difficulty is that experience shows that a person in a prone position with eyes closed simply cannot stay awake after the first night. Even without sleep deprivation, muscular relaxation leads to a tendency to fall asleep. Patients resting in the morning while waiting for a basal metabolic rate determination frequently fall asleep. Subjects trained with the Jacobson progressive relaxation procedure frequently lapse into sleep. With proper training, however, they can achieve the depth of relaxation asociated with partial sleep while still awake (Kleitman, 1939). But it is also possible that full muscular relaxation is not possible with the cortex still showing a wakeful pattern.

Since sleep is related so intimately to muscular relaxation the question naturally arises as to whether sleep functions to alleviate muscular fatigue. This would be consistent with the metabolic changes described in the previous section but specifically limited to muscular phenomena. Kleitman (1939) believed that muscular fatigue may lead to the muscular relaxation that results in sleep. On the other hand, Coriat (1912), while emphasizing the importance of muscular relaxation, points out that such relaxation takes place whether the organism is fatigued or not. Thus sleep may prevent fatigue on an innate, instinctive basis, but it is independent of the given state of actual muscular fatigue.

It is true that muscular fatigue is one of the most prominent symptoms of sleep deprivation. Here, too, the situation is complicated by the fact that it is very nearly impossible to do a sleep-loss study without having the subject engaged in activities that are known to produce muscular fatigue in their own right. Although a clear-cut study varying sleep and fatigue independently is not available because of these technical problems, some indirect and partial evidence suggests that the two are not identical.

In a sleep-deprivation study by Ax et al. (1957), which will be described in more detail later, an attempt was made to separate the effects of sleep deprivation from general muscular fatigue. The subjects lay on a comfortable bed in a darkened, temperature-controlled room all night, demonstrating that they were awake by pressing a hand switch in response to a buzzer sounded once a minute. Failure to respond resulted in loud bells. The authors, who tried this procedure beforehand, insist that it did not produce tension and irritability, but that it provided considerable bodily rest with little sleep. The significant finding was that on many tests of appropriately low interest, performance deteriorated in just about the same way it does after the more typical sleep-deprivation experiment, in which the subject is kept awake by frequent fatiguing activities. Of course it is obvious that Ax's subjects were not fully relaxed. Nevertheless, we can assume that Ax's subjects were less fatigued than the subjects in a typical sleep-deprivation experiment. If fatigue were the critical factor then there should have been some observable difference. More research along this line would be useful. Perhaps someone can find a chemical method of separating the two variables in a better way.

Another approach to this problem is to investigate the inter-action between sleep deprivation and induced muscular fatigue. This was done by Bowen, Ross, and Andrews (1956). They studied the performance of subjects in a visual tracking task after one night's sleep loss and found a marked decrement. This is the kind of paced task that typically shows an effect of sleep deprivation. Muscular fatigue was induced by five or ten minutes of stationary bicycle riding at 20 mph pedaling speed. This strenuous activity had no direct effect on the tracking task nor did it inter-act with sleep deprivation to worsen performance. Of course, this was a relatively brief period of muscular exertion, so that the possibility that prolonged chronic fatigue would interact with sleep deprivation cannot be precluded.

We see then that, while sleeping is associated with muscular relaxation, it is not clear whether sleep is necessary for the reduction of muscular fatigue or whether muscular relaxation is simply a necessary condition for sleeping. Muscular fatigue is not necessary for sleeping but may facilitate it. Although muscular fatigue is a common symptom of sleep deprivation, muscular exertion does not seem to account for all the effects of sleep deprivation. Our tentative conclusion is that the reduction of muscular fatigue is one of several functions facilitated by sleep. It is probably secondary to more basic metabolic functions. It is also quite possible that excessive muscular fatigue is *prevented* by a daily period of muscular relaxation.

NEUROPHYSIOLOGICAL FUNCTIONS

Perhaps the most dramatic change in sleep is the decrease in reactivity of the organism. Subjectively, we speak of this as a loss of consciousness. Perhaps most of the muscular and biochemical changes are simple consequences of the fact that the body's coordinating and controlling organ—the brain—decreases its waking function during sleep. The difference in waking and sleep brain activity has been described vividly by the great Sherrington (1940) in what is perhaps one of neurophysiology's most famous passages:

A scheme of lines and nodal points, gathered at one end into a great ravelled knot, the brain, and at the other trailing off to a sort of stalk, the spinal cord. Imagine activity in this shown by little points of light. Of these some stationary points flash rhythmically, faster or slower. Others are travelling points, streaming in serial trains at various speeds. The rhythmic stationary lights lie at the nodes. The nodes are both goals whither converge, and junctions whence diverge, the lines of travelling lights. The lines and nodes where the lights are, do not remain, taken together, the same even for a single moment. There are at any time nodes and lines where lights are not.

Suppose we choose the hour of deep sleep. Then only in some sparse and out of the way places are nodes flashing and trains of light-points running. Such places indicate local activity still in progress. At one such place we can watch the behavior of a group of lights perhaps a myriad strong. They are pursuing a mystic and recurrent manoeuvre as if of some incantational dance. They are superintending the beating of the heart and the state of the arteries so that while we sleep the circulation of the blood is what it should be. The great knotted head-piece of the whole sleeping system lies for the most part dark, and quite especially so the roof brain. Occasionally at places in it lighted points flash or move but soon subside. Such lighted points and moving trains of lights are mainly far in the outskirts, and wink slowly and travel slowly. At intervals even a gush of sparks wells up and sends a train down the spinal cord, only to fail to arouse it. Where however the stalk joins the headpiece, there goes forward in a limited field a remarkable display. A dense constellation of some thousands of nodal points bursts out every few seconds into a short phase of ryhthmical flashing. At first a few lights, then more, increasing in rate and num-ber with a deliberate crescendo to a climax, then to decline and die away. After due pause the efflorescence is repeated. With each such ryhthmic outburst goes a discharge of trains of travelling lights along the stalk and out of it altogether into a number of nerve-branches. What is this doing? It manages the taking of our breath the while we sleep.

Should we continue to watch the scheme we should observe after a time an impressive change which suddenly accrues. In the great head-end which has been mostly darkness spring up myriads of twink-ling stationary lights and myriads of trains of moving lights of many different directions. It is as though activity from one of those local places which continued restless in the darkened main-mass suddenly spread far and wide and invaded all. The great topmost sheet of the mass, that where hardly a light had twinkled or moved, becomes now a sparking field of rhythmic flashing points with trains of travelling sparks hurrying hither and thither. The brain is waking and with it the mind is returning. It is as if the Milky Way entered upon some cosmic dance. Swiftly the head mass becomes an enchanted loom where millions of flashing shuttles weave a dissolving pattern, always a meaningful pattern through never an abiding one; a shifting harmony of subpatterns. Now as the waking body arouses, subpatterns of this great harmony of activity stretch down into the unlit tracks of the stalk-piece of the scheme. This means that the body is up and rises to meet its waking day.

The psychological significance of these neurophysiological changes—particularly those of the cerebral cortex—becomes apparent when one considers that these are the substrata of the higher mental processes, including thinking, remembering, and conscious awareness (Morgan and Stellar, 1950; Lashley, 1954). Sleep involves a decrease in cortical arousal and its correlated psychological functions. For our purposes, we will roughly equate cortical functioning with general, conscious wakefulness and a decrease in cortical functioning with sleep. However, it is true that a primitive sleep-wake cycle, probably corresponding to "wakefulness of necessity," occurs in organisms without a cortex (Kleitman, 1937; Kleitman, 1939).

Actually, the brain is never completely electrically quiescent in sleep—although it ceases in deep hibernation in certain animals at various low temperatures (Suomalainen, 1961). Under other conditions, electrical activity can be observed in the brain both in wakefulness and sleep. This activity does not indicate the firing of neurones such as the trains of lights in Sherrington's analogy —a continuous firing would keep the individual in a state of convulsion. Instead there is a rhythmic flow of extracellular current, which appears to be a property of any aggregate of nerve cells. The function of this electrical phenomenon is not known —one theory is that there is a buildup and discharge of potentials by cellular metabolism. In any case, it seems to operate as a homeostatic mechanism of some sort that keeps the brain stable (Brazier, 1960).

The brain waves from this electrical activity may be measured at the scalp by the electroencephalograph (EEG). This useful instrument simply picks up and amplifies the brain waves in much the same way as receiving radio signals. The main difference between various psychological states is not the total level of activity as such but its rhythm. Recall that brain metabolism is not decreased and that some cortical cells are more active during sleep. When a person is resting with his eyes closed, a characteristic rhythm of 8 to 12 cps frequency and moderate amplitude is evident—this is the well-known alpha rhythm. When mental activity is going on the EEG record shows very fast, low amplitude waves. This is because the cells are less synchronized —each busy in a different direction in the drama of thought. When the person is sleeping, the record shows a very slow, high amplitude wave, indicating a high degree of synchrony—the lulling, deep rhythm of sleep (Ellingson, 1956).

The brain waves appearing during sleep can be classified into several categories. A five-stage system was devised by Loomis, Harvey, and Hobart (1937). The stages range from A, awake, to E, deep sleep. Emmons and Simon (1956) add a sixth stage, very deep sleep. Sample records of EEG tracings of these stages are

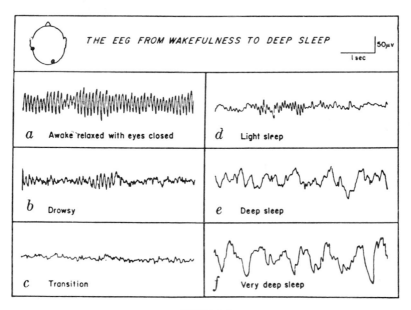

FIGURE 2

on our poster ✓

shown in Fig. 2. Stage A is the well-known alpha rhythm. For some purposes, this stage can be subdivided into four categories (O, A-plus, A, A-) depending on the amount of alpha present (see Simon and Emmons, 1956). Stage B is the drowsy period and consists of a mixture of fast alpha and delta waves of low magnitude. Most dreams seem to appear in Stage B. Stage C is a transition period and is characterized by very low voltage, 14 per second spindles. In Stage D the spindles continue but delta waves also appear. Stages E and F consist of the large, slow-rolling delta waves. Stage F has the larger, slower waves.

The Loomis system is widely used around the world, but the Kleitman group uses a somewhat simpler system that we will have occasion to discuss. In the Kleitman system there are four EEG stages. Stage 1 consists of an absolute lack of spindle activity and includes the Loomis A and B stages. Stage 2 is characterized by spindle activity. Stage 3 is intermediate with a mixture of spindling and slow waves. Stage 4 is the slow delta wave period (Dement and Kleitman, 1957 b).

The general behavioral significance of the EEG has been discussed by Lindsley (1957) who shows that it provides an index of activation. He orders behavior along a continuum from death to strong excited emotion. Many visceral, muscular, and brain changes accompany activation. However, the cortical EEG provides a clear measure of this, as is shown in Table I.

TABLE I

PSYCHOLOGICAL STATES AND THEIR EEG, CONSCIOUS, AND BEHAVIORAL CORRELATES

BEHAVIORAL CONTINUUM	ELECTRO-ENCEPHALO-GRAM	STATES OF AWARENESS	BEHAVIORAL EFFICIENCY
Strong, excited emotion (fear, rage, anxiety)	Desynchronized: low to moderate amplitude; fast, mixed frequencies.	Restricted awareness; divided attention; diffuse, hazy; "confusion."	Poor: (lack of control, freezing-up, disorganized).
Alert attentiveness	Partially synchronized: mainly fast, low amplitude waves.	Selective attention, but may vary or shift. "Concentration," "anticipation," "set."	Good: (efficient, selective, quick, reactions; organized for serial responses).
Relaxed wakefulness	Synchronized: optimal alpha rhythm.	Attention wanders—not forced. Favors free association.	Good: (routine reactions and creative thought).

TABLE I (*continued*)

BEHAVIORAL CONTINUUM	ELECTRO-ENCEPHALO-GRAM	STATES OF AWARENESS	BEHAVIORAL EFFICIENCY
Drowsiness	Reduced alpha and occasional low amplitude slow waves.	Borderline, partial awareness, imagery and reverie. "Dreamlike states."	Poor: (unco-ordinated, sporadic, lacking sequential timing).
Light sleep	Spindle bursts and slow waves (larger). Loss of alphas.	Markedly reduced consciousness (loss of consciousness). Dream state.	Absent
Deep sleep	Large and very slow waves (synchrony but on slow time base). Random, irregular pattern.	Complete loss of awareness (no memory for stimulation or for dreams).	Absent
Coma	Isoelectric to irregular large slow waves.	Complete loss of consciousness; little or no response to stimulation; amnesia.	Absent
Death	Isoelectric: gradual and permanent disappearance of all electrical activity.	Complete loss of awareness as death ensues.	Absent

After Lindsley, 1952.

During the course of a natural night of sleep, the individual will show a cyclical change in the EEG state corresponding to the variations in sleep depth. Loomis and his associates present graphs on subjects cycling from the A to the D or E stages four to six times a night. A loud or unusual stimulus shifts the EEG up toward the A stage, sometimes skipping a stage or two. Bodily movements are usually, but not always, associated with an upward change of stage.

Lester (1958) has shown that it is possible to electronically transform the complex EEG pattern into a simple frequency versus time graph. This simple frequency measure appears to correlate with depth of sleep. Lester had judges rate the original EEG records according to depth of sleep by the usual clinical methods, taking into account amplitude and patterns as well as frequency. The phi coefficients between the clinical judgments and the electronic frequency measure ranged from .75 to .91, showing a significant relationship almost as good as the reliability coefficients for the clinical judgments. This might be a useful research tool. His data, shown in Fig. 3, provide a good demon-

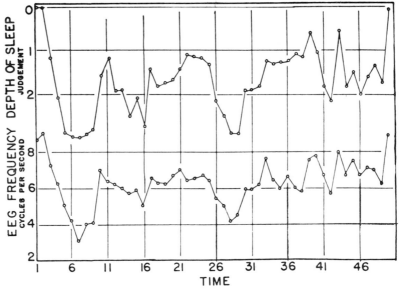

FIGURE 3

stration of the cyclical changes in depth of sleep throughout the night.

There are limits, however, to the usefulness of the EEG as a measure of sleep and wakefulness. Atropine and other drugs will produce EEG sleep patterns in animals that are awake behaviorally, although the implications of this for the physiological mechanisms are in dispute (Schmidt, 1957; Ellington, 1956; Kleitman, 1957; Ellingson, 1957). Also, the correlation between EEG patterns and wakefulness may be disrupted by head injuries (Walsh, 1957). Nevertheless, in the normal subject the EEG is an extremely useful indication of cortical activity and is probably related in a complex way to wakefulness and sleep.

At this point, we must discuss the issue of defining "depth of sleep." This issue has become complex and controversial. Earlier we cited studies in which depth of sleep was defined in terms of auditory threshold or general motility. In this section we have just seen that depth of sleep may be defined in terms of the character of the EEG—an aroused EEG is usually taken as light sleep and a synchronized EEG as deep sleep. All of these indications of depth of sleep make intuitive sense and in the past they have been used more or less interchangeably.

In recent years, however, it has been found that in some situations the several measures are unrelated. Specifically, during the dream stage of sleep the EEG is aroused but auditory thresholds are raised and certain muscle groups are relaxed. Thus the EEG suggests light sleep and the other measures deep sleep. This phenomenon is particularly clear in the case of cats and has led some investigators to describe dreams as occurring in deep sleep. In man and higher primates the discrepancy is not as marked and dreams appear to occur in light sleep. The issue has been discussed by Oswald (1964) and will be treated at length in the chapter on dreams in this book.

The problem at this time is to find some way of describing the various stages of sleep without making a prejudgment about the theoretical issues. The terms *light* and *deep* appear to be outmoded. Terms such as *telencephalic* versus *rhombencephalic,* neosleep versus archisleep, or forebrain versus hindbrain involve too many assumptions about mechanisms that are just beginning to be explored. After considering various possibilities, we have decided to use the terms *aroused sleep* and *synchronized sleep* in this book. These terms are descriptive of the EEG and do not necessarily imply that auditory threshold, motility, or any other measure of sleep depth is correlated with the level of cortical arousal. When applicable, sleep stages will simply be referred to by the number of the EEG stage (1, 2, 3, 4). Other measures —auditory threshold, motility, etc.—will be used in a strictly operational sense. If these usages are kept in mind, there should be no confusion about sleep depth.

Many of the physiological changes during sleep can be seen as due to the general raising of several thresholds. There is a decrease in tendon reflexes such as the knee jerk. There is a decrease in palmar sweating leading to a decrease in the Galvanic Skin Response. However, most other parts of the skin show no change in sweat production. There are also some complex effects on breathing rate which Kleitman attributes to a decrease in the irritability of the respiration center in the brain. Of particular interest is the fact that in synchronized sleep the positive Babinski reflex reappears. This is usually taken to indicate lessened cortical influence on subcortical centers.

Recent evidence (Caspers, 1961) shows that in addition to the waves of the traditional EEG, cortical d.c. potentials reflect the sleep-wakefulness cycle in rats. Negative d.c. shifts are associated with spontaneous locomotion, sensory stimulation, and arousal. Positive shifts reflect resting and sleep. During sleep the d.c. potential oscillates with the EEG level. Of particular interest is the observation that these d.c. potential changes are not always correlated with EEG changes. A d.c. change may precede the slowing of the EEG on going to sleep, and on awakening may trail the EEG waking pattern if the transition from sleep to wakefulness is gradual and with little motor activity. Caspers suggests a relationship between these cortical d.c. changes and a subcortical system, probably the brain stem reticular formation.

Becker and his associates (see Becker, Bachman, and Friedman, 1962) have stressed the importance of these d.c. potentials in a variety of growth, anesthetic, hypnotic, and pathological processes. They also find a relationship between positive d.c. shifts and sleep when measured from the frontal area to the occiput. Hypnosis, anesthesia, and local analgesia also produce shifts. Sleep can be produced in salamanders by a magnetic field that reverses the flow of current. Three sources of the d.c. current were demonstrated—at cranial, brachial, and lumbar neural enlargements. The current flows out from these "batteries," probably along motor nerves. The cranial source, at the occiput or base of the brain, may be an overall control system. Becker et al. think of these circuits as primitive communication systems. They are of great potential importance, although their exact significance is hard to evaluate at the moment.

What is the significance of these neurophysiological changes for the biological need for sleep? Several people have suggested that the cessation of cortical functions means that some reparative process takes place in the brain during sleep. This may be on the metabolic level as discussed earlier, or it may be changes unique to the nervous system. For example, Bartley and Chute (1947) suggest that the nervous system is so complex that periodically there has to be a "resolution of interrelational tangles." This may be analogous to sending a test program through a computing machine every now and then to see which circuits have burned out.

Hallowell Davis (1950) has postulated a homeostatic mechanism for regulating the excitability of the central nervous system, particularly cerebral excitability. The physiological state regulated is that which varies diurnally from sleep to wakefulness. When the homeostatic mechanism fails, coma may result at one extreme and convulsions at the other. Davis compares this homeostatic mechanism to others such as the muscle spindle or the carotid sinus. As in these mechanisms, the regulator of the excitability of the central nervous system must have a source of negative feedback: a source of information about danger to the tissues or an exhaustion of chemical reserves. Then some sort of recuperation can take place. The first sign of negative feedback in the case of overexcitability of the central nervous system is the subjective feeling of fatigue. This signals us to stop activity and rest in much the same way that hunger and thirst affect the person. The source of the subjective feeling, Davis believes, is somewhere in the central nervous system.

The criticism against muscular fatigue as the signal for sleep, mentioned earlier, can be raised against Davis' idea. Fatigue is not an adequate explanation of why we go to sleep. But here, too, sleep may function to *prevent* cerebral fatigue and thus the rest of Davis' theory is more acceptable. The idea of sleep as a general homeostatic mechanism is attractive and will be mentioned again.

One argument against the idea that sleep functions to permit a recuperation of the cortex is that there is an inverse relationship between the size of the cortex and the amount of sleep needed. As one proceeds up the phylogenetic scale the cortex becomes larger and more complex. One would expect that the more complex and overworked an organ, the more rest it would need. Nevertheless, the ability to extend the period of wakefulness over sleep also increases as one goes up the same phylogenetic scale (Kleitman, 1939). On the human level, sleep needs are greatest in infants without a fully functioning cortex and decrease with age, although the situation is complex in the elderly.

A rebuttal to this argument might be that the more complex cortex functions more efficiently and thus needs less sleep. However, the elderly arteriosclerotic, whose brain is certainly not functioning well, frequently suffers from insomnia (McGraw and Oliven, 1959). Another rebuttal might be that the more complex brain has so many parts that are interchangeable that one may spell the other during wakefulness, thus reducing neural fatigue and postponing the time when sleep is necessary. This theory, however, requires experimental evidence.

The most direct approach to the problem of brain restoration during sleep is simply to deprive the organism of sleep and examine neurological changes. Kleitman (1939) has reviewed the few studies in which this has been done; unfortunately they are all old and do not utilize modern neurophysiological and histological techniques. In 1894, Manaceine found hemorrhages in the gray matter of puppies who had died after 4 to 6 days of sleep deprivation. Tarozzi found degenerative changes in the cortex and cerebellum of dogs who died after 9 to 17 days of enforced sleep loss. Similar degenerative changes were found by Pieron. He kept 20 dogs awake from 30 to 505 hours and found the degenerative changes proportional to the length of sleep deprivation. Dogs permitted to sleep before sacrifice showed no changes. Okazaki reported comparable results on dogs kept awake 14 to 77 days. Rabbits show changes also.

In 1927, Kleitman himself performed the methodologically most adequate study, with negative results. Twelve puppies were kept awake from 2 to 7 days and their brains compared with those of their litter-mate controls. Degenerative changes were found but did not differ from the controls. Unfortunately, Kleitman's study used a mild deprivation period. A longer period or a procedure in which the animals died naturally instead of being sacrificed may have shown differences. At the present time, no firm conclusion can be drawn either way.

In spite of his negative findings on brain pathology, Kleitman believes that sleep deprivation does produce fatigue of the higher cortical levels. He bases this mostly on the psychological changes —irritability, hallucinations, and concentration difficulties. It is often difficult to evaluate the effects of sleep deprivation, he says, because of several confounding variables. First, muscular activity, and thus muscular fatigue, is essential for keeping the subject awake. Second, the sleep-deprived subject lapses into a protective semisleep in spite of all efforts to prevent this. Finally, the subject pulls himself together for short periods so that he may appear to be functioning normally.

If either the neuropathology or the psychological malfunctioning resulting from sleep loss indicates a cortical fatigue, then a good case can be made for the idea that sleep offers a time for a metabolic restoration, a network reorganization, or some other neural restoration. Again, the evidence is not conclusive. There is a strong possibility that the recovery of brain functions is a need fulfilled by sleep, but the case is not closed.

A NEED TO DREAM?

In the previous sections we have alluded to a stage of sleep that appears to be associated with dreaming. We will describe this stage in more detail in the next chapter, but for the moment we can say that dreams tend to occur periodically throughout the night when the EEG shows Stage 1 and when Rapid Eye Movements (REM) appear. The discovery of these objective measures of dreaming by Aserinsky and Kleitman (1955 a) has stimulated a good deal of research on dreams.

Traditionally, dreams have been viewed as phenomena of considerable psychological interest but of little biological significance. Freud (1961) assumed that they acted as a safety valve for the tensions of the day and thus enabled the sleeping person to remain asleep. However, William Dement (1960) has raised the possibility that we do not dream in order to sleep, but that we sleep in order to dream. In other words, dreams subserve a basic biological function.

Dement tested the theory of the necessity of dreams in an experiment that has become widely quoted. He deprived subjects of dreams while permitting them to sleep in other stages. This was possible because of the objective EEG and REM measures. After a baseline period, the subjects were watched during the night and awakened whenever they began to dream. Upon returning to sleep, they entered a new cycle of synchronized sleep before the next dream attempt. After a few days of this deprivation, however, they made more and more attempts to dream right after going back to sleep. Later on, when the subjects were allowed to sleep normally, they increased the time spent in dreaming above the baseline level. Thus it appears that the subjects needed dreams and compensated for the dream deprivation by dreaming more during the recovery period.

To control for the effects of sleep deprivation and awakening per se, the subjects returned at a later time for interruptions of sleep during nondreaming periods. The number and distribution of awakenings were duplicated for each subject except that they took place after a dream period. Neither increase in dream attempts nor extended dreaming in recovery was observed. Therefore the increased dreaming during the recovery period following dream deprivation is not due to the disturbance of being awakened.

Dement's basic finding has been confirmed in a number of laboratories (e.g. Snyder, 1963; Hoedemaker et al., 1963). Furthermore, amphetamine has been found to decrease REM periods, but when the drug is withdrawn there is a compensatory increase in dreaming (Rechtschaffen and Maron, 1964). The drug method clearly avoids the problem of disturbing the subject by awakening.

Dement also found that some dream-deprived subjects showed irritability, anxiety, concentration difficulties, and increased appetite. Dement (1961) observed various kinds of emotional disturbance in a subsequent series of dream-deprived subjects. This part of his findings has not been confirmed generally (Snyder, 1963; Hoedemaker, 1963). The most recent evidence suggests, however, that animals deprived of dreams show emotional changes. Dement is trying to demonstrate that dream periods are necessary for the discharge of some accumulated poison. There is no direct evidence for this as yet (Luce, 1965).

This exciting discovery needs much more work and amplification before its significance is fully understood. Nevertheless, it shows that dreams play a vital and positive role. It may be interpreted to mean that we do not dream in order to sleep, but sleep in order to dream. This conclusion is not, however, entirely warranted. First of all, Dement's data show a good deal of return to sleep during the first few nights and, although dream time increased during recovery, 77% of the time was still spent in dreamless sleep. In addition, the sleep-deprivation studies show that, during recovery, subjects spend more time in synchronized sleep. Williams et al. (1964) analyzed some EEG data from a sleep deprivation study at Walter Reed. During the first recovery night after 60 hours of wakefulness, there was an *increase* in stage 4 sleep and a *decrease* in dreaming. On subsequent nights total dream time did increase. A similar finding is reported by Berger and Oswald (1962). They deprived human subjects of sleep for

108 hours and then studied recovery. On the first recovery night the subjects showed a marked *increase* in synchronized sleep and a *decrease* in stage 1-REM sleep. On the second recovery night the dream time did show a compensatory increase but not as large as the increase in synchronized sleep on the first night.

Perhaps dreaming and synchronized sleep are both needed for different purposes. This is suggested by a study in which Dement (1961 a) restricted sleep to 4 hours a night. *Both* stage 4 sleep and dream time increased on successive nights! The time spent in stage 2 sleep was reduced and the initial sleep onset period was shortened.

Finally, an independent need for stage 4 sleep has been demonstrated by Agnew, Webb, and Williams (1963). In a procedure analogous to Dement's method of dream deprivation, they deprived subjects of stage 4 sleep. This was done by sounding a tone whenever the subject entered stage 4; no awakening was necessary. During recovery the subjects increased the proportion of time spent in stage 4 sleep as compared to their baseline rates.

Therefore we cannot conclude that we sleep only to dream. Both the dream stage of sleep and the synchronized stage of sleep appear to be necessary. Perhaps synchronized sleep fulfills one function and dreams fulfill another. The exact functions of each remain a mystery. They may well overlap in their functions. It would seem reasonable to assume, however, that the synchronized stage of sleep offers the best conditions for metabolic restoration, recovery from muscular fatigue, and neural reorganization. Other possible functions for dreams will be discussed in the next chapter.

SUMMARY

The biological motives most familiar to psychologists—hunger, thirst, temperature, etc.—are built-in mechanisms serving, on a behavorial level, the metabolic and homeostatic needs of the body. Other motives—curiosity, sex, affection, etc. —serve the general survival of the individual or the species.

Sleep is comparable to these motives, in a very general way, because it is necessary for survival—total lack of sleep results in death. Sleep is also important in one's general feeling of well-being and efficiency.

One specific function sleep may play is to conserve energy at times when other adaptive behavior is not feasible. All organisms—from plants to human beings—adapt their behavior to the seasonal and diurnal cycles of nature. The patterns used—diurnal, nocturnal, monophasic, polyphasic, tidal, seasonal—represent an adaptation in which energy is expended at times appropriate for the organism, and conserved at other times. The cycles vary in their fixity, with man showing a fair degree of modifiability. Sleep, then, may be viewed as an innate mechanism providing for periods of energy conservation.

Does sleep permit a more active restoration process? The fact that sleep involves a decrease in metabolism, a general muscular relaxation, a slowing of circulatory and respiratory functions, and a decrease in wakeful brain functions suggests that some sort of recuperation is going on in one or several of these systems.

Recent evidence supports some old theories about the possible anabolic functions of sleep. During sleep deprivation, the basic energy transfer system of cellular metabolism is under stress. Phosphorylation is accomplished by emergency measures, but these are exhausted after several days and behavior deteriorates. Sleep restores this. Thus, sleep may function to permit the build-up of energy reserves. The fact that digestion continues undiminished during sleep is consistent with this. The energy restoration would explain the decreases in muscular, brain, and other functions as well as the decrease in level of arousal.

The decrease in the expenditure of energy for active behavioral processes may facilitate other basic cellular functions, such as the repair of tissue, the fight against disease, general growth, and the prolongation of life. Some evidence supports such an idea, but it is largely hypothetical at the present time.

An argument against any restorative effect of sleep has been that sleep is not dependent on metabolic exhaustion, muscular or neural fatigue, or any other bodily signal of depletion.

Similarly, the fact that we are frequently less efficient upon awakening than on going to bed is often mentioned. However, this argument confuses the *function* of sleep with its mechanism of *control*. The onset and offset of sleep—which will be discussed in a later chapter—is certainly not entirely under the control of fatigue. Nevertheless, this is not an indictment against the idea that sleep functions to permit recuperation.

The nature of most homeostatic motives is preventative. Thus, hunger is aroused long before a total depletion of food substances in the organism occurs, thirst emerges before cellular dehydration reaches a critical point, and pain may precede mortal bodily injury. Likewise, sleep motivation occurs before energy reserves are exhausted and before fatigue sets in. When food is not available to an organism hunger may become ravenous and eventually the body weakens. So, too, with sleep; if sleep is not possible, subjective fatigue mounts and later there is a general deterioration and a collapse of the energy transfer system. Thus the motive for sleep has this built-in anticipatory feature of other homeostatic motives.

There are at least two distinct phases of sleep—the synchronized stage with a slow EEG and the REM-dream stage with an aroused EEG. Deprivation of either phase results in compensatory efforts by the sleeping organism. The two types of sleep are qualitatively different and may serve similar or quite different functions. It is possible that synchronized sleep facilitates the restoration of functions, while dreams play another role.

In conclusion, while the evidence is incomplete, the sleep motive appears to be comparable to the other homeostatic motives. A reasonable working hypothesis is that sleep permits: the conservation of energy; the diversion of energy for growth, repair, and resistance; and the restoration of energy reserves for muscular, neural, and all other bodily processes in advance of their actual exhaustion. The exact functions of the synchronized and dream phases of sleep are not known.

CHAPTER 3

Dreams and Sleep

In the last chapter we saw that dreams play a prominent part in sleep. It is not the purpose of this chapter to make an exhaustive analysis of dreams in relation to personality and psychopathology. Nor will a general phenomenological description of dream experiences be attempted. Rather, the relation of dreams to sleep will be examined because several theoretical issues are raised by the occurrence of dreams. After all, in the present theoretical analysis sleep has been described as the consumatory response for the motive to sleep. But instead of complete relaxation and dedication to restoration, people report those most interesting, fantastic, and emotional experiences that we call dreams.

The plan of this chapter is as follows: First, the thought processes involved during the process of falling asleep will be examined from both the physiological and subjective viewpoints. Then the recently discovered objective measure of dreams—rapid eye movements—will be described and evaluated in some detail. Using this measure, the occurrence of dreams during the night and in various subject populations can be determined. One major issue that can be answered with this technique is the level of arousal during which dreams occur. The cognitive nature and level of thought processes in dreams will be examined in order to see if they are simpler or as complex as in the waking state. Finally, the functions that dreams play in sleep will be discussed.

FALLING ASLEEP AND AWAKENING

The onset of sleep is accompanied by muscular relaxation, a decreasing responsiveness to afferent stimulation, and changes in brain potentials. As the individual closes his eyes, his EEG pattern shows a predominance of alpha; this is the A stage in the Loomis system. As drowsiness increases, the B stage appears. This is a transitional state with a mixture of alpha, beta, and theta waves. The sleeper has a sensation of "floating" or "drifting off." He may return to stage A or go on to C—a more definite state of sleep. On the average, sleep is attained in less than a half hour (Kleitman, 1963, part 2).

Muscular relaxation sets in before the individual is fully asleep. One criterion for sleep, used by the Kleitman group (1939), is the point at which an object—a piece of paper or a spool—which is held in the hand is dropped. The thumb-pressing used by Lindsley (1957) is similar. When subjects are questioned after muscular relaxation has been reached, however, they often report waking and thinking activity (Kamiya, 1961). Therefore, a person may give all outward appearances of being asleep but still be conscious and aware of being awake.

During the onset of sleep, a person's eyes show slow, drifting movements. The motion is pendulous and the two eyes are not coordinated. The slow eye movements are associated with the relaxation during sleep onset and with body movements later on during the night. They seem to occur during the drifting EEG phase (Aserinsky and Kleitman, 1955 a). Sleep-deprived subjects show these slow movements even with their eyes open. They also suggest that people can sleep with their eyes open (Miles and Laslett, 1931; Oswald, 1960). The slow eye movements should not be confused with the rapid eye movements that appear to indicate dreams. Under normal circumstances, rapid eye movements are not found during the onset of sleep (Dement and Kleitman, 1957 b), although they may appear in some special conditions such as narcolepsy (Rechtschaffen, Wolpert, et al, 1963), amphetamine withdrawal (Oswald and Thacore, 1963) and dream deprivation (Dement, 1960).

Phenomenologically, as people fall asleep they often pass through what is described as a "twilight phase," in which they are not fully conscious and still not fully asleep. Reports of this state include thinking, imagery, drifting, and dreams (Kamiya, 1961). There is some question whether the dreams at sleep onset are full-fledged dreams in the traditional sense. Dement and Kleitman's (1957 b) subjects describe the experience as "dream-like," but without the realistic quality of a dream. Their subjects report sensations of "floating," "drifting," and "flashing lights." The twilight phase has been compared with hypnogogic states (Slight, 1924), the aura that precedes an epileptic attack, and the experience of *déjà vu* (Isakower, 1938).

Typically, a person falling asleep perceives less and less of the external world and is more aware of his thought and his bodily sensations. Later he is less aware of his bodily sensations and concentrates on his thoughts. These thoughts tend to show a change from logical, verbal thought to more symbolic processes akin to dreaming. Slight (1924) gives a good example of this. One evening after a very fatiguing day he was in bed and thinking about a particularly difficult patient he had worked with. The patient was schizophrenic and at the insistence of relatives he had attempted psychoanalysis with little success. In a semi-sleeping state but still awake, Slight began visually experiencing himself bicycling after the patient up a steep hill. He felt tired and that he could go no further. Finally a bus came along and carried the patient off, leaving Slight feeling pleased.

The level of thinking in this example resembles that in dreams. It shows symbolism, a pictorial representation of feelings and ideas, and is clearly wish-fulfilling. At the same time he was thinking about the patient in normal, logical fashion using language. He was aware of having a fantasy. This kind of state appears to be intermediate between normal waking thought and regular dreams. It seems a little closer to daydreams than to night dreams. All this suggests a continuum of integrative thinking from wakeful, to semiwakeful, to dream states.

Arnold (1960, pp. 149-150) has proposed a theory of neural mechanisms that could account for some of the phenomena associated with falling asleep. She identifies an amygdala circuit of the limbic system with imagination, a hippocampal circuit with memory, and a number of limbic and other brain structures with action. These three systems have an increasing density of synapses, which are thought to be particularly susceptible to fatigue. Thus, as sleep approaches, first action, then memory, and finally imagination should drop out. This is in accord with the introspective reports. Recently, Jouvet and Mounier (1962) demonstrated that limbic circuits are involved in dreams.

Awakening seems to involve a comparable twilight phase. The return of psychological functions and awareness is in an order reverse to that in which they dropped out while falling asleep. Logical thinking is said to replace associative forms of thinking slowly. Things are timeless and without problem. There is a change from awareness of the inner self, to an awareness of one's own body, to an awareness of external reality. Awakening may differ according to the manner in which the person arises. Regular, daily awakening may occur promptly with little of a transition state. Sudden awakening in an unusual place may produce some disorientation and emotional disturbance. Gradual awakening is of greatest interest because the changes in thinking may be observed and reported (Grotjahn, 1942). Gradual awakening produces more reports of thinking activity during both REM and non-REM periods (Goodenough et al., 1963).

Awakening has been described by Federn (1934) in terms of degree of ego, or cognitive, functioning. During sleep the level of thought, or the degree of ego organization, resembles that of the embryo. As the ego awakens for the purpose of dreaming, it functions only to the extent necessary. In many cases the degree of organization of the awakened ego resembles that which was true at some early level of development of the person. Thus, the level of thought is that of an infantile ego or of a child. This can be extended to awakening in general and to falling asleep. In awakening there may be a recapitulation of the cognitive development of the individual, and in falling asleep, a regression.

In the only quantitative study of awakening known to this

author, Twente (1964) had graduate students fill out questionnaires and telephone him for a structured interview just after awakening. Later he administered several psychological tests. A measure of degree of activity upon awakening, which was obtained from a behavior inventory, was found to correlate positively with a measure of pleasure and negatively with a measure of pain, obtained from an adjective check list. A measure of contact with external reality was obtained from items on the behavior inventory concerning vision, hearing, smell, touch, and communication. This measure of reality contact was correlated positively with the Fisher-Cleveland Barrier score from the group Rorschach. The Barrier score indicates the degree to which a person experiences a definite body boundary. The high Barrier person tends to be independent, achievement-oriented, and self-steering. Twente suggests that there are two types of awakeners. One type finds awakening pleasant, regains contact with reality quickly, springs out of bed, and begins the day's activities. The other type finds it difficult to wake up, regains contact with reality slowly, and hates to face the day's activities.

Thus, both the physiological and subjective data indicate that the process of falling asleep involves passing through a transitional phase characterized by an intermediate level of arousal and consciousness. Thought processes become more dreamlike, but true dreams ordinarily do not occur at this time. A somewhat similar process occurs upon awakening. Thus, there are several levels of integrative thought involved. First, there is the complex thought of wakefulness; then, the semi-wakeful thought of falling asleep or awakening; and, finally, the thought of dreams.

DREAMS AND RAPID EYE MOVEMENTS

Research on dreaming has suffered long because no one knew exactly when dreams occurred. Speculations ran from the idea that dreams took place only during the instant of awakening to the assumption that dreaming was continuous throughout the night. The recent development of an objective measure of dreams by Aserinsky and Kleitman (1955 a) has opened this area for productive research. As mentioned in the last chapter, these investigators found that in addition to the slow pendulous eye movements described in the last section, the sleeper showed rapid eye movements (REM's) periodically throughout the night. When awakened during the REM periods, subjects more frequently reported dreams than at other times. REM's occur only in the aroused Stage 1 sleep. Actually, the relationship between dreams and eye movements was anticipated by a psychologist over half a century ago (Ladd, 1892).

In the original study by Aserinsky and Kleitman, about 74% of the awakenings during REM periods resulted in detailed reports of dreams, while only 17% of non-REM awakenings did so. In subsequent studies Dement (1955) and Dement and Kleitman (1957 a) found dream reports in from 60% to 88% of REM awakenings, depending on the population, and 0 to 7% in quiescent periods. Kales, Hoedemaker, and Jacobson (1963) report 83% dream recall during REM awakenings and 6% during the non-REM times.

On the other hand, a number of investigators report somewhat different results. Goodenough et al. (1959) found dreams in 46 to 93% of REM awakenings and in 17% to 53% at non-REM times, depending on whether the subject was a habitual dreamer or not. Orlinsky (cited in Kamiya, 1961) got figures of 85% and 27%. Foulkes (1962) found an 88% recall during REM periods and 74% at other times. This is the highest non-REM recall reported. In general, the discrepancies in these studies concern non-REM recall rather than REM recall. Everyone seems to agree that dreams are recalled at a high frequency upon awakening from a REM period. A controversy has grown up as to whether dreams also occur during non-REM periods. How can these discrepant findings be reconciled?

First, Goodenough et al. (1959) suggest that memories of dreams persist after recent REM periods, and thus may be reported after a non-REM awakening. In line with this, Wolpert and Trosman (1958) obtained an 85% recall during REM's and a

69% recall during body movements following a dream episode. Five minutes after eye movements stopped only fragments of dreams were recalled. Ten minutes after the REM's very few fragments were reported—the EEG now showing a synchronized record. However, other observers (see Kamiya, 1961) report at least some dreams from the synchronized stages of sleep, although most are from the aroused stages. Finally, Goodenough et al. (1963) failed to obtain evidence for their lingering memory hypothesis. They found no difference in dream recall in non-REM awakenings following REM periods in which the subject was allowed to dream and those which were interrupted to prevent dreaming. At the present time it does not seem that all non-REM dreams can be explained as memories of dreams in preceding REM periods.

Another possibility is that non-REM dreams are not true dreams. There is a real problem in defining a dream. Some of the discrepancies in the studies mentioned above are due to different definitions of dreams. The Kleitman group accepts only the more detailed dreams. Orlinsky worked out a scale of 0 to 7 describing degrees of dreaming. The percentage of dream recall changes with the inclusion or exclusion of different categories of dreaming. It is possible that non-REM dreams are really semiconscious thought processes.

The possibility that non-REM reports are not of true dreams is suggested by Foulkes, who found such a high percentage of non-REM dreams. First of all, the reports from synchronized sleep —the non-REM periods—resembled waking thought more than dreams. This was related to Foulkes' broader questioning set; he asked the subject for anything "going through his mind." Thus, the conclusion which Foulkes reached was that synchronized sleep involves more highly integrated thought, while aroused sleep consists more of dream thought. Of course, this is diametrically opposite to the point of view presented here.

Somewhat similar results have been reported by Rechtschaffen, Verdone, and Wheaton (1963). Subjects were awakened by a buzzer during REM and non-REM periods. They had been briefed previously to describe all mental content and, in addition, an illuminated bulletin board at the foot of the bed outlined a series of questions. The results were that ". . . as compared with REM mentation, subjects describe NREM mentation as more poorly recalled, more like thinking and less like dreaming, less vivid, less visual, more conceptual, under greater volitional control, more plausible, more concerned with their contemporary lives, and occurring in lighter sleep." The fact that the experiences were more under "volitional" control suggests that something approximating wakeful thought was being reported.

The difference in the reports from REM and non-REM awakenings is discriminable. Monroe, Rechtschaffen, and Foulkes (1963) found that raters could make a correct judgment of the stage from which a report came with an accuracy of as high as 88%. Obviously we are dealing with two kinds of mentation.

If non-REM mentation is more like waking thought than dreams it is possible that it is produced by the experimental awakening itself, i.e., the person is actually reporting experiences that occurred in the time between the arousing stimulus and the verbal report. This seems particularly apparent in the study by Foulkes. During the awakenings from synchronized sleep, Foulkes found it necessary to arouse the subject fully in order to get a coherent report. His interview covered at least three or four minutes of intensive probing. It is quite possible that this vigorous, lengthy arousal resulted in reports of thought that had occurred during the several minutes *after* being awakened. Thus, Foulkes' subjects may have been describing mental activity from a near-wakeful state, not actually recalling anything from synchronized sleep.

Kremen (1961) takes the position that Foulkes' results are due to the intensive probing. Kremen further suggests that the nature of the probing may introduce a bias for or against reporting dreams from non-REM periods. Kremen demonstrated this by giving different instructions to subjects. First he ran a group under the usual conditions that lead the subject to believe he should be reporting dreams. He obtained a dream recall of 87% in REM and 36% in non-REM. Then he changed the instructions and made it clear to the subject that dreams were not necessarily expected. The results were 75% for REM and 12% for non-REM. Kremen even believes the few non-REM dreams here were due to the arousal process.

The case is not yet closed. Rechtschaffen, in particular, maintains that true dreams can be obtained from stage 4 on occasion. Furthermore Rechtschaffen, Vogel, and Shaikun (1963) report that identical key elements are found in the REM and non-REM reports in a subject awakened several times in the same night. However, even in synchronized sleep dreams may occur in periods of temporary arousal that may not be picked up clearly by the EEG. The individual sleeping naturally has periods of temporary arousal, even in synchronized sleep, associated with body movements and slow eye movements. Recent evidence suggests that slow eye movements build up into REM's over a five- to ten-minute period (Kamiya, 1961). Thus, it is possible that a dream is built up slowly, becoming more vivid and organized at peak REM periods. This would account for the occurrence of some dreams in non-REM periods.

While there is, as yet, no direct evidence that non-REM thought represents a partial arousal, data from an analogous problem—the occurrence of sleep talking—offers some support. It has often been thought that sleep talking is associated with dreams—a kind of verbal acting out. Kamiya (1961) reports, however, that many incidents of sleep talking occur in synchronized sleep, in conjunction with bodily movements. In a recent study, Rechtschaffen, Goodenough, and Shapiro (1962) confirmed this: of 84 sleep-talking incidents, 8% were found in REM periods, 63% in Kleitman's stage 2, and 29% in stages 3 and 4. But non-REM speech had less affect, was associated with little recalled mental content, and tended to be related to the experimental situation. In a few instances the REM talking was shown to be clearly related to dream content. Rechtschaffen et al. also found non-REM sleep talking to be associated with bodily and facial movements. These movements tended to produce artifacts in the EEG records, but in one uncontaminated instance it appeared that the non-REM talking was dependent on a cortical arousal. Talking during REM periods was not frequently associated with movement. The authors conclude that non-REM sleep talking takes place during a borderline state between true sleep and clear wakefulness. Is it not likely that reports of mental activity during non-REM periods are also dependent on partial arousal?

Arousal is a major technical problem in all dream research. In addition to the spontaneous arousal due to body movements and the activity of internal organs, experimental procedures may produce arousal. In order to get a dream report, one must wake up the subject. In going through the waking process the subject passes through the twilight phase in which semiwakeful thoughts occur. Considering the disorientation that is frequently associated with unusual wakening (Grotjahn, 1942), how can the subject be sure he is reporting only mental activities which occurred when he was definitely asleep? Perhaps this is where highly trained introspective observers, in the best 19th century tradition, could be of real help—Watson notwithstanding.

While REM's are usually associated with dreams, they may not be essential to nonvisual imagery. Dement (1961 b) mentions several cases of individuals, blind for long periods, capable of eye movement who do not show REM's during sleep. Periods of aroused EEG do occur, however, and are associated with nonvisual dreams. This has been confirmed by Berger et al. (1963) and Offenkrantz and Wolpert (1963). Thus, the REM's may be simply a peripheral manifestation of a central dream process, playing a significant role only in the specifically visual imagery. Still, since most dreams of normal individuals are predominantly visual (Hall, 1959), the REM's remain useful.

The problem needs more experimental study, of course. In the meantime, rapid eye movements can at least be used as a sufficient, if not necessary, criterion for dreams. Even Kamiya (1961) concludes that dreaming, in the traditional sense, is best predicted by a drifting EEG stage and rapid eye movements. We shall accept it, for the present purposes, as an index of dreaming in normal subjects.

The character of the REM's associate them closely with dreams. Unlike the slow, pendulous motions, both eyes are coordinated in REM's. The eyes are not in constant motion; they make a shift in about one-tenth of a second and then take up a fixational position for varying times. Movements are in all directions. They are comparable to eye movements during normal, waking perception. In fact, the REM's give the subject the appearance of looking at a movie (Aserinsky and Kleitman, 1955 a; Dement and Kleitman, 1957 b).

There is a correspondence between observed eye movements and visual imagery. For example, Dement and Kleitman (1957 a) describe a case where a series of vertical eye movements was associated with a dream of ladder-climbing in which the person looked up and down. A series of horizontal movements was associated with watching two people throw tomatoes at each other. A lack of eye movement may indicate fixation or watching action at a great distance. Mixed movements usually indicate dreams of people close by. Dement and Wolpert (1958) also report that frequent large movements suggest an active dream, while minimal motions go with passive dreams. This was confirmed by Berger and Oswald (1962).

REM periods may be preceded or followed by a bodily movement, but during the period itself the person is usually rather quiet. Small movements of the hands or limbs may occur (Dement and Kleitman, 1957 b). Although body movements do not occur frequently during REM's, when they do occur the subject frequently reports an interrupted dream or two unrelated dreams (Dement and Wolpert, 1958).

REM periods range from about 3 to 50 minutes in length. The length of the REM is related to the subjective length of the dream. Dement and Kleitman (1957 a) awakened subjects after either 5 or 15 minutes of REM, in a random order, and asked them to guess which time period had elapsed. They were correct in about 83% of the trials. There was also a correlation between the duration of REM's and the number of words in dream narratives the subjects were asked to write. Certainly the old popular idea that dreams occur in the split-second of awakening is wrong.

In brief, visual dreams appear to be related to rapid eye movements. A number of technical problems have yet to be solved in this research area. Still, the REM's are related to the content and length of the subjective dreams. The movements suggest that the dreamer is perceiving a visual image.

THE OCCURRENCE OF DREAMS

When do dreams, as measured by REM's, occur? As mentioned in Chapter 2, the degree of arousal waxes and wanes throughout the night. This is shown by the EEG and measures of motility (Kleitman, 1939; chapter XII). Increases in heart and respiration rates are also found in the aroused stage of sleep (Aserinsky and Kleitman, 1955 a; Kamiya, 1961). REM's were found by the Kleitman group to occur only in EEG stage 1 (Loomis A and B) when most dreams are also reported (Teplitz, cited in Kamiya, 1961). Some dreams occur at an extremely aroused EEG level close to consciousness. Dreams are also reported at other levels, but decrease in frequency the more synchronized the sleep. In general, dreams seem to occur in a state of partial arousal, although this particular issue will be discussed in more detail in the next section.

REM periods and synchronized sleep alternate throughout the night in a consistent fashion. In uninterrupted sleep, Dement and Kleitman (1957 a, 1957 b) found a cyclic variation with an average length of 90 to 100 minutes. The EEG shows minor fluctuations as often as 50 times a night. These are associated with body movements but do not necessarily reach stage 1. However, the major, long-lasting upswings associated with REM periods occur about 3 to 6 times during a 6- to 8-hour sleep period. They are accompanied frequently by major bodily movements. The REM periods, at the crest of the upswings, range from 3 to 50 minutes in length. The REM periods are shorter at the beginning of the night and lengthen more or less regularly as the night goes on. Conversely, the longest period of synchronized sleep takes place shortly after going to sleep; during the course of the night the synchronized part of the cycle becomes shorter and shallower. All this is shown in Fig. 4.

Events during a typical night's sleep take the following

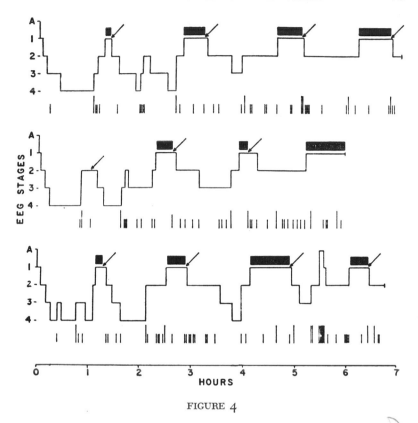

FIGURE 4

course: on going to sleep the subject passes through the stage 1 twilight phase, usually without dreams or REM's. Ignoring individual differences for the moment, synchronized sleep is reached fairly soon—say, in a half hour—with the EEG showing large delta waves. No body movements occur during this sleep stage unless they are accompanied by an EEG upswing. The sleeper remains in this initial synchronized sleep for about a half hour and then shows an arousal. The arousal is fairly abrupt and accompanied by body movements. The EEG may show brief periods of stage 3 and then 2 before reaching stage 1. The evidence of Kamiya (1961) suggests that the body movements give rise to slow eye movements that evolve into rapid eye movements. After the REM period, gross bodily movements may resume as the subject goes down through stage 2 to 3 or 4. After a shorter period of synchronized sleep, a body movement again brings on an abrupt progression to stage 1 and REM's which last a little longer. After the second cycle, the EEG returns only to stage 2 in between REM's. The person usually wakes up after a very long REM period at the end of the night.

There are important individual differences in these cyclic variations. Dement and Kleitman (1957 b) report two subjects who were quite regular in their patterns night after night, although the patterns of the two differed. On the other hand, two other subjects were quite irregular. It is possible that degree of sleepiness, anxiety, endocrines, drugs, and many other factors influence the individual patterns.

Sensory stimulation has often been thought to be the source of dreams. Freud (1958) reviewed this evidence many years ago. For example, Maury subjected himself to various stimuli such as tickling, the smell of cologne, pinching, heat, light, and a drop of water. The stimulus was represented in the dream. Thus, after the drop of water on his forehead, he dreamed "he was in Italy, was sweating violently and was drinking white Orvieto wine" (p. 25). Intraocular stimulation and sensations from diseased internal organs also influence dreams. Nevertheless, Freud felt that these stimuli play a minor role in dream formation; they do not account for the complex part of the dream unrelated to the stimuli.

Vindication of Freud's position has come from the recent research with the REM method. Dement and Wolpert (1958) used tones, a flashing light, a bell, and a spray of water. Some of these were woven into dreams. Berger (1963) reports a similar phenomenon with spoken personal names. But these stimuli were effective only during the rapid eye movements. In other words, external stimuli do not create dreams, but may be incorporated into an ongoing dream. It is not known whether this finding would be applicable to stimuli from internal causes.

How universal is the dream cycle? Jouvet (1961) has described phenomena in the cat that closely resemble the pattern in man. In addition to the usual slow sleep waves, the cat periodically shows something called "paradoxical sleep." The cortical EEG changes to an arousal pattern, postural muscles completely lose tone, and short rapid eye movements occur. Twitches of the vibrissae, jaws, and tail can sometimes be seen. The paradoxical phase lasts about 10 to 15 minutes and is repeated every 20 to 30 minutes. Similar fluctuations have also been observed in the cat by Dement (1958) and Grastyan (1959). Comparable cycles have been found in the monkey (K.L. Chow, cited in Kamiya, 1961, and Weitzmann, 1961). Snyder (1963) cites similar findings with dogs and sheep.

Rapid eye movements have been observed in the human being from birth to old age (Aserinsky and Kleitman, 1955 b; Dement, 1961 b; and, especially Roffwarg et al., 1964). In neonates the percentage of dream time is 55 to 80 and in young children it is about 40. At around age 3 or 4 there is a significant drop to about 20 percent, where it remains to young adulthood. In the older age group (50–70) there is a lessening of dream time. The pattern of progressively lengthening dream periods throughout the night begins around age 3 or 4 and is reversed in the older age groups.

Naturally, the question arises as to whether REM's in animals signify dreams as we know them. A recent study by Vaughn (cited in Luce, 1965) suggests that animals do dream during REM periods. During wakefulness, monkeys were trained to avoid shock by pressing a bar whenever images were flashed on a screen. Later, when they were asleep, the monkeys pressed the bar during REM periods, but not during non-REM periods. This suggests that they were responding to internal images during REM periods.

The age-old question of whether everyone dreams, in spite of the fact that they do not recall dreams, has finally been answered. Goodenough et al. (1959) compared habitual dreamers (every night) with nondreamers (less than once a month). When the habitual dreamers were awakened during REM's, they reported dreams 93% of the time; at other times, 53%. Nondreamers reported dreams in 46% of REM awakenings and 17% in non-REM periods. Every S had at least one dream—even those who said they had never had a dream in their lives. The conclusion seems to be that everyone dreams several times every night.

Goodenough et al. (1959) also found that habitual dreamers and nondreamers had the same number and distribution of REM periods. This suggests that the difference in recall is due to personality characteristics. Indeed, several studies (Schonbar, 1959; Lachman, Lapkin, and Handelman, 1962; Tart, 1962) have shown that recallers are more overtly anxious and use sensitizing defense mechanisms, while nonrecallers rely on repressive defense mechanisms. The main findings of Goodenough et al. were confirmed by Antrobos et al. (1964) but with some modification. While it is true that recallers and nonrecallers do not differ in the number of REM periods, recallers have longer REM periods and nonrecallers show more frequent eye movements during a shorter period. Antrobus et al. interpret this last finding in terms of visual avoidance, i.e., the nonrecallers tend to avoid the dream images. This would be consistent with the repressive defenses used by nonrecallers.

DREAMS AND AROUSAL

In the previous section it was stated that dreams occur in a state of partial arousal. The situation is actually more complicated than this statement would suggest. Dement (1961 a) points out that *arousal* is a relative term depending on the measure used. For example, the EEG suggests that the most synchronized sleep occurs in the first two or three hours, but heart rate reaches its lowest level after 6 or 7 hours of sleep, and body temperature is lowest around the middle or later part of the night. Dement suggests that the discrepancies are produced by shorter cycles superimposed on an overall diurnal rhythm. It is also possible that heart rate and metabolism are more influenced by the prone position (Kleitman, 1939), while neural changes operate by a different mechanism. In any case, Dement says that most measures tend to go in the same general direction.

During dreams some measures suggest arousal but others indicate deeper sleep (Dement, 1961 a). The EEG, mental activity, and variations in heart rate and respiration suggest an arousal. Actually, the circulatory and respiratory changes are irregular, but this might depend on the specific emotions involved in the dream. On the other hand, a deeper stage of sleep during dreams is suggested by an increased skin resistance, the lack of body movements, and an increased auditory threshold. In the most elaborate study in this area, Snyder et al. (1963) found that heart rate, respiratory rate, and blood pressure were higher during stage 1-REM than during any other sleep stage. Furthermore, the variability in these measures was increased significantly during these dream periods. Vividness of reported dreams was found to be related to the degree of respiratory variability.

The most dramatic indication of arousal during dreams is the recent discovery by Fisher et al. (1965) that dreams are accompanied by penile erections in males. About 95% of REM periods in males from birth to old age were found to involve an erection. Typically, the erection starts a minute or so before the REM period and subsides just before the end of the REM period. The accompanying dreams are rarely manifestly about sexual topics. The erection seems to be part of a general arousal reaction.

The recent findings of Evarts (1962, 1963) on the activity of individual neurones in the visual cortex of the cat support the idea that the dreams occur during periods of arousal. The earlier work of Evarts (1960, 1961) seemed to indicate that more neurones were active during sleep than during wakefulness. The more recent studies show that more neurones are active during wakefulness than sleep, but that during the paradoxical or dream stage more neurones are active than during slow EEG sleep.

Jouvet (1961) has studied a phenomenon in the cat that seems to be related to dreams. He distinguishes between "telencephalic" and "rhombencephalic" sleep. The former is the traditional slow EEG pattern seen during falling asleep and periodically thereafter. Rhombencephalic sleep, also called the "paradoxical phase," follows slow sleep periods and consists of cortical arousal, extreme muscular relaxation, and raised thresholds. The paradoxical phase is also accompanied by rapid eye movements; twitches of the vibrissae, jaws, and tail; and cardiovascular variations. For all intents and purposes, this is an arousal reaction and strongly suggests dreaming.

Jouvet goes on to say, however, that the paradoxical phase represents a more profound state of sleep—he talks about "neo-sleep" and "archisleep." One reason for believing this is that the paradoxical phase is controlled by a lower brain stem mechanism. However, this could just as likely be some sort of primitive arousal mechanism. The area involved in the paradoxical phase is close to the brain stem activating and de-activating mechanisms that will be reviewed in the next chapter. Jouvet found, as did Batini et al. (1958), that transactions at the rostral end of the pons produced cortical sleep records. Furthermore, Jouvet reports that it is possible to evoke the paradoxical phase by stimulating the pontine reticular formation when the animal is in a slow sleep phase but *not* when he is awake. Along this line, Williams et al. (1964) found that in human subjects there was a smooth progression from EEG stage 0 to stage 4 when sleep was deepening, but when sleep was lightening towards a dream period stages were often skipped. This study is important because the finding that dreams are followed by a progression to EEG stages 2, 3, and 4 is difficult to reconcile with Jouvet's idea that dreams occur in a more profound state of sleep. All of this suggests that the paradoxical or dream phase consists of some sort of partial arousal.

The sudden loss of muscle tonus, on the other hand, looks more like a de-activation. In *cerveau isolé* preparations Jouvet found, in addition to the usual slow sleep cortical record, periods of behavioral wakefulness alternating with paradoxical phase relaxation. In the intact animal, of course, the behavioral sleep is unbroken. These phenomena are difficult to show on the human level since muscle tonus is low all night. Dement (1961 b), however, reports a case of Bell's palsy in which muscle tension disappeared completely during REM periods. Berger (1961) has demonstrated a decrease in the tonus of the human laryngeal muscles during dream periods. Thus the pontine dream mechanism appears to have both excitatory and inhibitory effects. The ascending effect is arousal and the descending effect is relaxation.

It should be noted that the relaxation is not complete since the twitches of the vibrissae and the internal emotional changes continue. It would appear that dreams involve a complex and selective operation of both activating and de-activating brain stem mechanisms.

What other evidence would suggest that dreams represent a deeper level of sleep? The main observation is a behavioral one —auditory thresholds are higher during dreams in man and the cat (Dement and Kleitman, 1957 b; Jouvet, 1961). In a study on this specific point, Buendia, Goode, and Sierra (1962) found that while auditory pitch discrimination is moderately decreased in classical, slow sleep, it is reduced markedly during paradoxical sleep in the cat. Furthermore, the threshold for direct stimulation of the reticular formation during the paradoxical phase is 2 to 3 times that of slow sleep. On the other hand, cortical responses evoked by an auditory click in monkeys and men indicate that a similar arousal takes place in wakefulness and REM periods. Furthermore, Williams (1961 and personal communication) found that while ordinary auditory discrimination responding decreases during dream periods, the responding increases markedly when a failure to respond results in the presentation of a noxious stimulus. Thus, when the sleeping person is motivated sufficiently he can respond to external stimuli during dreams.

In an important study, Adey, Kado, and Rhodes (1963) report that auditory thresholds are not raised during the REM sleep of chimpanzees. In fact, they report that chimpanzees are easy to wake up during the paradoxical phase. The sleep pattern of chimpanzees is very close to that of man. The authors caution against generalizing from the simple mammals to the higher primates about the profound nature of the dream stage of sleep.

Dement and Kleitman (1957 b), and Snyder (1963) believe that the increased threshold is due to a focusing of attention on the dream imagery. The dreamer is too preoccupied to respond to external stimuli. In the chapter on physiological mechanisms, an inhibitory effect of the reticular formation on irrelevant afferent stimuli will be noted (Magoun, 1958; Lindsley, 1960). Thus the cat intent on the visual stimulus of a mouse in a beaker shows an increased auditory threshold. Kleitman (1961) believes that the EEG—which, of course, shows an aroused stage of sleep during dreams—should be the final criterion for level of cortical activity.

What conclusions can be drawn from this? It is apparent that some sort of cortical arousal is involved in dreams. But how can one account for the raised afferent thresholds? It seems to this writer that two mutually exclusive conclusions can be drawn: either dreams represent a profound stage of sleep involving cortical and autonomic arousal or dreams are an aroused stage of sleep involving profound concentration. The latter conclusion seems simpler and fits in better with the other facts presented in this chapter.

Perhaps part of the difficulty in this controversy is the concept "deep." Rhombencephalic sleep may be more "primitive" but not as "deep." This is particularly true if one defines "deep" in terms of cortical and autonomic arousal. If one defines "deep" in terms of auditory threshold the difference between the two types of sleep is at best equivocal. Some muscles relax during paradoxical sleep but others are more active as in the rapid eye movements and the twitching of the extremities. Snyder (1963) has suggested that rhombencephalic sleep is phylogenetically and ontogenetically more primitive but is characterized by a higher level of arousal. The fact that lower animals and neonates spend more time in rhombencephalic sleep than the adult human being supports this. Snyder also cites observations by Jouvet on newborn kittens showing that only wakefulness and rapid EEG sleep occur. Slow EEG sleep develops later. Synchronized sleep, then, is an evolutionary product that results in less aroused sleep. According to Kleitman (1963) this may be correlated with a higher degree of alertness during wakefulness and a capacity for more prolonged wakefulness. While all this is speculative it does show that there is no necessary correlation between the degree of arousal and the primitiveness of sleep stages.

COGNITIVE ASPECTS OF DREAMS

What is the level and nature of the thought process during dreams? According to our hypothesis, dreams occur in a state of partial arousal, suggesting a reduced level of cognitive functioning. According to Freud (1958) the dream process is a complex phenomenon; this is not in keeping with the theoretical development of the sleep motive made so far.

For Freud, dreams are determined primarily by psychological events: the memories of experiences of the previous day or so. For example, Freud reports that his young daughter dreamed her mother gave her a bag of chocolates. The day before she had been refused the candy by the mother. Two points are illustrated here: the role of the frustration of the previous day and the wish-fulfilling character of the dream. The dream also permitted the child to continue sleeping.

Still, these residues of daily experience do not account fully for most adult dreams. The motive force behind the daily experience in the dream, according to Freud, is in the basic instincts and conflicts of the person dating from early childhood. For example, an adult may dream of the death of a parent or a sibling. This may have been occasioned by a letter from the relative that day, but the feelings of hostility date back to the competition for affection in the early family situation. The dream represents the fulfillment of an infantile death wish.

Most of the primitive sexual and hostile material, which Freud finds stemming from early childhood, is too unacceptable to the socialized adult to be directly represented in the dream. Thus these basic feelings, which Freud calls the latent dream thoughts, are changed and disguised to appear as the manifest dream content. This deception enables the dreamer to accept the basic feelings without waking up with anxiety, and at the same time to achieve some partial discharge of the forbidden wish. A number of mechanisms are utilized in this transformation, including displacement, condensation, and representation by symbols. For example, an Oedipal conflict may be represented by a young man shooting an elderly banker and making off with the money.

Various attempts have been made to validate experimentally Freud's ideas about dreams. The studies using hypnosis (Rapaport, 1951) have supported the ideas about symbolism and the incorporation of external ideas, although the use of hypnosis raises questions about the amount of experimenter suggestion. A series of studies has been done on the so-called Poetzl phenomenon (Fisher, 1960; Shevrin and Luborsky, 1958). Tachistoscopic presentation of pictures is made to subjects; they consciously perceive some parts and do not seem to notice others. The parts not consciously attended to appear later in reproductions of dream images—often in a disguised form. Unfortunately, when adequate controls are used in this kind of study no effect is found (Johnson and Ericksen, 1961). It is difficult to find direct and unequivocal experimental support for the theory.

The entire process of changing and hiding the meaning of the wishes Freud calls the dream work, which involves an archaic but complex form of thinking. But Freud believes this may take place in a state of partial sleep. He comments as follows: "We have found evidence in the dream-thoughts of a highly complex intellectual function, operating with almost the whole resources of the mental apparatus. Nevertheless, it cannot be disputed that these dream-thoughts originated during the day, and it is imperative to assume that there is such a thing as a sleeping state of the mind. Thus even the theory of partial sleep has shown its value, though we have found that what characterizes the state of sleep is not the disintegration of mental bonds but the concentration of the psychical system which is in command during the day upon the wish to sleep" (Freud, 1958, p. 590).

The increased concentration during dreams is consistent with the findings about the heightened stimulus thresholds. This would be explained on the physiological level by the focusing of the systems mediating consciousness—the ascending activating system and/or the neocortex—or the paleocortically-mediated fantasies.

While the Freudian theory explains a good deal about the nature of dreams, there is some dissatisfaction with the impression left of highly complex mental operations that must be going on to provide the disguises, subterfuges, and deceptions that are assumed. Such a view does not fit in with the present theoretical analysis of sleep as a time of reduced thinking. Hall (1953 a) has developed a cognitive theory of dreams that accounts for many of the Freudian observations without assuming the complex thought processes that would be unlikely during sleep.

First of all, Hall bases his theory on a careful statistical analysis of thousands of dreams gathered in an elaborate research program (1951, 1956, 1959). He found that for the population as a whole, a dream is a succession of images, predominantly visual in quality, resembling a motion picture in which the dreamer is a participant-observer. Generally, a dream has one or more scenes, several characters in addition to the dreamer, and a sequence of actions usually involving the dreamer. Hall's theory (1953 a) is that this material represents a simple form of thinking. Whereas ordinary wakeful thinking involves translating ideas or conceptions into language, dreaming translates the same ideas into visual images. In other words, dreaming is pictorialized thinking. Concrete perceptual forms of conceptualizing are usually thought of as a simple form of cognitive activity not dependent on the highest cortical functions. Such primitive forms of thought may be found in young children, regressed schizophrenics, and brain-damaged individuals.

Piaget's (1960) observations on children are relevant to Hall's characterization of dreams as pictorialized thought. Very young children confuse dreams with perceptual reality; they think a person or thing is actually in the room. At around school age, the child no longer believes the dream to be real, but thinks of it as external to himself—a projected image. A few years later, the child understands the dream as an internal image—it may be described as a picture or a thought, with some confusion between the two.

Hall goes on to say that dreams contain pictorialized forms of conceptions about the self, other people, the world, impulses, prohibitions, penalties, problems, and conflicts. Thus, if a person conceives of his father as stern and rejecting, he will be given a role in keeping with this conception. Hall found that most themes in dreams are related to intimate, personal problems rather than to world events or external physical stimuli (1959). The major themes include sex and aggression, competition for love in the family, freedom versus security, moral conflict, sex role conflict, and life versus death.

What about dream symbols? The Freudian theory with its emphasis on disguise can account for a pistol in a sexually exciting dream as a phallic symbol. But Hall also has a cognitive theory of dream symbols (1953 b). He makes several criticisms of the Freudian theory of symbols on the basis of empirical observation. First, he notes that if one obtains a long series of dreams from the same subject, dreams with frankly sexual content alternate with symbolized dreams. Second, Hall noted that a naïve subject was often able to give his own sexual interpretation of a dream with little or no information about Freudian symbols. Third, in a study of slang and figures of speech, Hall found that slang expressions for sexual organs and acts were quite similar to the Freudian symbols. Finally, Hall asks why there are so many symbols for the same referent. Why so many disguises for genitals, intercourse, and masturbation?

Hall rejects the Freudian theory of dream symbols as disguised representation of anxiety-arousing thoughts. His cognitive theory of dream symbols assumes that a symbol is the best way of representing one's conception of a person, impulse, or other topic. For example, a nurturant mother may appear as a cow— providing the dreamer thinks of cows as nurturant. If the dreamer thinks of his mother as hostile, he may picture her as a witch. The advantage of the dream symbol is that it is economical in time and effort. Such a theory of dream symbols, like the general cognitive theory of dreams, supposes only a moderate amount of a simplified form of thinking. This is in agreement with the present interpretation which assumes an incompatibility between sleep and highly complex intellectual tasks.

Some support for Hall's position has been obtained in research at Western Reserve University (Hall, 1956). Students made a Q-sort of items drawn from Hall's theory of conceptual systems; this was correlated significantly with a Q-sort done by a psychologist who had analyzed the dreams of the students. Another Q-sort, based on the TAT, was correlated with both dreams and self-sorts. Generally, dreams contain *more* socially unacceptable material than the TAT. The relationship between motives revealed in dreams and TAT stories depends on both the strength of the motives and their inhibitory forces; this is comparable to the relationship between the TAT and overt behavior (Lazarus, 1961). In general, dreams are related to the conceptual systems of the individual and may include material inhibited in other situations.

A simplified form of thinking in dreams has also been described by French (1952, 1954). He sees dreams as a type of problem-solving activity with the same adaptive processes seen in rational behavior and neuroses. In the dream a conflict may arise, for example, where an infantile dependent striving emerges but also injures the pride of the individual. Resolving this conflict constitutes a problem and the individual may show a number of possible solutions in successive dreams. For example, a patient was insecure about his mother's love because of a younger sister. But the more jealousy he showed, the less the mother approved of him. In one dream he was nurturant instead of hostile toward the sister and thus won the approval of the mother. Did the solution originate in the dream? Not necessarily. The idea was probably being worked out in the patient's waking state and continued in the dream.

The quality of thinking which French perceives in the dream is also at a simple level and does not pose a problem. He says that dreams show a "practical grasp" of problems and deal with conflicts in terms of symbols and illusions. He suggests that dreams involve "thinking in terms of things." In fact he finds that Freud himself hinted at this in a paper on the unconscious (Freud 1950, pp. 98-136). Here Freud concludes that a conscious idea involves both a concrete image and a verbal concept; an unconscious idea involves just the concrete image. While Freud was referring mostly to schizophrenic thinking, the notion is obviously applicable to dreams as well. In dreams as well as schizophrenic thought, concrete things are treated as though they were abstract.

Thus, the best conclusion that can be drawn at the present time is that dreams involve a simple form of thought. This thought is primitive and may have much in common with the thinking of children, schizophrenics, and brain-damaged individuals. The thought is concrete, symbolic, and pictorialized. It may be goal-directed and involved in problem-solving, but it is limited because of the absence of abstract reasoning. This picture suggests strongly that lower integrative structures of the brain—probably the limbic system—are activated during dreams but that the higher cortical levels mediating abstract, verbal functions remain relatively quiescent. The evidence also suggests that dreams represent a level of thought that is intermediate between dreamless sleep and semiwakefulness.

THE FUNCTION OF DREAMS

The most influential theory of the function of dreams is that proposed by Freud (1958). As is well known, he believed that dreams serve as wish-fulfillments. It is less well known that the primary wish, which Freud thought was fulfilled, was that for sleep. "Dreams are the guardians of sleep and not its disturbers" (p. 233). Freud believed that the residues of the day were the true disturbers.

According to Freud, the frustrations and tensions of the day threaten to disrupt sleep by arousing the individual to worry or take action. The frustrated wishes initiate the dream and are fulfilled in dream fantasy. The number of these wishes is as great as the number of frustrations in civilized life. They range from the desire of a child for candy to the wish to prove Freud's theories valid. Freud gives examples of wishes for revenge, for not being pregnant, for social gatherings, for proving the analyst wrong, for a lost child, for money, and for achievement. Of course, Freud thought that the deeper wishes in many dreams stemmed from infantile sexual and aggressive wishes, particularly those associated with the frustrations of Oedipal competition.

As mentioned earlier, Freud believed that physical stimuli play a secondary role in dream formation. External and somatic stimuli threaten to disturb sleep and are woven into the ongoing dream so that action does not have to be taken. However, the physiological need to urinate may arouse a psychological wish to get out of bed which would disturb sleep. If the person dreams he 'is urinating, the wish is dissipated and sleep can continue. The critical factor is the wish, not the stimulus.

Several criticisms have been made of Freud's wish-fulfillment theory. First, the occurrence of dreams in lower animals seems, to some, to preclude their having a psychological function. Kleitman (1939) believes that general observations on the horse, the cow, and, especially, the dog are convincing enough to assume that they have dreams. The REM technique has established more objectively the existence of dream cycles in the cat, monkey, and other species (Snyder, 1963). Why, however, can these animal dreams not serve a function similar to that in man? Again, the casual observations which can be made by any dog owner suggest that the animal is acting out fantasies of running, attacking, and so forth. Surely, domesticated animals face the frustrations of the leash, the fence, and the dictatorship of the master. Wild animals face even more terrors and frustrations. In defense of his wish-fulfillment theory in connection with animals, Freud (1961, p. 132) quotes an old proverb "What do geese dream of? Of maize."

A criticism aimed more directly at the sleep-protective function of dreams has to do with the occurence of anxiety dreams. Actually, most dreams are associated with affect of some kind (Hall, 1959; Arnold, 1960). But anxiety dreams, or nightmares, wake the person up and thus do not fulfill the wish to sleep. Freud (1958, pp. 580-587) explained this as a failure of the dream to discharge a tension because of the strength or fear of the impulse. The wish conflicts too much with conscience so that it cannot be discharged. The dream does not arouse anxiety itself, but the wish is linked with anxiety and this is what wakes the person up. The dream is thought of as a compromise adjustment, like a neurotic symptom, but, as in the case of neurotic symptoms, where the anxiety is too great, the compromise adjustment fails.

The most extensive analysis of nightmares, from the psychoanalytic viewpoint, has been made by Jones (1959). Phenomenologically, nightmares show a marked dread, oppression on the chest, and a feeling of paralysis and helplessness. Jones believes the origin to be sexual—especially incestuous impulses—and symbolized by vampires, witches, devils, etc. Actually, this explanation of the origin of anxiety dreams is not in accord with observations on war neuroses (Grinker and Spiegel, 1945). Here the cause of anxiety may stem from the fears aroused in combat. Feldman (personal communication) found that half of a group of normal subjects had had nightmares within the previous year. Moreover, he found that the themes were mainly helplessness and death. He interprets his results as being more consistent with an existential approach than with the Freudian sexual theory. For our purposes, we can assume that a variety of dangers are reflected in anxiety dreams.

It is true that later on Freud, in "Beyond the Pleasure Principle" (1950), changed his views on dreams, as he did on so many other things. He was impressed by the persistence of anxiety dreams stemming from traumatic war experiences. He suggested that these operate in obedience to a compulsion to repeat, in order to master or "psychically bind" the traumatic impressions. But this he sees as a primitive function that does not contradict the later function of fulfilling wishes, including the wish to sleep. In his final book, Freud (1949) again calls dreams the "Guardian of Sleep."

The most cogent criticism of Freud's "Guardianship of Sleep" theory of dreams has been made by Ullman (1958 a, 1958 b), Snyder (1963), and Trosman (1963). This criticism concerns the regularity in the dream cycle. Nearly all researchers using the REM technique report that for a given individual, the dream periods occur with a more or less predictable periodicity. This suggests a basic biological process involving an endogenous rhythm. While there might be some reason to expect something like hunger to occur rhythmically, why should the cares of the day erupt at predictable times each night? This observation is not consistent with the idea that dreams are *initiated* by impulses and wishes. Of course, this does not preclude the possibility that wishes are integrated into ongoing dreams just as external stimuli are.

One possible counterargument to the line of thought presented above is that the alternation of dream and synchronized sleep is due to conflict. Fisher and Dement (1963) take this position and "propose that the total dream time level in any given night is the outcome of the balance between the pressure of instinctual drives towards discharge and the adequacy of the defensive and controlling forces of the ego." In support of this, they describe a subject who had a psychotic episode in the middle of a sleep study. During the acute phase, REM-dream time increased to about 50% of the night. The dream periods were atypical, however, and much closer to wakefulness than usual. A tranquilizer reduced the dream time. Lester et al. (1963) also report an infant who showed more REM time when upset. Recall that anxiety, while not related to the frequency of REM periods, is related to the length of these periods. However, other studies do not support these observations. Depressed patients, while spending more time awake, show a normal ratio of dream sleep to deep sleep (Oswald et al., 1963). So, too, in a study of good and poor sleepers, Monroe (cited in Luce, 1965) found that poor sleepers, who tended to be psychologically maladjusted, awakened more during the night, but spent less time in REM periods. In other words, emotional conflict leads to disrupted sleep and fewer dreams.

At this time, the evidence is not strong for the conflict interpretation, but more research is needed. In any case, the effect of emotional factors would most likely be on the length of dream periods rather than on the basic rhythm.

One would expect that drug research would shed some light on the role of emotional factors in the appearance of dreams. However, the effects are complex. Alcohol decreases dream time (Gresham et al., 1963) but so does the stimulant amphetamine (Rechtschaffen and Maron, 1964). LSD increases the amount of time spent in REM sleep, according to recent reports (Luce, 1965). In general, the effects of drugs are complex and difficult to assess at this time (see Kleitman, 1963).

Freud also assumed that, in addition to protecting sleep, dreams provide a safety valve for the tensions of the day. Most psychoanalytic theorists have gone along with this basic idea. For example, Sullivan (1956) believed that the "self-system" drops out during sleep except for vestigial traces in the form of dreams. The needs which could not be discharged during the day, provided there is not too much tension, are satisfied through the symbolic operations of the dream. Sullivan says "If it were not for that, we would all blow up early in life and the human race would become extinct, for the social order is such that unnumbered needs for direct satisfaction have to be more or less thwarted, postponed, or something of the sort. We succeed, however, in discharging the urgencies of things by operations in sleep" (p. 20).

Dement and Fisher (1963) have emphasized the "safety valve" theory in recent years. They cite the emotional disturbances after dream deprivation as evidence and suggest that prolonged dream deprivation could produce psychosis. Here, too, if dreams function as a safety valve, one would expect an increase in dream time with emotional disturbance. As we saw above, the evidence that this is so is inconclusive. While the safety-value theory can not be discounted it does not seem to be supported strongly by the research available at this time.

Ullman (1958 a, 1958 b) has proposed still another function for dreams. He suggests that the natural waxing and waning of sleep is related to an innate anxiety mechanism. Through evolution, a periodic near-awakening occurs for purposes of vigilance and orientation. The organism samples the environmental stimuli, appraises them, and then either wakes up fully or goes back to sleep. Anxiety dreams are seen as an adaptive preparation for awakening. As evidence for this, Ullman cites the regularity of the cycles. However, it is not clear why the dream periods get longer and longer—surely vigilance is required as much at the beginning of the night as at the end. Then, too, the fact that in some species, at least, thresholds are higher during dreams would seem to indicate that dreaming would be a period of exceptional vulnerability rather than an adaptive mechanism. Finally, most anxiety dreams seem to have internal sources— memories of disturbing events, childhood conflicts, and the like. It is possible that the periodic lightening of sleep serves a vigilance function. But why dreams? Why not a brief period of wakefulness during which all of the senses—including vision—could be used for orientation? Some animals do this. For example, Liddell reports that the seal raises its head every ten seconds to survey the surroundings even during sleep (see May 1961, p. 78).

There is also the possibility that dreams serve no particular function in relation to sleep. In other words, dreams are the result of an aroused stage of sleep that occurs on an endogenous basis. Recall that Snyder (1963) suggested that stage 1-REM sleep constitutes a primordial state that antedates synchronized sleep both phylogenetically and ontogenetically. Dreams may be the experiential consequence of the organism passing into this primitive but partially aroused phase of sleep. This is essentially the position taken by Gerard (1955), Snyder (1963), and Kleitman (1963).

What this means is something like this: During normal sleep the person moves from a synchronized stage to an aroused stage. The cortex is partially aroused and thought processes occur. The arousal can be thought of as lowering thresholds for thought associations, but not for all thought associations at random. Prepotent associations—those connected with the tensions of the day, conflicts, etc.—would be closer to threshold and emerge first.

This theory would be consistent with Hall's description of dreams as directly representing conflicts in concrete pictorialized form. The level of thought that would appear in a partial state of arousal would most likely be primitive. Dream interpretation would still be valid but could be described as supplying abstract verbal labels for this concrete thought so that reasoning and problem solving could occur.

The problem of the source of the endogenous rhythm would remain. This could be due to a hunger rhythm (Wada, 1922; Pierce, Lester, and Mathis, 1963) although the evidence is not strong on this point. It could also be due to a basic rest-activity cycle, as Kleitman (1963) suggests. The two types of sleep could also represent von Economo's (1930) idea of brain sleep versus body sleep.

SUMMARY

The occurrence of dreams during sleep challenges the theoretical analysis presented so far because sleep has been assumed to be a period of reduced arousal. The recent discovery of rapid eye movements associated with dreams provides an objective measure, to be combined with subjective reports, in evaluating the role of dreams in sleep.

Physiological and introspective data concerned with the phenomena of falling asleep and awakening show that people pass through a transitional stage of consciousness—sometimes called a twilight phase. Thought processes become dreamlike, but do not have the vivid, illogical quality of dreams. A continuum of integrative thought from wakefulness to semiwakefulness to dreams to deep sleep is suggested.

Rapid eye movements are associated with dreams but not with semiwakeful thought. These REM's occur only during EEG stage 1. The degree of association between dreams and REM's is still a matter of debate, with some investigators finding a considerable number of dream reports from non-REM periods. Nevertheless, these non-REM reports are more like normal thought and may be due to methods of arousing the sleeper. In spite of these technical problems, nearly everyone agrees that dreams are best predicted from a combination of REM's and an aroused EEG stage.

Using these measures, it has been shown that the level of arousal during sleep waxes and wanes throughout the night, with dreams taking place during the crests. There are about four to six cycles during the night with the synochronized sleep periods getting shorter and shallower, as the dream periods get longer. The EEG upswing to dream periods may be accompanied by body movements, slow eye motion, and gastrointestinal motility. External stimuli are woven into ongoing dreams, but do not instigate them. The dream cycle seems to be universal, having been observed in animals, children, and people who believe they never dream.

Whether dreams constitute a lighter or deeper stage of sleep has been a matter of controversy. Cortical and emotional arousal during dreams is clear, but increased stimulus thresholds in some species and muscular relaxation suggest a deeper sleep. Neurophysiological findings suggest that dreams depend on lower brain stem mechanisms, and constitute a qualitatively different kind of emotional arousal—but arousal nonetheless. The increased stimulus thresholds during dreams can be explained as due to concentration on the dream imagery. It has been suggested that the aroused state in which dreams occur represents a phylo-genetically and ontogenetically primitive state of sleep.

Dreams appear to involve a simpler level of cognitive func-tioning than waking life. Freud's description of dreams, involving complex censoring and disguising functions, does not seem to be necessary. Hall has criticized Freud's theory and offers empirical evidence for dreaming as a simplified form of concrete, pictorialized thinking. Symbols are direct representations of the dreamer's verbal concepts. There seems to be a continuum of integrated thought from synchronized sleep to dreams to semiwakefulness to wakefulness.

Several functions have been suggested for dreams—the protection of sleep, the discharge of daily tensions, and the maintenance of primitive vigilance. It had also been suggested that dreams have no function in relation to sleep but are simply the result of an endogenous rhythmic period of primitive, aroused sleep. The evidence is inconclusive on all these theories.

In conclusion, regardless of the exact function of dreams, they occur in a unique stage of sleep. This stage is characterized by cortical and autonomic arousal, loss of muscle tonus and possibly heightened thresholds, rapid eye movements, and primi-tive thought processes.

CHAPTER 4

Physiological Mechanisms for Arousal, Sleep, and Dreams

In previous chapters the physiological changes occurring during various stages of arousal and sleep were described. The purpose of this chapter is to investigate those physiological processes that control the onset, maintenance, and termination of states of wakefulness, synochronized sleep, and aroused sleep. Factors such as peripheral stimulation, hormones, and brain mechanisms have been found to be important in regulating physiological motives such as hunger and thirst (Morgan, 1959). The problem under consideration here is whether the physiological mechanisms associated with sleep are similar to those of other motives, in that they have similar effects on behavior.

The plan of this chapter is as follows: First, the physiological mechanisms of the better known motives, such as hunger, thirst, and sex will be described for purposes of comparison. Then the system that appears to control wakefulness and general arousal will be presented. Next the question whether sleep results primarily from a deficiency of external stimulation will be considered. The influence of the internal milieu will be mentioned. Finally, the complex neural mechanism underlying sleep and its several stages will be examined.

MECHANISMS FOR PHYSIOLOGICAL MOTIVES

Early theories of the physiological mechanisms of motivation pointed to peripheral events as the critical factors in determining behavior (Cannon, 1934). So, for example, thirst was said to be due to a local dryness of the mouth, and hunger was said to be due to stomach contractions. However, experimental evidence does not indicate that these peripheral events are crucial (Morgan and Stellar, 1950; Morgan, 1959). Thus removal of the salivary glands does not affect the amount drunk by an animal, although it may increase the frequency. Similarly, removal of the stomach does not eliminate hunger, nor stop learning for food reward. This can be extended to emotional behavior, where it has been shown that visceral reactions are not essential for the expression of rage or fear (Cannon, 1929). Similarly, hormones and other biochemical factors may not be sufficient, by themselves, to elicit motivated behavior (Beach, 1949).

This is not to say that these various peripheral events are not typically involved in motivation. Rather, it is that they do not seem to account for all of the phenomena. This has led thinkers, from Sherrington to Lashley, to postulate some sort of brain mechanism which controls motivation. Such a mechanism has been referred to as a "central excitatory state" by Beach (1942), and a "central motive state" by Morgan (1959). Such a mechanism, sensitive to internal and external events, would arouse and integrate motivational behavior. In discussing the modern view of the physiological mechanisms of motivation, several topics will be covered: brain stem mechanisms, hypothalamic mechanisms, cortical mechanisms, the influence of the internal milieu, and the role of environmental stimulation.

To many of those who postulated a "central motive state," the recently discovered reticular activating system has appeared to fulfill theoretical expectations (e.g., Morgan 1959; Samuels, 1959). This brain stem mechanism, which will be described more fully in the next section, stimulates the rest of the brain and the body as a whole. It has the generally arousing effect on the organism that is often associated with motivation. It is also more than a simple reflex-arc mechanism: a stimulus may set off the reticular activating system, but the arousal continues long after the stimulus is terminated. In addition, since the system is responsive to environmental stimuli, it offers a physiological basis for "sensory" motives, such as curiosity, as well as the more traditional homeostatic motives. For these reasons, many current textbooks associate motivation with the reticular activating system (Bindra, 1959; Berlyne, 1960; Brown, 1961; and Young, 1961).

Proceeding up the brain, the next important subcortical structure involved in motivation is the diencephalon (see Stellar, 1960). This structure is, of course, influenced by the reticular system from below and is also closely related to the higher centers of the cerebrum. However, the diencephalon appears to be the area of the brain in which specific patterns of motivational and emotional behavior are organized. Thus Hess (1957) stimulated various parts of the thalamus, and hypothalamus, and was able to produce changes in visceral functions, such as blood pressure, respiration, salivation, and vomiting. He was also able to elicit normal behavioral patterns, such as the crouching and covering which is characteristic of defecation in the cat. Other effects included rage, fear, eating, and, as we shall see later, sleep.

Subsequently, more specific mechanisms have been found, in the hypothalamus, involving hunger, thirst, temperature, sex, rage, maternal behavior, and general activity. In the case of thirst, it has been found that, if a sodium chloride solution is injected into a restricted area in the hypothalamus, goats will show a marked increase in drinking (Andersson and McCann, 1955). The authors also found that electrical stimulation would produce similar results. Furthermore, destruction of this hypothalamic area in dogs caused a decrease in drinking (Andersson and McCann, 1956). One dog died, and the other two required supplementary fluid because of extreme dehydration. Miller (1957) was able to increase and decrease drinking with hypothalamic injections of salt water and pure water, respectively. Of course, a number of other factors also influence thirst (Morgan and Stellar, 1950).

Some of these hypothalamic mechanisms exist in antagonistic excitory and inhibitory pairs (Stellar, 1954). For example, there is a lateral area that excites hunger, and a medial one that inhibits it. Stimulating the medial area, or destroying the lateral one, results in decreased food intake—even starvation. When both of these areas are destroyed the result is starvation—the same as destroying the medial area alone. This suggests that the function of the inhibitory, medial area is to suppress the excitatory, lateral area. There is also some antagonism between the anterior and posterior hypothalamus—in general, the anterior hypothalamus is associated with parasympathetic functions, and the posterior hypothalamus with sympathetic ones (Gellhorn, 1957).

The cerebral cortex is also important in motivation (Stellar, 1960). A distinction may be made between the outer neocortex and the phylogenetically older paleocortex, in closest proximity to the brain stem. The paleocortex, together with parts of the diencephalon, make up the limbic system, which is now thought to be intimately related to emotion and motivation (Nauta, 1958; Brady, 1960; MacLean, 1960). It is in this older system that the classic "sham rage" of decortication is produced. Both emotional expression and restraint are centered here. Influences on oral and sexual behavior have been reported. It is also here, in the limbic system, that self-stimulation has been found to be positively reinforcing (Olds and Milner, 1954) and negatively reinforcing (Delgado, Roberts, and Miller, 1954). This has led a number of theorists to identify this archaic part of the brain with motivation and emotion. It has been pointed out that, while the neocortex has shown great development during mammalian evolution, the paleocortex is essentially unchanged.

The neocortex does, however, play a significant role in motivation. While the evidence is fragmentary, most studies show a decreased emotionality with neocortical destruction (Brady, 1960). In the best studied motive, a clear connection between the neocortex and sexual behavior has been established (Stellar, 1960). The larger the cortical lesion, the greater the decrement in sexual behavior—particularly in males. This effect is more marked as one proceeds up the mammalian scale. Lindsley (1951,

1957) has emphasized the role of an aroused cortex in motivation and emotion.

The internal milieu of the organism would logically be expected to have some influence on central motive mechanisms, and in fact it does (Stellar, 1960). The interaction is largely through the hypothalamus. This part of the brain stem has a rich vascular supply, and is situated on the third ventrical; thus, it may be influenced by biochemical factors in the blood and cerebrospinal fluid. Research has shown that the hypothalamus has receptors for temperature, blood sugar, salt concentration, sex hormones, and other substances. Only minute quantities of these substances are needed in the hypothalamus to produce behavioral change. If the sexual areas of the hypothalamus are destroyed, sexual hormones are ineffective in influencing behavior.

Dell (1958) has reported that various internal biochemical events will produce a reticular arousal. Epinephrine will elicit a reticular arousal reaction that is independent of the effect of epinephrine on blood pressure. Furthermore, decreasing the oxygen level or increasing the carbon dioxide level of the blood may activate the reticular formation directly. Dell suggests that bodily needs in general may affect the reticular formation in this way, to serve the adaptive functions of increasing alertness and exploratory behavior. The normal route for these chemical substances was not demonstrated, although it could be through the hypothalamus.

In addition to these chemical substances the central nervous system, of course, receives information about internal events— through internal afferent paths. Thus, the aching of a muscle due to strain, the distension of the bladder, or the pain from a wound, may motivate various kinds of behavior.

Finally, the importance of environmental stimulation should be mentioned. Learned stimuli are, of course, of extreme importance in motivation, but what is meant here is the innate influence of stimuli. Thus some taste substances appear to be more rewarding than others, on an innate basis. Some environmental stimuli evoke fear, without previous training. Sexual behavior is strongly influenced, in certain species, by temperature, illumination, season of the year, fighting for territories, and the chemical, visual, and auditory stimuli afforded by the sexual partner (see Young, 1961). The ethologists have been especially concerned about the environmental release of instinctive mechanisms (Tinbergen, 1951). In sensory motives, e.g., curiosity, stimulus parameters such as novelty are critical (Berlyne, 1960).

Furthermore, it should be noted that the cortex is not a passive partner in its relation to the reticular formation. Livingstone (1958) has demonstrated descending cortical influences on the reticular system. Thus, the cortex can participate in its own level of arousal. Morgan (1959) describes the waking brain in terms of a reverberatory transaction between the cortex and the reticular formation.

Much is still not known about the neurophysiological mechanisms of motivation. Nevertheless, it does appear that the concept of reticular arousal is extremely useful in explaining motivation. A centrally located reticular system receives information from the external environment, through the sensory paths, and from the internal environment, predominantly from the hypothalamus. In turn, the reticular system activates the limbic system and the neocortex, which organize the behavior on the basis of innate reaction and past experience. The cortex also influences the reticular system.

THE AROUSAL SYSTEM

The basic neurophysiological mechanism responsible for wakefulness is the same as that for aroused motivational states—the reticular activating system. From an adaptational point of view, one can see wakefulness, and the activities it makes possible, as subserving the purposes of most motives. For the moment, arousal and wakefulness may be equated, although there are some instances in which consciousness and muscular activity are dissociated. Let us begin by describing those parts of the brain stem that are most important for an understanding of arousal.

There exists, in the central core of the brain stem, an anatomical structure known as the reticular formation (Magoun, 1954, 1958). This is a mesh of cell bodies, transverse and longitudinal fibers, extending from the medulla to the thalamus (see Fig. 5). It is separate from the classical sensory and motor path-

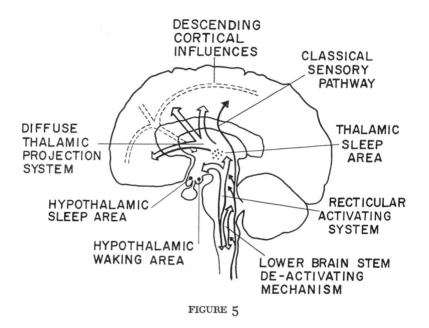

FIGURE 5

ways, although the sensory tracts give off collaterals to the brain stem reticular formation, and it is influenced by motor areas of the cerebrum and cerebellum, as well as other parts of the brain, and the internal milieu. This is, both anatomically and functionally, a complex area, with both excitatory and inhibitory effects. We will focus on the excitatory aspects now, because they are most relevant to the problem of arousal, but we will return to the inhibitory part later.

Certain parts of the brain stem reticular formation have a general arousing effect on the organism, and have been labeled the "reticular activating system." Generally speaking, the rostral parts of the reticular formation—from the pons forward—are predominantly activating. There is so much intermingling, however, that this is a relative statement; facilitory fibers do extend down to the spinal cord. Nevertheless, the general statement can be made that the anterior parts of the reticular formation are mainly activating while, as we shall see again later, the posterior section is more inhibitory.

The reticular activating system has a descending facilitory influence on spinal reflexes and motor performance. It also activates visceral and endocrine reactions through the hypothalamus and limbic system, and thus participates in emotions, stress reactions, and possibly psychosomatic disease. Perhaps the best known effect is on the EEG arousal response in the cortex. This has been related to attention, consciousness, perception, and learning (Lindsley, 1960).

The reticular activating system has several routes to the cortex—through hypothalamic projections directly via the subthalamus, and by way of a diffuse projection system in the thalamus proper. This latter system, described by Jasper (1954), is separate from the specific sensory projections. It has widespread effects on electrical activity in the cortex—probably arousing the paleocortex as well as the neocortex (Lindsley, 1960). There is some indication that the part of the activating system in the lower brain stem has a more generalized, tonic, and less differentiating arousal effect, while the thalamic portion is more capable of sudden shifts of attention from one part of the cortex to another (Magoun, 1958).

The evidence for the reticular activating system has been well summarized by Lindsley (1960). In a now famous experiment of 1949, Moruzzi and Magoun found that electrical stimulation of the reticular formation produced an EEG pattern of desynchronization and behavioral signs of wakefulness in the cat (see also Segundo et al., 1955). Destruction of the same area produces EEG and behavioral signs of sleep.

These results require a reinterpretation of the famous, older experiments by Bremer (1954): behavioral and EEG signs of wakefulness remained in a spinal preparation—his *encephale isolé*. However, a high midbrain transection isolating the cerebrum from most of the rest of the brain—the *cerveau isolé*—resulted in EEG and behavioral sleep. Bremer explained this as due to de-afferentation, since his *cerveau isolé* preparation had eliminated all but olfactory and visual afferents. Lindsley's studies show clearly, however, that it is the reticular formation that is responsible. When the sensory pathways were severed, but the reticular formation left intact, the animals showed normal wakefulness. On the other hand, transecting the reticular formation, but sparing the sensory pathways, resulted in sleep.

Anesthesia is now thought to be due to a blocking of the reticular activating system (Magoun, 1958). French, Verzeano, and Magoun (1953) showed that ether and pentobarbitol sodium blocked the transmission through medial parts of the brain stem, but not the lateral part, where the classical sensory pathways are. Anesthetics may also act on the thalamic projection system (King et al., 1957).

Lindsley (1960) also reviews studies on the diffuse thalamic projection system. Here the picture is confusing, and suggestive of several overlapping mechanisms. High frequency stimulation of some areas produces arousal. Lesions have effects on attention, to some extent, but clear-cut evidence of sleep is harder to find. One study did report "somnolence and lethargy," as a result of lesions in thalamic intralaminary nuclei (Schreiner et al., 1953).

There is still another way in which the reticular activating system may influence wakefulness (Magoun, 1958). The skeletal musculature and the viscera may be activated by the descending part of the reticular formation. This peripheral activity may, in turn, provide proprioceptive stimulation helpful in maintaining wakefulness. Kleitman (1939) puts a great deal of emphasis on the role of muscle tension in maintaining wakefulness. Similarly, the regulation of afferent stimulation from the environment, by the reticular formation, is another means by which this subcortical mechanism controls wakefulness.

In addition to producing wakefulness, many neurophysiologists have assumed that the reticular activating system, by its cessation of activity, produced sleep. This is really a more sophisticated version of the de-afferentation theories of Bremer

(1954), Kleitman (1939), and others (see Lindsley, 1960). These theories view sleep as a passive state, which, if correct, would disprove the sleep motive hypothesis under discussion here. In fact, until recently most neurophysiologists would probably have said that the known physiological mechanisms would *not* suggest sleep as an independent motive.

There has been a strong resistance among neurophysiologists to the concept of neural mechanisms producing sleep. This is in spite of the long-standing positive evidence of Hess and Nauta (which will be treated in a later section). Reading the three fine symposia in this area—*Brain Mechanisms and Consciousness, Reticular Formation of the Brain,* and *The Nature of Sleep*—one is struck by the strong distaste of many, although not all, of the contributors, for the idea of a sleep system. The preference is for some intrinsic avalanche of fatigue in the reticular activating system itself. Nevertheless, the evidence against the passive concept of sleep is mounting.

The preceding paragraphs may have left the impression that the cortex is a passive organ, to be aroused at will by sub-cortical mechanisms. Indeed, the Bremer de-afferentation sleep theory would suggest such a passivity to an even greater extent. This is not the case, however, since the cortex exerts a good deal of control over its own arousal.

Electrical stimulation of several parts of the cortex will set the reticular activating system in motion, and awaken a sleeping animal (Livingston, 1958). Effective areas include frontal regions (including the cingulate gyrus), certain occipital regions, and certain temporal regions. It has been proposed (see Magoun, 1961) that in the normal animal during sleep, environmental stimuli reach the cortex first via the classical sensory pathways. The initial cortical arousal produced by this message is probably quite small, and localized. Thus, the cortex may or may not send impulses to the reticular activating system. If it does, then the activating system will arouse the cortex as a whole, and amplify incoming signals. Thus, the cortex determines its own arousal.

The fascinating question is what determines the cortical impulse to the bain stem. Sokolov (see Magoun, 1961) has proposed that there is a matching mechanism at the cortical level. Stimuli received during sleep are compared with models based on past experience. If they do not match, an "orienting reflex" (à la Pavlov) is elicited, which includes impulses to the brain stem activating system, and general cortical arousal. If the incoming stimuli do match the existing model, then no arousal occurs. This hypothesis helps explain the reaction of the sleeping organism to novel stimuli, and the phenomenon of habituation (see Lindsley, 1960). A novel or unfamiliar stimulus evokes an EEG arousal reaction, without necessarily waking the subject. After a few presentations, however, the stimulus no longer evokes the arousal. It has been compared to experimental extinction. Such a matching mechanism may also explain the oft-told tale of the mother who sleeps through the rumbling of trucks but awakens at her baby's cry. Danger signals would have a similar effect.

SLEEP AND ENVIRONMENTAL STIMULATION

It is apparent that external environmental stimulation has to do with sleep. When we wish to go to sleep, we close our eyes and seek quiet and darkness. The worker on the night shift may purchase ear plugs and eye shades. Noises wake us up: the loud soldier returning to the barracks late at night is an object of hostility. Actually, it would be more accurate to say that an absence of strong, unfamiliar, and changeable stimuli favor sleep. This would account for the example of the miller who could not sleep when his grist mill was out of order and no longer groaned through the night (MacNish, 1834). Another exception is the nocturnal animal (Richter, 1922-23). Here the peculiarities of the perceptual apparatus may result in more meaningful stimulation at night.

In any case, a number of theorists have placed a good deal of emphasis on environmental stimulation. Lindsley (1960) calls these "stimulus deficiency theories," and relates them to the reticular activating system. One example would be Bremer's

(1954) idea that de-afferentation produces sleep. Kleitman (1939) also should be included, although he stresses internal afferents more than the environmental stimuli. In these theories, a decrease in environmental stimulation (other things held constant) would lead to a cessation of the reticular activating system, and thus sleep. If this is true, then experimentally decreased stimulus situations should produce sleep.

Such experimental situations do exist and are known, of course, as sensory deprivation studies (see Solomon et al., 1961). In the classical study in this area (Bexton et al., 1954, and Heron, 1961) college students were paid to lie on a comfortable bed in a lighted cubicle for several days. They wore translucent goggles and cardboard cuffs around the hands. Masking sounds, and the use of a pillow, limited auditory perception. There was time out only for eating and going to the toilet. The subjects tended to spend the earlier part of the experimental session in sleep, as indicated by a measure of motility. Later, they slept less and began to have difficulties in concentrating. They experienced perceptual distortions, bordering on hallucinations, and had emotional disturbances. Some of the men reported difficulty in discriminating between sleep and wakefulness. A slight slowing down of the EEG suggests that the men were sometimes in a drowsy state, which would account for some of their difficulties.

A similar study by Vernon and his associates (1961) supports the idea that sleep occurs mainly at the beginning of the sensory-deprivation period. They measured the Galvanic Skin Resistance of both experimental and control subjects and, since this resistance *increases* during sleep, it can be taken as an index of behavior. The experimental subjects, confined in a sound- and light-proof, floating room, were expected to show an *increase,* because the conditions were thought to be conducive to sleep. Instead, all of the experimental groups showed a *decrease* in resistance, suggesting an arousal. Controls showed an increase. Furthermore, the longer the period of confinement the greater the degree of alertness. The authors conclude that "The confined subject 'sleeps-himself-out' in the first 24 hours of confinement, and remains progressively more awake in 48 and 72 hours."

Actually, there seem to be important individual differences in sleeping during sensory deprivation, which may be associated with personality variables (Ruff et al., 1961, and Mendelson et al., 1961). Using GSR, EEG, ERG, and motility as indices, it seems that some subjects use sleep as an escape from the stress of the situation, while others are so overtly anxious that they are unable to sleep. Some of the subjects who slept terminated the experiment, as they are typically allowed to do, after a sleep period, apparently fearing the long stretch of wakefulness coming up. Some subjects had one long, relatively sound sleep, while others seemed to revert to a polyphasic cycle with less extreme variations. By and large, however, the records from these two studies suggest that most of the sleeping was done early in the deprivation period.

Goldberger and Holt (1958, 1961) report on a sensory-deprivation study in which Holt's Rorschach measure of the degree of ego control over primitive, primary process thinking, was employed. Generally the more mature, ego-controlled subjects fared better in the isolation situation, showing a flexible use of many means of adaptation. Of interest here is the finding that the average amount of sleep per hour during this short, one-day deprivation period, was positively correlated with the Rorschach measure. In fact, it is the highest and most significant correlation reported. This suggests that the sleep occurring in the sensory-deprivation studies is a highly adaptive mode of behaving in a difficult situation.

None of these studies was specifically designed to determine the effects of sensory deprivation on patterns of sleep, and most of the observations are fragmentary. It would be extremely interesting to see, for example, whether the sleep pattern eventually becomes polyphasic in most individuals. A systematic investigation is sorely needed. The present studies do show that decreased stimulus availability or variation will favor sleep initially, but that, at least in complex human adults, it is not sufficient to maintain sleep. Anxiety may have contributed to the wakefulness, but it is also possible that it was the result of the satiation of the motive to sleep.

Another line of evidence against the de-afferentation theory is that on animal immobilization, or hypnosis (see Coriat, 1911-12, and Kleitman, 1939 for reviews). It has been shown, with animals ranging from crayfish to puppies, that a sleeplike state can be produced by holding the animals immobile. Kleitman, for example, held puppies on his arm against his body with the hand covering the head and eyelids, but with the body and limbs free. After a few minutes the puppy would relax, yawn, and fall into a deep sleep.

For some time it was believed that this phenomenon was due to an elimination of sensory stimulation, or a decrease in stimulus variability, producing monotony. Kleitman and Coriat argue, however, that muscular relaxation is the cause. Coriat showed that human subjects, sitting in a comfortable chair in a darkened room, late at night, would fall asleep not only when listening to monotonous sounds, but when simply asked to relax. On the other hand, sleep would not occur if the body, or just one limb, showed muscular tension. Kleitman also reports that subjects trained with Jacobson's relaxation method sometimes, but not always, fall asleep when in an extremely relaxed state. Coriat believes that inattention to the environment leads to muscular relaxation and thus to sleep.

Even muscular relaxation may not be sufficient to invariably result in sleep. Species differences, related to the evolution of the brain, may be significant. Thus, Magoun (comments summarized in Solomon et al., 1961, p. 235) mentions that with curare relaxing muscles, and with specific environmental stimulation, rabbits show a sleep EEG, but monkeys one of wakefulness. Obviously, cortical influences make the difference. Magoun sees the need for revising the classical theory that sleep is the inevitable result of de-afferentation.

Therefore muscular relaxation, while important for sleep, is not a sufficient condition for its production. Muscular relaxation, after all, is controlled by brain mechanisms. The inattention mentioned by Coriat is probably the more important condition. It has always intrigued this writer that the most frequently used example of monotony causing sleep is listening to a boring sermon. From a psychodynamic point of view, it is possible that the moralistic content of the sermon may have motivated what Sullivan (1953) calls "selective inattention," and thus sleep.

The preceding studies were concerned with one kind of stimulus influence on sleep: the effect of stimulus insufficiency, lack of variation, or monotony. A different kind of stimulus effect is related to a special acquired property—inhibition. Pavlov (1957) has developed an entire theory of sleep based on the inhibitory properties of environmental stimuli.

Pavlov felt that sleep was produced by a stimulus that produced inhibition in one part of the brain which then spread to the whole brain. At first, Pavlov thought that this inhibition was cortical, but later included subcortical areas as well, in order to account for the fact that de-cerebrated animals show a sleep-wakefulness cycle. In short, his theory was that sleep is generalized inhibition, and inhibition is localized sleep. The model experiment on which he bases this is the trace-conditioned reflex, in which the conditioned stimulus (e.g., buzzer) is presented for a brief instant, but then is followed by a time interval of several seconds, or more, before the unconditioned stimulus (e.g., food) is presented. During this trace reflex, conditioned salivation is inhibited by the dog until near the end of the time period. The interesting thing was that whenever the time interval was a half-minute or more, the dog became drowsy, and often went to sleep. Pavlov said the inhibition of the salivation spread to the whole brain. Pavlov also deprived dogs surgically of smell, sight, and hearing, with the result that they slept for 23½ hours a day. Instead of attributing this to decreased sensory stimulation, Pavlov explains it as due to the monotonous and inhibiting stimulation of the remaining senses of the dog in prone posture.

Pavlov's theory has been challenged by many people (Kleitman, 1939). Kleitman himself observed that dogs with no conditioned reflexes fell asleep when left alone in the experimental room. Wendt (1937) argued that sleep occurred in Pavlov's trace-reflex situation because the animal was restrained in a harness, in an environment with little varied stimulation. Sleeping was about the only response, outside of salivation, available to the animal. He said that in order to inhibit a response, an incompatible response is necessary. So when salivation had to be inhibited, sleeping occurred. Wendt goes on to describe analogous experiments of his own, in which monkeys were required to delay for 8 to 16 seconds the response of opening a drawer to get food. Unlike Pavlov's dogs, the unrestrained monkeys showed little drowsiness. Instead they showed such behavior as grooming, scratching, rough play, galloping in place, vocalizing, and biting the cage—depending on the type of monkey. Therefore, it does not seem that sleep is an inevitable result of inhibition, but may occur when the variability of stimulation is decreased and response possibilities are limited.

In a recent series of studies of conditioned responses during sleep, Rowland (1957, 1961) varied the duration of an auditory clicking stimulus, that previously had been paired with shock. This is somewhat analogous to Pavlov's delayed reflex. The stimulus was extended from the original 5 seconds to 2 minutes. The EEG's of these sleeping cats showed only brief desynchronization at the beginning of this period, and then a pattern of synchrony for the first half. During the second half of the two-minute period desynchronization reappeared. Again this seems to be an induction of sleep by a prolonged stimulus involving delay.

Here too, one can ask if the sleep pattern, or synchrony, occurred simply because no other response was possible in the situation. If some other response was possible, this may have served the purpose. Actually, this is the case because the study also included observations on animals which were completely awake. Some of these cats were engaged in prolonged grooming when the clicking commenced. After a brief interruption grooming continued for the first minute, but then dropped out during the second half of the period. The EEG in these wakeful cats remained desynchronized during the entire stimulus period. During a tone signaling no shock, the animals also showed grooming behavior.

These results suggest that during a delayed response period a variety of irrelevant responses can, and do, occur. The particular response that occurs depends on the situation, the species, and the state of a number of irrelevant motives. At the onset of the delayed stimulus a brief anticipatory response occurs—a few drops of saliva, an EEG arousal, or a startle pattern. Next occurs a response that serves the purpose of inhibiting the anticipatory response. In Wendt's study this was galloping in place—a response probably determined by the freedom of the situation and the nature of monkeys. In Rowland's waking cats the reaction was grooming—again determined by the possibility of this response in the wakeful state and the propensity of cats for this activity. In Pavlov's dogs the response was sleeping—one of the few responses available to the dog in the situation and one that the dogs often exhibited in the harness on other occasions. Finally, in Rowland's sleeping cats the response was a synchronization of the EEG, i.e., a continuation of sleeping. What other response is available to a sleeping animal? Furthermore, Rowland reports that to get this result consistently, it is necessary to deprive the animal of sleep for a day, indicating the need for a heightened sleep motive. Rowland also reports that the synchrony is enhanced by decreasing the shock, and eliminated by increasing it. The occurrence of the sleeping response, then, depends on the relative strength of the sleep and anxiety motives.

Pavlov (1957) also found that animals in his laboratory fell asleep during the extinction of a conditioned reflex. This is seen most dramatically in the inhibition of the investigatory reflex. It is related to the neurophysiological habituation phenomenon, in which novel stimuli at first evoke an EEG arousal, which decreases with subsequent trials in a manner suggestive of extinction. For example, subjects in the typical EEG recording situation will show a disruption, or blocking, of the alpha rhythm with sufficient stimulation. Gastaut and Bert (1961) have shown that when visual or auditory stimuli are presented repetitively, subjects show a habituation of the alpha blocking. Furthermore, the subjects who habituated most rapidly showed EEG signs of sleep during the period of habituation. The authors suggest that certain individuals might be more prone to the hypnotic effects of monotonous stimuli. This might be of significance in various practical situations requiring prolonged vigilance, such as in long-distance truck driving. The important theoretical issue is what brings on the habituation.

Moruzzi (1960) made a careful analysis of the habituation phenomenon in relation to Pavlovian sleep. He finds that it is not due to an inhibition of the sensory pathways or the sensory cortex, nor is it due to a general inhibition of the reticular activating system. This latter is shown by the observation that arousal may be habituated to one tone but not another. Moruzzi concludes that habituation is due to the active intervention of the lower brain stem inhibitory system, in response to the monotonous stimulation.

We would only add that in most situations in which EEG habituation, or inhibition of the investigatory reflex, is studied, sleep is the only readily available alternative to the curiosity pattern. There are many studies of experimental extinction in which responses other than sleep appeared—especially if the animal was in a freely moving situation. To cite one clear case, take the example of Brady's (1955) conditioned fear experiment. Rats had been trained to press a bar at a steady rate for water reinforcement, in an operant procedure. Then, in a classical Pavlovian conditioning procedure, a clicking signal was paired with electric shock. Subsequently, the clicking stimulus alone elicited a fear reaction, one manifestation of which was a decrease in the unrelated bar-pressing. During extinction of the fear-provoking clicking stimulus, the bar-pressing response returned to full strength. Therefore, an increased responsiveness rather than sleep was the result of extinction in this freer situation. Sleep is not an inevitable accompaniment of inhibition.

It can be seen that Pavlov's idea that the inhibitory properties of a stimulus cause sleep can be more easily explained by other factors. The monotony of the stimuli used, and the lack of alternative responses in the conditioning situation account for many of the results. Inhibition, extinction, and habituation do not produce sleep in and of themselves. This does not mean that a stimulus cannot be associated with sleeping and come to evoke it. In the Pavlovian situation the stimulus was related to salivation and food reward, but not to sleep—at least initially. The attachment of stimuli to sleep behavior itself is quite a different problem. Thus sight of our own beloved bed, after a week of uncomfortable hotels, may evoke an anticipatory relaxation. Similarly, meeting a very boring acquaintance may result in an embarrassing yawn. The thought of the lawn mower on a Saturday afternoon has put many a man into a deep slumber. These are learned cues and will be dealt with at greater length in subsequent chapters.

The interpretation of Pavlovian sleep may explain to some extent why monotony and stimulus deficiency favor sleep. In Pavlov's conditioning harness, the dogs could make few responses other than sleeping or salivating. Similarly, since most of our behavior is associated with environmental cues (discriminative stimuli more than Pavlovian conditioned stimuli), the lack of such cues would diminish the available response repertoire. In extreme situations the only response left would be sleeping. Since we are not *entirely* dependent on our environment for responding, however, sleep would not always, or continuously, occur. Not only would stimuli from distended bladders and stomach contractions awaken us, but the activity of that great repository of memories, ideas, images, and fantasies—the cortex—would also arouse the organism and produce wakefulness—sometimes of a distorted kind.

THE ROLE OF THE INTERNAL MILIEU IN SLEEP

Since ancient times there have been theories of sleep based on brain influences from the internal processes of the body. Processes thought to be important include cardiovascular changes, digestion and elimination, muscular fatigue, metabolism, and fluid balance. These processes influence the brain by humoral, chemical, or neural mechanisms. It is all part of the homeostatic balance of the organism. Kleitman (1939) has reviewed the evidence for these theories, and finds fault in most of them. Nevertheless, it appears that internal processes may play a contributing role. We will first review the evidence for chemical and neural stimulation related to fatigue, and then the effects of satiation of sexual and hunger motives.

The best known of the chemical theories of sleep is Pieron's hypothetical "hypnotoxin" (see Kleitman, 1939; Morgan and Stellar, 1950). According to this theory, some sort of fatigue product is accumulated during the day in the blood and cerebrospinal fluid. This produces sleep when it reaches a certain level, and is metabolized away during sleep. Pieron attempted to demonstrate this by removing cerebrospinal fluid from a fatigued dog and injecting it into the fourth ventricle of a rested dog. The rested dog then fell asleep. Pieron found that normal cerebrospinal fluid had no such effect. The results support hypnotoxin theory.

The experiment by Schnedorf and Ivy (1939) is often quoted as disproving Pieron's theory. These experimenters repeated Pieron's cerebrospinal fluid study. Injections of fluid taken from dogs kept awake from 7 to 16 days, into 20 rested dogs, produced sleep in 45% of the cases. They used injections from rested dogs, a dog's own fluid withdrawn and reinjected, and normal saline as control conditions. Such control injections were administered to 24 dogs, with the result that 4, or 17%, fell asleep. The authors also noted a rise in temperature and cranial pressure with these injections, and conclude that the evidence does not support hypnotoxin theory. Yet the difference between the groups is large. If one calculates a t-test for the difference between the 45% and 17%, it turns out to be significant at the .05 level. Furthermore, the authors report that the control animals did not show as deep a sleep as the others.

Another sort of evidence cited against hypnotoxin theory is that Siamese twins may not show fully synchronized sleep-wake behavior. One may sleep while the other is awake (Kleitman, 1939). As Kleitman concedes, however, this is not conclusive evidence. He suggests that the state of the nervous system may increase its resistance to chemical agents. This points to a multifactor theory.

Kety (1961) has reviewed some recent studies on brain metabolism during sleep. Most changes are not significant, or are secondary to the sleep posture. There is no evidence that cerebral blood flow, or oxygen consumption, is responsible for sleep. One change that is significant and important, however, is that during sleep there is an increase in arterial carbon dioxide tension. Of particular interest is that fatigued subjects showed a high carbon dioxide level *before* going to sleep. Furthermore, those fatigued subjects who went to sleep immediately had a higher carbon dioxide tension than those who elected to stay up longer. Kety points out that it would have been possible to pre--

dict who would fall asleep, on the basis of the carbon dioxide tension. Of course, this is most likely a result of shallower breathing, and thus is not independent of neural control. These factors are probably all interrelated.

Quite recently, Monnier and his associates (cited in Luce, 1965) were able to obtain a membrane-filtered substance from the brain blood of a sleeping rabbit. This substance produced sleep when it was injected into an alert rabbit. So, too, a substance from the blood of an awake animal produced arousal in a sleeping one. The specific substance has not yet been identified.

At the present time one tends to agree with Morgan and Stellar (1950) that the influence of a chemical factor in producing sleep can be neither rejected nor fully accepted. They feel that at best, chemical factors play a contributing role. Obviously, more research is needed here. Nevertheless, it is difficult to see how someone can dismiss the hypnotoxin and related theories as Kleitman does. The evidence for neural factors related to fatigue is a little clearer, however.

Kleitman (1939) has emphasized the importance of internal afferent stimulation from receptors in the muscles, joints, and organs of the body in producing wakefulness. This is an aspect of the internal milieu, although it involves neural pathways. During sleep, thresholds for internal stimulation are raised. Even so, stimulation from these receptors will interfere with sleep. According to Kleitman, mild stimulation from cramped muscles and joints produces some arousal and causes the person to turn over; with the cessation of the stimulation, synchronized sleep is resumed. Severe pain will interfere with sleep, and may make it nearly impossible. Emotional disturbance may prevent the onset of sleep. These factors operate cortically, but may involve afferent stimulation through arousal of visceral and other responses.

There may also be an effect of internal afferent stimulation in the direction of de-activating the organism. During periods of great muscular fatigue or overexhaustion, one would suspect that a homeostatic mechanism would act to produce inactivity and, in some cases, sleep. Dell and his colleagues (1961) have shown that stimulating somatic nerves, ordinarily carrying proprioceptive messages, first sets off the reticular activating mechanism, but then secondarily triggers a de-activating mechanism. In animals sectioned just above the medulla, the stimulation of somatic afferents regularly sets off long-lasting, descending inhibitory impulses. Thus the body can protect itself from muscular strain by a de-activating influence.

Another danger of overexertion is overwork of the heart and high blood pressure. Dell and his associates showed that this aspect of the internal milieu may be related to sleep. One of the chief homeostatic mechanisms the body has for controlling blood pressure is in the carotid artery in the neck. When blood pressure mounts, and the carotid sinus is distended, stretch receptors in the wall send nervous impulses to the brain stem and blood pressure is lowered. Dell and his associates showed that mechanically distending the carotid sinus, while surgically maintaining normal blood flow to the brain, resulted in a change in the EEG from a wakeful to a sleep pattern. Carotid stimulation also inhibits postural tone. This mechanism may account for sleep after prolonged emotional strain or exhausting activity, as well as some of the symptoms of narcolepsy or syncope (see Lindsley, 1956, although his explanation is somewhat different). It is interesting to note that the Greek meaning of *carotid* is "to produce sleep" (Brownlow, 1941).

Adrenaline and noradrenaline affect the level of cortical arousal indirectly through the carotid sinus (Nakao et al., 1956). Adrenaline and noradrenaline raise blood pressure and, if the carotid sinus is intact, produce a slowing down of the cortical EEG. This effect does not occur if the carotid sinus area is denervated. In other words, these excitatory hormones have a de-activating effect because of the homeostatic action of the blood pressure receptors in the carotid sinus. Hypotensive drugs such as acetylcholine produce a cortical arousal, which is also dependent on the intact carotid sinus.

Sexual hormones may also lead to sleep. Sleepiness after coitus is frequently reported anecdotally on the human level. Sawyer and Kawakami (1961) report laboratory studies of this phenomenon in the female rabbit. Estrogen-primed female rabbits fall asleep after coitus. For a few minutes to a half-hour the EEG shows the slow waves of synchronized sleep. This is followed by a period of paradoxical fast-wave sleep and then wakefulness. The effect can also be produced by a number of pituitary hormones that are ordinarily released after coitus. The same effect can also be achieved in the estrous rabbit by electrical stimulation to the hypothalamus.

The relationship between stomach contraction and activity, as mentioned in an earlier chapter, is well known. While stomach contractions are neither necessary nor invariably present in hunger and action, they probably play some sort of contributing role in the intact organism. Stimulation from the digestive system may also lead to de-activation, inactivity, and sleep. Everyone is familiar with the soporific effects of a very heavy meal, when the stomach is distended. More systematic observations on rats (Richter, 1922-23), dogs (Kleitman and Camille, 1932), and infants (Gesell and Ilg, 1943) show that sleep and inactivity typically follow eating when there are no competing interests. The infant wakes, eats, has a bowel movement, and returns to sleep. "The baby eats to sleep and he wakes to eat . . ." (Gesell and Ilg, 1943, p. 300). As Kleitman (1939) points out, digestion is enhanced by sleep and inactivity. Magoun (1963) cites a study by Anokhin in which an EEG synchrony was produced by tube-feeding into the stomach or glucose injections into the blood stream. The effect of the digestive system on the central nervous system is probably achieved through vagal stimulation, although humoral elements may also participate. Both have been demonstrated experimentally.

In *encephale isolé* preparations, the Dell group stimulated the cut end of the vagus nerve. Stimulation of some of the rootlets leads to cortical arousal, but stimulation of others produces deactivation. Thus, changes in the cardiovascular and gastrointestinal systems may contribute to sleep. Another influence is by a liver hormone acting on the bulbar inhibitory mechanism, with ascending and descending effects. Distending the bile duct releases the hormone, and after several minutes of latency there is an internal postural inhibition and a synchronized cortical sleep record.

Therefore, there is some evidence of a general hypnotoxin, and, furthermore, a number of internal factors—stimulation of somatic nerves, blood pressure, hormones, satiety, etc.—have a de-activating or sleep-producing effect. These internal factors appear to act on brain mechanisms for de-activation and sleep.

THE SLEEP SYSTEM

In contrast to the passive concept of sleep, in which sleep occurs because of a cessation of the reticular activating system or a lack of environmental stimulation, an impressive array of evidence for a system of neural mechanisms producing sleep activity has been gathered over the years. This system includes influences from the lower brain stem, the thalamus, the hypothalamus, the limbic structures in the paleocortex, and the neocortex. We will describe these influences in turn and review several theories suggesting that they form an integrated system. We will consider both synchronized sleep and the aroused sleep associated with dreams.

Lower Brain Stem Mechanisms

While the activating system in the reticular formation has received the most attention in recent years, it has long been known that this formation also contains inhibitory mechanisms (Magoun, 1958). Although excitatory and inhibitory mechanisms are intertwined throughout the length of the reticular formation, the inhibitory part seems concentrated in the lower brain stem in the medulla and caudal pons (see Fig. 5 for a rough placement). In conjunction with descending parts of the activating system, the inhibitory reticular formation has a generalized effect on spinal reflexes. The two systems also appear to act, in a reciprocal way, on specific sets of antagonistic muscles, e.g., at a joint. These two reciprocal systems also influence spinal control of the viscera. The descending influences of the reticular formation are controlled, in turn, by the extrapyramidal motor cortex, several basal ganglia, and the cerebellum (see also Lindsley, 1960; Morgan and Stellar, 1950, Chapter 13).

Another kind of inhibitory function of the reticular formation is on the transmission of incoming afferent impulses (Magoun, 1958; Lindsley, 1960). While potentiating effects have been found, most of the studies show an inhibitory effect. Thus, stimulation of the reticular formation reduces the transmission of incoming afferent impulses (Magoun, 1958; Lindsley, 1960). Stimulation of various parts of the reticular formation reduces the transmission of proprioceptive, auditory, visual, and olfactory messages. This effect may be important in the focusing of attention. Thus a drowsing cat will exhibit a certain magnitude of neural response to a click stimulus. When the cat's attention is attracted by a visual stimulus (mice in a beaker), however, or an olfactory one (fish odor), the magnitude of the evoked auditory response is reduced. Magoun thinks that this is due to an inhibitory process preventing irrelevant afferent information from passing beyond its first synapse. Such inhibition of afferent impulses may also be involved in sleep.

The inhibitory influences mentioned so far are only indirectly related to sleep. However, a recent series of studies, carried out mainly by Moruzzi and his associates at the University of Pisa, has indicated an area in the lower brain stem that very clearly has to do with sleep (see Moruzzi, 1960, and Magnes et al., 1961 b, for summaries of these studies). There are three kinds of evidence for this sleep influence: from brain stem transection, from chemical infusions, and from electrical stimulation. The first line of evidence comes from a series of studies in which the brain stem was completely transected (e.g., Batini et al., 1958). If a transection was made at the rostral or forward end of the pons, the EEG and behavior indicated sleep, similar to the *cerveau isolé* of Bremer. Unlike Bremer's preparation, these animals could be aroused briefly by olfactory stimuli. Wakefulness could not be maintained, however. If the transection was performed in the middle of the pons, the result was just the opposite—EEG and behavioral indications of increased wakefulness. For example, the EEG showed a waking pattern 70% to 90% of the time, as opposed to 20% to 50% in the normal cat. The animals also showed visual following and pupillary dilation in response to the stimulus of a mouse. It should be emphasized that the sensory input in both the rostro-pontine and mid-pontine preparations was the same.

These results suggest that the pons contains two important mechanisms. The forward part of the pons is essential for continuing wakefulness, although more anterior parts of the reticular formation are sufficient for temporary arousal. Somewhere behind the middle of the pons there must be a sleep-inducing system. Since these results are obtained in *encephale isolé* preparations the critical area must be in the caudal part of the pons or the medulla. In all probability the structures involved are part of, or related to, the inhibitory part of the reticular formation described above.

A second line of evidence comes from barbiturate infusion of various parts of the brain stem (see Moruzzi, 1960). The blood supply to the rostral pons and forward parts of the brain was surgically separated from that reaching the caudal pons and medulla. *Encephale isolé* preparations were used so that indirect circulatory effects could be controlled. Very small amounts of thiopental, injected into the blood supply to the rostral areas, changes the EEG from a wakeful pattern to one of sleep. Contrariwise, similar or even larger doses of the barbiturate, infused into the lower pons and medulla, change a sleep record into an aroused one. In other words, sedating the activating mechanism results in sleep, while sedating the sleep mechanism produces wakefulness.

Finally, an EEG synchronization was produced by electrical stimulation of the area in question (Magnes et al., 1961 a, and Magnes et al., 1961 b). In *encephale isolé* cats, low-frequency stimulation of two areas in the medial part of the medulla (nucleus of the solitary tract and nucleus reticularis ventralis), resulted in EEG synchronization that often lasted beyond the stimulus. The frequency of the electrical impulse was important —high-frequency stimulation at the same spot resulted in EEG arousal. Nevertheless, the synchronizing area was very small— moving the electrode up or down just 1 mm. resulted in EEG arousal even with this low-frequency stimulation. The synchronizing effect was difficult to obtain when the background EEG was one of intense arousal, and could be abolished by sensory stimulation. The effect may be similar to the carotid sinus reflex, but appears to be independent of it. The extent of the synchronizing structure, rostrally and caudally, was not determined.

In the above experiment descending influences of this bulbar, de-activating mechanism could not be seen, since an *encephale isolé* preparation was used. In an earlier and unrelated study, however, Sprague and Chambers (1954) made an interesting observation on a cat. The animal had been decerebrated at the pontine level and then stimulated somewhere in the medial reticular formation of the medulla. At this particular point the stimulation produced the behavioral manifestations of sleep—circling and curling up in the sleeping position. At the same time, the eyes remained open and the cat appeared to be fully awake. This dissociation of "brain and body sleep" was, of course, due to the pontine transection. Jouvet (1961) has observed that in cats with a rostro-pontine or mesencephalic transection, the forward part always shows the sleep EEG of the *cerveau isolé*, while the part caudal to the transection shows general rapid activity during periods of behavioral wakefulness, and spindles from the caudal-pontine reticular formation during periods of behavioral sleep. It is possible that some sort of functional block at the pontine level could account for cases of sleep paralysis (Levin, 1957) in which the individual awakens but cannot move. In the intact organism we would expect that the bulbar mechanism would produce EEG and behaviorial signs of sleep at about the same time.

More recently it has been found that mechanisms in the lower brain stem are important in the production of aroused sleep and, presumably, dreams. Jouvet (1961) reports a series of experiments that localize this area. In the intact cat the cortical arousal in the paradoxical phase is correlated with spindling activity in the pontine reticular formation. Separating the cerebrum from the pons by a midbrain transection results in a continuous synchronized sleep pattern at the cortical level and cyclical bursts of spindling at the pontine level. Destroying an area in the lower brain stem at the level of the pons eliminates the paradoxical phase entirely. Since destroying the ascending reticular pathways in the midbrain does not eliminate the paradoxical phase, Jouvet suggested that paradoxical sleep originates in the pontine area and arouses the cortex via the more ventral limbic circuit.

The relationship between the pontine mechanisms for paradoxical sleep found by Jouvet and the two pontine mechanisms described by Batini et al. is not entirely clear. It is possible that there is an intermingling of wakeful arousal, synchronized sleep, and aroused sleep mechanisms at the pontine level. The mechanisms for synchronized and aroused sleep may be the same but depend on stimulus frequency. Rossi (1962) has shown that stimulating the reticular formation at a variety of points at the level of the medulla, pons, or midbrain with low-frequency stimuli produces cortical EEG synchrony and, eventually, behavioral sleep. When the cat is in an intermediate stage of sleep, high-frequency stimulation produces paradoxical sleep. All investigators agree that aroused sleep cannot be produced directly if the animal is awake; aroused sleep can only be produced after a period of synchronized sleep.

Jouvet's theory that the pontine mechanism affects the cortex via the limbic system was tested by Carli et al. (1963). They destroyed large areas of the midbrain including all the connections between the limbic system and the pontine area, but found that the aroused sleep stage was essentially unmodified. The cortical arousal appeared periodically; the loss of tonus in the neck muscles and the twitches in the extremities remained. Nevertheless, they did observe one important change: rapid eye movements frequently disappeared after these lesions. This suggests that the limbic system is the route by which the pontine mechanism controls rapid eye movements.

The most recent evidence presented on this point is by Jouvet (cited in Luce, 1965). His evidence was based on a systematic series of lesions along the limbic circuit. Lesions at four different limbic levels eliminated paradoxical sleep. Lesions in the midbrain reticular system eliminated wakeful arousal but not the paradoxical phase of sleep. The results are not consistent with those of Carli et al. (1963) but possibly have greater weight because they are more systematic. It seems likely that paradoxical sleep involves the pontine mechanism operating through the limbic circuit.

The pontine area is connected to the lateral geniculate bodies that control eye movement. Stimulation of the pontine mechanism results in responses in the lateral geniculate bodies but only during the paradoxical phase. Stimulation of the lateral geniculate bodies never results in a response in the pontine area. Thus, the pontine mechanism seems to be critical in the rapid eye movements of aroused sleep (Bizzi and Brooks, 1963).

It appears, then, that there are three functional mechanisms in the lower brain stem—for wakeful arousal, for synchronized sleep, and for aroused sleep. They may or may not overlap anatomically. The ascending reticular system appears to be the pathway for the wakeful arousal and synchronized sleep influences. The ascending pathway for the aroused sleep influence is not definitely established but seems to be the limbic circuit.

Thalamic Mechanisms

We will now turn to thalamic mechanisms that might be involved in sleep. More than thirty years ago Hess discovered a vaguely defined area in the thalamus that, when properly stimulated, evoked normal sleep behavior in the cat— including circling, curling up, and sleeping (see Hess, 1957). For some time it was difficult for neurophysiologists to duplicate Hess' work, for two reasons: the crucial area was hard to specify, and the frequency of the stimulation was more important than many realized. As with the de-activating mechanism in the lower brain stem, it was necessary to use a low-frequency (4-12 cps), and low-voltage (1-2v) impulse. The area is a little better defined now; it is not far from the midline, runs lateral to the massa intermedia, and probably includes the intralaminary regions (see Lindsley, 1960). In recent years a number of scientists have been able to produce the effect, including Hess' son, R. Hess et al. (1953), Akert et al. (1952), Akimoto et al. (1956) in the dog, Monnier et al. (1960), and Hernández-Peón (1964).

Another line of investigation suggesting a sleep mechanism in the thalamus, is that on the Morison-Demsey thalamic "recruiting response" (see Jasper, 1954, and Lindsley, 1960, for reviews). Stimulation of areas overlapping with Hess' "sleep center," with the same sort of low, slow electrical impulse resulted in a partial synchronization of the cortical EEG. Slowly, more and more cortical elements are brought into harmonious rhythm. Stimulating the same area with a higher frequency caused de-synchrony, or, in other words, arousal. Subsequently, Hunter and Jasper (1949), using the same procedure in unanaesthetized cats, showed that the recruiting response was related to a behavior "arrest" pattern and, in a few cases, actual sleep.

Monnier and his associates (1960) have duplicated the above phenomena, and have gone further in postulating two thalamic projection systems: the thalamic reticular activating system and the "intralaminary moderating system." These two systems are thought to be intermingled in the thalamus, so that they have not been distinguished anatomically. Here too, a low, slow stimulation produces cortical synchrony, while a stronger stimulus at the same point is arousing. In a microelectrode study on single neurones in the cortex, the authors were able to show that the two systems are antagonistic and reciprocally related.

Monnier and his colleagues were also able to show differential effects on the two systems with drugs. Centrally stimulating drugs such as LSD, amphetamine, and coramine facilitate the activating system and inhibit the moderating system. Centrally depressing drugs such as morphine, chlorpromazine, and reserpine act in just the opposite way; they decrease the activity of the activating system and enhance the moderating system.

The thalamic moderating or recruiting system does not respond to low-frequency stimulation during aroused sleep, according to a study by Rossi (1962). In addition, injection of a barbiturate during aroused sleep leads to synchronization at the thalamic lead. Rossi concludes that paradoxical sleep is due to an inhibition of the thalamic synchronizing mechanism.

Thus, we see that the thalamus has antagonistic systems for wakeful arousal and synchronized sleep. Aroused sleep may involve an inhibition of the thalamic synchronizing mechanism.

Hypothalamic Mechanisms

On the basis of the presence of other physiological motivational mechanisms, one would also expect some sleep-regulating mechanism in the hypothalamus. The involvement of the hypothalamus in the regulation of sleep was first shown clinically in cases of *encephalitis lethargica* (see Kleitman, 1939, Chapter 23, and Nauta, 1946, for summaries). Von Economo (1930) mentions several kinds of hypothalamic disturbances that cause sleep symptoms: hemorrhage, tumor, or inflammation. In *encephalitis lethargica* a virus appears to have an affinity for sleep mechanisms in the hypothalamus and related areas, as opposed to areas for other vegetative functions. Von Economo and others distinguish several stages of the disease: an acute stage with psychotic symptoms, a stage of marked insomnia, and a stage of excessive sleepiness. One or another stage may predominate. The symptoms of sleepiness, often accompanied by diplopia, are usually associated with lesions in the posterior part of the hypothalamus. The insomnia symptoms, which may be accompanied by a muscular chorea, are related to the anterior part of the hypothalamus. Thus, there is evidence for a waking area in the posterior hypothalamus and a sleep area in the anterior hypothalamus (see Fig. 6).

Parenthetically, two other interesting symptoms of *encephalitis lethargica* might be mentioned: inversion of the sleep-wakefulness cycle, and a dissociation between body and brain sleep. According to Kleitman (1939) the inversion of the sleep cycle is due to difficulty in getting to sleep at night, and thus catching up during the day. In some cases the person stays awake for two or three days, and then sleeps several days. The inversion can be treated by keeping the person awake during the day. Von Economo (1930) tried to explain the dissociation phenomenon by postulating two sleep areas: one rostral one controlling consciousness, and one in the midbrain controlling somatic and visceral functions (see also Lindsley, 1960). It is conceivable that the lower brain stem mechanism discussed above would fulfill this latter role.

Returning to the problem of hypothalamic sleep mechanisms, we turn to the experimental studies of Nauta (1946). This research on rats supports the clinical observations and suggests antagonistic sleep and waking areas in the hypothalamus. First, Nauta demonstrated a waking area by making bilateral, slicing surgical wounds in the posterior hypothalamus, in the region of the mammillary bodies. Synchronized sleep and a temperature drop was the result. The animals, which had to be fed artificially,

FIGURE 6

could be aroused by handling and pinching, but they would yawn, stretch, and rapidly fall asleep again. Those animals surviving long enough showed a tendency to recover from the synchronized sleep, although all the animals died eventually from secondary infections.

These results suggest the existence of a waking area in the posterior hypothalamus. If this area is destroyed, or if its connections are disrupted, sleep results. Nauta also found that lesions just anterior to the mammillary bodies, especially in the lateral hypothalamus, produced a state of drowsiness in which the animals were neither fully awake nor fully asleep. Lesions more than 2mm. in front of the mammillary bodies, and lesions not fully bilateral, did not produce any signs of somnolence.

More data suggesting a waking area in the posterior hypothalamus are available. Ranson (1939) placed lesions in the posterior hypothalamus of monkeys and found that they resulted in somnolence. Meyer and Hunter (1952) reported comparable results in the cat when they put lesions in the mammillo-thalamic tract, one of the routes by which the posterior hypothalamus conceivably influences the cortex.

Thus, there is evidence in the rat, cat, monkey, and man for a waking mechanism in the posterior hypothalamus. Lindsley (1960) does not see any conflict between this and the idea of a reticular activating system, since reticular substance extends into the hypothalamus. However, the hypothalamus is most sensitive to changes in the internal milieu that might influence wakefulness (Gellhorn, 1957).

Nauta's evidence for a sleeping mechanism is based on a group of rats with complete bilateral lesions in the anterior half of the hypothalamus, in the area of the preoptic nucleus. The animals in this group showed complete sleeplessness. For the first 24 hours they appeared normal and ate well. Then they began to be fatigued, ceased eating and drinking of their own accord, and showed less interest in their environment. Nevertheless they did not fall asleep, as shown by their open eyes and spontaneous activity. After about three days they became exhausted, showed an unsteady gait, fell into a coma, and died soon after. There was never a suggestion of the return of the ability to sleep. Nauta concludes that a mechanism for sleep exists in the anterior hypothalamus. Lesions anterior to the preoptic nucleus had no effect on sleep or wakefulness. Nauta's results on both the sleeping and wakeful areas of the hypothalamus have been collated in a single diagram by Morgan and Stellar (1950); this is presented in Fig. 7.

The mode of interaction between the sleep and waking mechanisms is of great theoretical interest. Von Economo thought that the sleep mechanism was fully independent, directly inhibiting the cortex and other parts of the brain. Ranson and others who did not accept the existence of a sleep area, believed that sleep and wakefulness were the result of intrinsic variations in the activity of the waking area. Nauta suspected that the sleep area inhibits the waking area. The ideal experiment would be to first make an animal somnolent by a lesion in the posterior hypothalamus, and then see if a second lesion in the anterior part would restore wakefulness. For technical reasons this experiment was not possible, and so Nauta made both lesions simultaneously. The result was animals showing a typical sleep

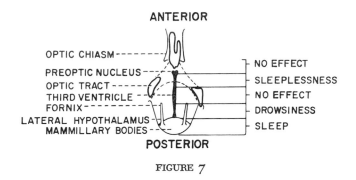

FIGURE 7

pattern. This means that an anterior lesion, which by itself can produce sleeplessness, cannot overcome the somnolence due to a posterior lesion. Nauta concluded that the sleep mechanism ordinarily functions to inhibit the action of the waking mechanism. It is unlikely that the sleep mechanism affects the cortex directly. Nauta also believed that supplementary sleep mechanisms existed lower in the brain stem to control muscular changes involved in the sleeping position. Today, Nauta believes that the dual hypothalamic mechanisms act on the reticular activating system (personal communication).

Direct confirmation of Nauta's early work has come from electrical stimulation studies (Clemente and Sterman, 1961; Sterman and Clemente, 1962 a; Sterman and Clemente, 1962 b; Sterman, Wyrwicka, and Clemente, 1962). Stimulation in the region of the preoptic nucleus in the hypothalamus, with both low- and high-frequency stimulation, produced an EEG synchrony and behavioral sleep. If the stimulation was persistent, the paradoxical phase of sleep appeared. The sleep produced by preoptic stimulation can be conditioned to an external sensory stimulus. The sleep produced by preoptic stimulation resembles normal sleep in every way.

Structures adjacent to the preoptic region are also effective in producing sleep when stimulated; the Sterman-Clemente group has therefore described the whole area as a basal forebrain inhibitory mechanism. Stimulation of the preoptic region produced synchrony in the thalamic intralaminary system and, at a high voltage, in the limbic system and cortex.

The basal forebrain inhibitory mechanism appears to operate antagonistically to the reticular activating system. Stimulation of the reticular formation produced the well-known cortical arousal, but if the basal forebrain mechanism was stimulated during the cortical arousal, synchronization resulted. So, too, reticular stimulation reversed ongoing synchronization produced by basal forebrain stimulation. This is a little different from Nauta's idea of the sleep mechanism inhibiting the wakefulness mechanism. They appear to be mutually antagonistic.

The existence of a sleep-inducing mechanism in the preoptic region was confirmed by Hernández-Peón (1962), using both low-frequency electrical stimulation and chemical stimulation with acetylcholine. Typically, the animal passes first into synchronized sleep and then into aroused sleep. Thus, hypothalamic mechanisms appear to be important in wakefulness, synchronized sleep, and aroused sleep.

Limbic Mechanisms

While the hypothalamus can now be considered important in sleep, its real importance is in its involvement in a larger system including the paleocortex and midbrain—Nauta's (1958) limbic-midbrain circuit or limbic system.

The three chief parts of the paleocortex—the septum, the amygdala, and the hippocampus—seem to be involved in sleep.

Sleep can be produced by stimulating the septum (Rosvold and Delgado, 1956), the amygdala (Sterman and Clemente, 1962), and the fornix, which is the chief pathway from the hippocampus to the hypothalamus (Segundo et al., 1955). On the other hand, lesions in the fornix and septum result in an exaggerated alertness (Brady and Nauta, 1953).

The hippocampus seems to be especially important in sleep. This large projection area shows an unusual EEG pattern in connection with the sleep-wakeful cycle (Green and Arduini, 1954). It responds in just the opposite way from the cortex: synchronized waves during wakefulness and aroused sleep but fast waves during cortically synchronized sleep. The hippocampus reacts to sensory stimuli during the paradoxical phase of sleep when the cortical responses are decreased (Cadilhac et al., 1962). Green and Arduini suggest that the hippocampus shows a "specialized paleocortical arousal reaction."

This evidence suggests strongly that the hippocampus is important in dreaming. Jouvet (1961) found that the hippocampus was associated with his rhombencephalic phase of sleep. Cadilhac et al. (1962) were able to produce paradoxical sleep by stimulating the hippocampus. These authors conclude that the hippocampus—at the far end of the limbic system from the pontine mechanism for paradoxical sleep—acts as the "moderator" for aroused sleep.

The most extensive and systematic study of the limbic circuit in relation to sleep has been done by Hernández-Peón and his associates (Hernández-Peón, 1962; Velluti and Hernández-Peón, 1963; Hernández-Peón et al., 1963). As mentioned earlier, small crystals of acetylcholine were tamped into cannulae placed along the limbic circuit in different cats. At nearly all points along the limbic circuit the acetylcholine produced a pattern of synchronized sleep passing into aroused sleep. A rough diagram of the limbic circuit is shown in Fig. 8.

According to Hernández-Peón and his associates the sleep system, or hypnogenic circuit, starts in the limbic forebrain (amygdala, septum, and hippocampus), descends via the preoptic region and lateral hypothalamus to the limbic midbrain area, caudal to the midbrain reticular arousal system. Connections also descend further to the pontine mechanism.

There is evidence in these studies that the direction of influence along the limbic circuit is from the forebrain to the midbrain. Lesions were made along the route in the medial forebrain bundle. Cholinergic stimulation to points anterior to the lesion was no longer effective while points posterior to the

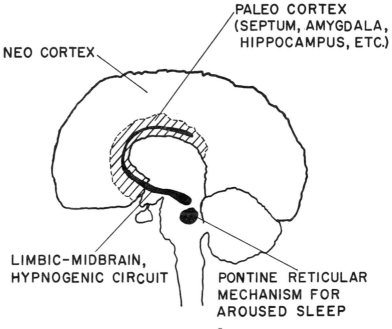

FIGURE 8

lesion still produced sleep. The latency of the reactions also seemed to indicate that sleep-inducing influences are initiated in the paleocortical limbic structures, are transmitted down the limbic circuit, and act to inhibit the midbrain reticular activating system.

The entire limbic system is thus involved in the induction of both synchronized and aroused sleep. It seems to act by a descending inhibitory influence on the brain stem activating system rather than directly on the cortex.

Cortical Influences

There is also some evidence that there are positive neocortical influences facilitating sleep. Burns (1957) was able to produce sleep with repeated bursts of 5-volt, 60-cycle impulses through electrodes in the occipital cortex of rats. Stimulation of the frontal areas did not produce the sleep. The sleep appeared to be normal behaviorally, but the EEG was not a normal sleep record. It is possible that this result is related to the recent use of electrical anesthesia (Hardy et al., 1961). A low amperage 25-volt, 700-cycle current, applied through the temples, was effective in producing unconsciousness and inactivity during major surgery. It is difficult to say exactly how these phenomena occurred. An interference with activation cannot be ruled out.

Possibly the unique role that the cortex plays in the sleep-wakeful cycle is to prolong the period of sleep and wakefulness. All animals capable of voluntarily stretching out their sleep and awake periods, have a well-developed cortex, although the reverse may not be true (see Morgan and Stellar, 1950). Such a conception of the role of the cortex also fits some clinical facts (Davison and Demuth, 1946).

An experimental verification of the role of the cortex in prolonging wakeful and sleep periods has been presented by Kleitman and Camille (1932). Four dogs survived a total removal of both hemispheres of the cerebral cortex. The dogs did sleep and could be aroused by environmental stimuli, hunger cycles, and micturition needs. Their distribution of sleep patterns, however, became polyphasic; they showed an alternation of short periods of sleep with wakefulness. The authors point out that normal dogs can stay up all day and sleep all night. Young puppies, as well as human infants in whom the cortex has not yet developed, show a polyphasic sleep pattern, so that the de-corticated dogs resemble puppies. Kleitman and Camille also cite the case of a child born without a cortex, who at age 4 had not learned to sleep all night and stay awake all day.

Finally, the early finding by Bremer (1961) that the cortex separated from the rest of the brain shows a continuous synchronized EEG record, has been disproved by Batsel (1960). He was able to produce Bremer's synchronization by almost any midbrain transection. However, Batsel was able to keep his dogs alive for long periods after the operation. He found that after a few days of continuous synchronization the cortex began to show a normal alternation of arousal and synchronization. This is further evidence that the cortex is not entirely a passive organ and that it may participate in its own level of arousal.

Jouvet (1961) removed the entire neocortex in one series of studies in connection with his work on paradoxical sleep. This operation eliminates slow waves and spindles in subcortical structures. The paradoxical phase of sleep continues in a normal cyclical fashion. Therefore, Jouvet postulated his two types of sleep—synchronized *telencephalic* sleep controlled by the neocortex and paradoxical *rhombencephalic* sleep controlled by the pontine mechanism.

The cortex then plays an active role in synchronized sleep. It seems to be particularly important in the prolongation of sleep as well.

Interrelation of Mechanisms

The sleep system certainly seems to be a Chinese puzzle of complex mechanisms. One can simply say, as does Hernández-Peón (1962), that in contrast to the compact wakefulness system, the sleep system is scattered about the brain. Hernández-Peón postulates influences from the medulla, limbic system, and neocortex acting to inhibit the recticular arousal system.

Magoun (1963) relates the mechanisms in a more detailed way. First he assumes that the synchronized EEG is produced by the thalamo-cortical system. The thalamo-cortical synchronizing system is driven in turn by the pontine mechanism to effect a general reduction in visceral processes by reducing the level of arousal of the brain. The hypothalamic and limbic sources drive the thalamo-cortical synchronizing system on the basis of satiety and as an endocrine homeostat. Finally, the thalamo-cortical system is driven by basal ganglia and the cortex in the service of Pavlovian internal inhibition. The sleep mechanisms together operate opposite the reticular activating system according to Sherrington's principle of reciprocal innervation.

Magoun also attempts to account for the qualitatively different stages of sleep. In synchronized sleep the cortex is inhibited, but not the subcortical mechanisms. Aroused sleep involves an inhibition of the thalamo-cortical synchronizing system and the reticular activating system. Dreams consist of an aroused cortex with emotions supplied by the activity of the hippocampus. We would just add here that the dream stage of sleep constitutes a special kind of arousal, probably mediated by the limbic system.

There are a number of problems remaining. The exact mechanisms controlling the transition from synchronized sleep to aroused sleep are not known. Does the pontine mechanism operate on an entirely endogenous basis or is it influenced by some bodily process? Or could it be that the cortex cannot maintain synchronized sleep indefinitely and so a more primitive form of sleep occurs? The mechanism controlling sensory thresholds during aroused sleep in various species is not clear. The possibility that limbic thresholds are lowered as cortical thresholds increase is intriguing, and argues further against the usefulness of the terms *light* and *deep* sleep. Many other relationships between the various mechanisms for wakefulness, synchronized sleep, and aroused sleep remain to be understood.

SUMMARY

A review of the physiological mechanisms of arousal, sleep, and dreams was undertaken in order to compare the motive to sleep with other physiological motives. Most physiological motives involve a multiplicity of internal and external factors, but brain mechanisms are of critical importance.

The reticular activating system seems to be particularly important in most motive states.

The reticular activating system in the brain stem and a diffuse thalamic projection system appear to be important in wakeful arousal. The cortex also participates in its own level of arousal. One can speak of a general reticular arousal system that underlies wakefulness and is identical with the arousal mechanism involved in most motive states.

Environmental stimuli can awaken a person and to some extent keep him awake, while the lack of stimuli or of stimulus variation has a soporific effect. Although stimulus deficiency, as it is sometimes called, favors going to sleep, it is not sufficient to maintain sleep, as sensory-deprivation studies have shown. The production of sleep by monotonous stimulation or immobilization, may be due to the muscular relaxation which the situation encourages, although sleep does not inevitably follow relaxation. The sleep, during the trace-conditioned reflex and extinction described by Pavlov, is probably not due to inhibitory properties of the stimulus, but to the monotony of the situation and the lack of other response possibilities.

The internal environment of the organism has its influence on sleep, as it does on all kinds of wakeful activities. Neural stimulation from the muscular, circulatory, and digestive systems has been shown to have a de-activating effect, as well as the better known activation. Several hormonal factors have been shown to produce sleep. The old issue of a general hypnotoxin is still in dispute, however, although it cannot be casually dismissed.

There is a sleep system in the brain but it seems to be more complex than the activating system. There are at least three major components of the sleep system—a sleep-inducing mechanism in the lower brain stem, a descending limbic hypnogenic circuit, and the neocortex. All of these influences affect a thalamic moderating system and the reticular arousal system. The complex sleep system appears to be antagonistic to the reticular arousal system important in wakefulness and most motivational states.

The dream stage of sleep seems to be controlled primarily

by a lower brain stem mechanism and to involve a special, limbically mediated cortical arousal. Synchronized and aroused sleep may be produced by stimulating the same structures so that the mechanisms may overlap. Synchronized sleep frequently passes over to aroused sleep by as yet unknown processes. In any case, although the dream stage of sleep involves arousal, it is a special kind of arousal. Furthermore, dream arousal does not appear to be mediated by the same system as wakeful arousal.

How do the physiological mechanisms for sleep compare with those for other physiological motives? The sleep mechanisms in the lower brain stem, thalamus, hypothalamus, and limbic system are analogous to other motives in location and variety. The role of the cortex in the more phylogenetically advanced phase of sleep is similar to the increased role of the cortex at higher evolutionary levels in other physiological motives, such as sex. The influence of sensory stimulation and the internal environment also compares well with hunger, sexual, and other motives.

There is one important difference between the motive to sleep and most other motives. While other motives depend on the reticular arousal system and often result in behavioral activation, the mechanisms for the sleep motive are inhibitory and antagonistic to the reticular arousal system. Even the arousal stage of sleep depends on a different mechanism and is a qualitatively unique biological state with many inhibitory properties.

Finally, the existence of a complex sleep system in the brain, which may be stimulated electrically or with acetylcholine, and which is responsive to the influence of internal bodily processes as well as external stimuli, is strong evidence for the concept of a positive motive to sleep. Sleep can no longer be viewed as a passive state, but is an active, inhibitory process.

CHAPTER 5

Sleep Motivation, Learning, and Performance

Possibly the most important relationship between a motive and behavior is its effect on the learning process. In fact, Miller (1959) emphasizes this as the chief criterion for classifying a variable as a motive. An organism deprived of food will learn and perform a response to get food. This prime observation leads us to postulate a hunger motive. Even the proven existence of a physiological need is less important than its effects on learning. For that reason, for example, Miller and Dollard (1941) do not classify the need for oxygen as a motive. Oxygen deprivation does not lead to the learning and performance of a response to get oxygen.

If sleep is to be considered a motive, it must be shown to have the same relationship to learning and performance as the other motives. Therefore, it is startling to read through the literature and find that in most cases, increasing the sleep motive by keeping human subjects awake either had no effect, or a deleterious effect, on the learning and performance of a great variety of tasks. For example, Edwards (1941) found a decrement of nearly 50% in the scores on an intelligence test, after 96 hours of sleep deprivation. Learning of telegraphy, typewriting, and associated pairs of words was possible only with greatly increased difficulty and effort. In fact, Edwards had to discontinue the learning tasks because the subjects refused to go on with them. Williams, Lubin, and Goodnow (1959) showed that the acquisition and retention of an information-learning task was impaired by sleep deprivation. A number of other tasks also showed decrements.

At first glance, these results seem to rule out the possibility of considering lack of sleep as a motive. If sleep deprivation does not increase learning and the performance of learned responses, it is unlike other motives.

The kind of learning used in these experiments on sleep deprived human beings, however, is not comparable to the paradigmatic situation of the hungry rat pressing a bar to get a pellet of food. The responses used in these studies are *not relevant* to the sleep motive—they do not result in a reduction of the sleep motive. The responses involved may reduce other motives, such as the desire to please the experimenter, but they do not reduce the sleep motive.

Furthermore, the responses required in the usual learning situations during sleep-deprivation studies are, to a large extent, *incompatible* with the sleep responses. There is a good deal of evidence, as we shall see later, that during sleep deprivation subjects are unable to avoid short lapses of consciousness, or what has been called microsleeps, of several seconds. Research has shown that learning is difficult or impossible during actual sleep. Therefore, it is clear that under some conditions, which will be discussed later, it is difficult for learning or related thought processes to take place during some periods of a sleep-deprivation period.

In order to test the validity of viewing sleep as a motive against the criterion of the motive-learning relationship, the proper conditions must be met. First of all, the response must be made relevant to the sleep motive. Ideally, a sleep-deprived animal should be able to learn a response leading to an opportunity to sleep. Secondly, if the response is incompatible with sleep, care should be taken to see that the organism is awake. The effect of sleep and sleep deprivation on other kinds of learning is of considerable interest, but for other reasons.

THEORETICAL ANALYSIS
OF MOTIVATION, LEARNING
AND PERFORMANCE

The purpose of this section will be to lay the theoretical foundation for understanding the complex effects of sleep deprivation on learning and performance, to be discussed in the next section. First, the role of deprivation in motivating learning and performance, and of motive reduction in reinforcing learning and performance, will be reviewed. Then, it will be shown that the actual occurrence of a response is also determined by conflicting motives producing other, sometimes incompatible, responses. In many studies on the effect of physiological motives, such as hunger or noise, the main disturbance is of attention and is probably due to competing responses. Following this, it will be pointed out that sleep is a response that is incompatible to a large extent with learning, thinking, highly organized performance, and cognitive activities in general.

The Motivation of Learning
and Performance

Learning is one of the fundamental processes studied by psychologists. Nearly all of social behavior is learned. The child learns to love and to fear, to think logically, to behave badly or well, to acquire knowledge in school and on the back fence, and to distinguish between a model citizen and a price-fixer. The basic element is the acquisition of ways of responding to the world. The essence of the process is found in the lower animals learning the lore of the jungle or pressing bars for experimental psychologists. What are the basic conditions of learning?

The most effective way of producing learning is to provide a motive and to make the reduction of that motive contingent upon the occurrence of a given response, under the proper conditions of environmental stimulation. For example, a hungry rat will learn to press a bar to get a pellet of food. On the aversive side, an animal will learn to make a response to turn off an electric shock. In human learning the role of motivation is no less significant, as many a frustrated school teacher who has faced a class of indifferent and resentful children will testify.

The term *habit strength* is often used to refer to the associational variables involved in learning. Habit strength is primarily a function of past reinforcement. In the examples given, the reinforcement is the reduction of the appropriate motive, e.g., providing food in the case of hunger. Habit strength is a function of the number, nature, amount, delay, and scheduling of the reinforcements. The actual performance is the result of the habit strength and the motivational conditions in the particular stimulus situation (see Hull, 1943; Deese, 1958).

The nature of reinforcement is an area of intense controversy in psychology. Reinforcement may involve intrinsically motivated behavior, innate rewarding stimuli, and brain mechanisms for pleasure and pain (Murray, 1964 b). There is, however, the empirical observation concerning the connection of the phenomena of deprivation, satiation, and reinforcement: in a given situation, generally speaking, those substances of which the organism has been deprived will prove most reinforcing. Furthermore, substances that have the initial satiating effect of reducing relevant behavior have the long-range effect of reinforcing, or increasing the probability of, the same responses. An analogous observation exists for aversive stimulus drives (Miller, 1959).

This is not to say that there is convincing evidence that all learning involves motivation (see Deese, 1958). For example, classical Pavlovian conditioning often does not reduce a motive, although such learning may be influenced by various motives. Similarly, the latent learning experiments have shown that an animal may learn the location of food in a maze although he is not hungry. Here other motives may be involved, such as curiosity or a learned motive. Nevertheless, for the purposes of the present analysis the universality of the motive-reduction principle is not critical. It is sufficient to know that learning *can* be produced by the reduction of a motive. This is what Miller (1959) calls the "weak" form of the motive-reduction hypothesis.

There is little controversy over the efficacy of motivation in influencing the performance of a response once it has been learned. For example, Hull (1943) presents evidence for the hypothesis that the performance of a response is a multiplicative function of motivation and habit strength. So, for example, the number of bar-pressing responses during an extinction session is a function of the number of food reinforcements during the initial learning period, and the number of hours of food deprivation just prior to the extinction session. Similar results have been found with most of the known biological motives (see also Tolman, 1932; Lewin, 1938; Skinner, 1938).

It should be noted that any measure of performance reflects both habit strength and motivation. Unless one is held constant, it is impossible to say which is influencing the performance and to what degree. Many studies have not kept these two variables separated and a good deal of confusion results. When one wishes to assess the effect of motivation on performance, motivation should be varied with prior training held constant, or varied systematically for each level of motivation.

There are also a number of studies showing that an irrelevant motive may facilitate the performance of a response learned and rewarded on the basis of a different motive (see Brown, 1961). Thus, electric shock or anxiety may help maze performance based on hunger, or drinking behavior based on thirst. Hunger may increase performance motivated by light avoidance, or intracranial stimulation. It should be clearly noted, however, that in these situations the irrelevant motive does not elicit responses competing with the originally learned response. As we shall see in the following section, if conflict is involved the effects of the irrelevant motive may be anything but facilitating.

What are the objective manifestations of performance strength? Traditionally, four measures have been used by psychologists: the magnitude of the response, as illustrated by the degree of deflection of a GSR apparatus; their reaction latency, as in measures such as time before commencing to eat; resistance to extinction, as in the unreinforced bar-pressing situation; and probability of occurrence, as in accuracy and error scores (see Hull, 1943). Many other ingenious measures have also been devised—ranging from strength of pull to tolerance for quinine (see Miller, 1957), most of which are related to probability or magnitude dimensions. With the emphasis on partial reinforcement, rate of responding is also often used (Skinner, 1938) as a more general form of the resistance to extinction measure. Thus, the main indicators of performance are: magnitude, latency, rate, and probability of occurrence.

Possibly the most general statement is in terms of probability of occurrence. It is possible to make reinforcement contingent upon the force of lever depression (magnitude), the speed of leaving a starting box (latency), or the rate of panel pecking (see Skinner, 1953; Logan, 1959). In such cases it is not appropriate to use these measures for assessing degree of motivation or habit strength. In other situations, however, they typically continue to serve as sensitive measures. Nevertheless, the most general statement is that behavior strength is shown by the probability of the occurrence of responses.

Performance Modified by Conflicting Motives

In the previous section the simple direct effects of motivation on learning and performance were emphasized. In many natural and social situations, however, there is more than one motive operating. In his natural habitat, the rat approaching food is also constantly alert for danger. If we wish to get along in society, our competitive and achievement needs have to be tempered by some concern and responsibility toward our fellows. The interaction of motives and their responses will be of considerable importance in understanding the effects of sleep deprivation.

Ordinarily, motives themselves are not conflicting. An organism can be deprived of food, sexual outlet, and sensory stimuli with no interaction between the motives per se. But the responses required for the reduction of these motives may or may not be compatible. For example, eating and sexual responses are very difficult to perform at the same time. On the other hand, a motive like curiosity (see Berlyne, 1960) may possibly be satisfied along with either eating or sexual play.

As mentioned earlier, Brown (1961) summarizes a number of experiments showing that an irrelevant motive may facilitate the performance of a response learned on the basis of a different motive. In order for this to happen it is necessary that the irrelevant motive does not produce an incompatible response. For example, an electric shock administered just prior to putting an animal in a drinking cage results in a facilitation of drinking (Amsel and Maltzman, 1950). On the other hand, if cues associated with the shock are actually put into the drinking cage, the result is a suppression of drinking (Amsel and Cole, 1953) presumably because of incompatible responses such as crouching.

When two or more motives produce responses which are incompatible, then a conflict is established. This is most clearly seen in the approach-avoidance conflicts studied by Miller and his associates (see Miller, 1944, and Miller, 1959). In the typical experiment, hungry rats are trained to run down an alley to get a pellet of food in a cup. After this approach training is completed, the animals are shocked at the food cup until they fear it and avoid it by withdrawal. The response of approaching the food cup is patently incompatible with avoiding the same place.

Before the avoidance training, the approach tendency down an alley, as shown, for example, by the strength of his pull against a restraint, is stronger as the rat gets closer to the food cup— the principle of the goal gradient. Similarly, the avoidance tendency drops off as distance from the goal increases. The key assumption is that the avoidance gradient is steeper than that of approach. The conflict point around which the animal will oscillate is at the intersection of these two gradients. This is shown schematically in Fig. 9.

Of particular significance is the observation that the gradients of either approach or avoidance may be raised or lowered by manipulating the two motives involved, even when habit strength is equated. This results in a shift in the conflict point. For instance, if the rat is made hungrier by depriving him of food for an extra day, he will go further down the alley. If the fear is raised, possibly by an increased shock, he will retreat even further back down the alley. Thus the balance of the conflict is a function of the relative strength of the two opposing motives. Since the rats oscillate a good deal, not only is the conflict point shifted forward or backward, but also the probability that a goal response may occur increases or decreases.

FIGURE 9

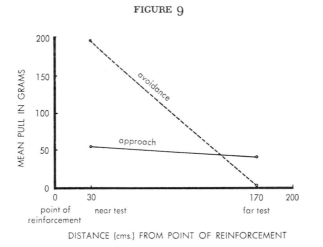

DISTANCE (cms.) FROM POINT OF REINFORCEMENT

After Miller, 1944.

This conflict model has been applied to a variety of experimental and clinical situations. It has been extended to displacement phenomena (Miller, 1948; Miller and Kraeling, 1952; Murray and Miller, 1952; Miller and Murray, 1952; Murray and Berkun, 1955). It has also been found useful in explaining some of the phenomena of psychotherapy (Dollard and Miller, 1950; Murray, 1954; Murray, Auld, and White, 1954; Murray, 1956). With appropriate knowledge of the social and personal conditions making up the specific conflict, this model can be useful.

With respect to the effect of motivation on performance, the conflict model would point to two critical factors in making any sort of prediction. First, the situation must be examined carefully to see what motives are operating; a man may be highly motivated to perform a task but his muscles may be so fatigued that he makes errors. The motivations in a situation may not be simply the ones the experimenter has chosen to study: e.g., the man may do poorly because he is anxious about his relationship with his girl—something of which the experimenter may be completely ignorant. Second, the degree to which the various relevant and intruding motivations interfere with one another by producing incompatible responses, or have other adverse or facilitative effects, must be evaluated.

Human Performance and Physiological Motives

In the preceding sections the emphasis has been on animal studies of motivation. There is little doubt that motives operate in a similar fashion on the human level. Unfortunately, while most animal studies use physiological motives such as hunger, most research with people involves social motives such as achievement. Studies of physiological motives with human subjects, or social motives with animals, are harder to find, and have played a relatively minor role in motivational theory. Since most of the sleep-deprivation studies were with human subjects, we will examine what studies are available on physiological motives and human performance, to make meaningful predictions about sleep.

Physiological motives such as hunger and thirst have motivated the learning and performance of many behavioral responses during the history of mankind. Even in our highly developed civilization, under appropriate conditions physiological motives can override the most powerful social controls. For example, if famine continues long enough it causes a loosening of social ties and a decrease in moral standards. Families are abandoned, prostitution increases, and thievery becomes widespread. Migrations, riots, and rebellions occur. On rare occasions cannibalism and murder have been reported (see Keys et al., 1950).

On the other hand, as with sleep deprivation, many of the experimental results are difficult to interpret. For example, hunger may lead to decreased performance. One reason for this is that in the experimental situations, to a greater degree than in natural ones, more than one motive is operating. The paradigm of the research in this area is to deprive subjects of something, for a period, and then test them. The subjects are volunteers and cooperate in refraining from ingesting the substance being studied. For example, in one study on semistarvation (Keys et al., 1950), the men had a restricted food allowance but walked about the campus as they wished. Occasionally, someone broke down and went on a malted milk shake bender. Obviously, some motive was conflicting with hunger to enable them to continue in the study—some motive such as achievement, need to please the authority figures, or, since these men were conscientious objectors, a complex religious and antiwar feeling.

Most of the research on physiological motives with human subjects relies on some unspecified social motive to keep the subjects in the experiment. Sometimes money is given, and while this is a clear example of such a motive, it is rarely the sole motivation involved. Whatever the motive, the subjects are nearly always in conflict. Perhaps many of the confusing results can be understood by keeping this in mind: the performance is motivated by task-oriented social motives. The physiological motive operates as a competing motivation, distracting the subject from this task. Thus, attention and concentration would be most affected by the conflict. Let us see.

In the well-known series of experiments done at the University of Minnesota, both acute and partial hunger deprivation were studied (Keys, et al., 1950; Brozek, 1955; Brozek and Taylor, 1958). Under all these conditions, performance on tests involving muscular exertion and coordination deteriorated markedly—partly due to weakness. Manual performance depending on speed was also impaired, particularly in acute starvation. Tests of intellectual functions such as reasoning, memory, spatial relations, and general intelligence did *not* show decrements. While the men were *capable* of good intellectual performance, however, their *actual* intellectual activity during prolonged semistarvation decreased considerably, due to a narrowing of interests and a general apathy.

Similar results are obtained when thiamine is removed from an otherwise adequate diet (Brozek, 1947). While manual performance and coordination were adversely affected by the thiamine deficiency, intelligence tests were not. Other observers have emphasized the appearance of apathy and disturbances of attention (Wohl and Goodhart, 1955; Wilder, 1952).

Temperature extremes constitute motivating conditions and have negative effects on performance. This was well illustrated by an examination of the accident rate in a British munitions plant requiring precise manual skills (Vernon, 1936). Accidents increased as temperature either increased or decreased markedly. In an experimental situation, Mackworth (1946, 1947) showed that raising the temperature beyond 90°F. impaired the reception of Morse telegraphic messages. Raising motivation by coaxing, pleading, and praising the subjects resulted in better work. Chiles (1958) showed that heat affects work on a complex mental matching problem only when the apparatus is set up in such a way as to maximize the role of attention.

Dusek (1957) summarized a number of studies showing that as temperatures drop below 60°F., manual dexterity is affected more and more. The evidence suggests that the effect is on performance and not on the intellectual processes (Teichner and Wehrkamp, 1954; Teichner and Kobrick, 1955). For instance, in one study using a pursuit-rotor, it was found that while performance was lowered during the cold period, the actual learning and retention of the task was unaffected.

It is not surprising to learn that fatigue impairs work efficiency (see Chapanis et al., 1949). Watch-keeping tasks are especially sensitive to fatigue (Bartlett, 1948; Mackworth, 1948). In a simulated long-range instrument flight, pilots were required to reset dials. The longer the pilot worked at this the worse his performance became, although periodic eye tests showed that this could not be explained by impaired vision. Instead, it seemed that the subject's motivation changed and that his standard for an adequate performance was lowered. Later we will discuss the role of "blocking" in accounting for the results of fatigue.

Noise also disturbs functioning primarily through attention changes. Many tests of performance and intelligence are unaffected (Stevens, 1946), but a continuous vigilance task is sensitive (Broadbent, 1958; Plutchik, 1959). The concept of auditory "blinking," analogous to fatigue blocks, is useful here and will be mentioned again later.

Sensory deprivation, which appears to have motivational characteristics, results in performance decrement; much of this can be explained by the difficulties in concentrating that the subjects report (Bexton et al., 1954; Heron, 1961). In a more general confinement situation, Gaite et al. (1958) found decrements in tasks depending heavily on vigilance, such as visual tracking, while tests of judgment, learning, reasoning, and intelligence held up. The men felt that "monotony" was a significant factor in their performance decrements.

Unfortunately, none of these studies were set up to examine the effects of motives on attention. Still, as a group, they strongly suggest that the physiological motives act as distractions, probably by evoking escape responses of one sort or another. Some of the effects may be explained by physical weakness, although it is difficult to see how this can explain the effects of sensory deprivation, which are so similar to those of semistarvation. Then, too, some results can be seen as due to biochemical changes in the brain. Why, then, is there an effect on simple performance items but not on difficult reasoning questions? The most parsimonious explanation of all these results is that the physiological motive, which is irrelevant to the task, produces responses incompatible with the performance. The result is a decrease in the attention devoted to the task, and a decrease in those aspects of performance requiring full attention.

The Incompatibility of Sleeping with Learning and Performance

The assumption made in this theoretical analysis is that the nature of sleep is such that it is incompatible with most forms of learning, performance, and cognitive activities. It is true that during the course of a night's sleep we maintain a certain amount of muscle tonus, turn over when some muscles or joints are strained or fatigued, and dream. However, most of these activities usually occur for only short intervals during periods of desynchronized sleep preceding and following dreams. Kleitman (1939) and others have shown that the EEG level varies cyclically through the night, with perhaps a dozen or more times when the sleeper shows stage 2 or 3 EEG patterns. During these periods, bodily movements of various kinds occur and are followed by a shift upwards in the EEG level. Stage 1 and dreams occur after some but not all of these peaks of activity.

Many learned stimulus-response habits, and even some innate reflexes, cannot be elicited during sleep (Kleitman, 1939; Simon, 1961). Reflexes, such as the knee jerk and galvanic skin response, drop out. Reactivity to electric shock and other kinds of pain decreases. Kleitman reports on a dog which was injected with morphine as an unconditioned stimulus, and was then conditioned to salivate. The conditioned salivation decreased from time to time when the dog became drowsy, and disappeared entirely during sleep. It is common knowledge that a sleeping person's threshold for verbal and other social stimuli is raised considerably. Nevertheless, some selectivity is involved, as illustrated, for example, by the sleeping mother's response to the cry of her child in distress.

These age-old observations on the ability of the sleeping organism to continue to make discriminations have been validated experimentally. Rowland (1957) trained six cats in a classical conditioning procedure. The conditioned stimulus was a ten-second tone followed by the unconditioned stimulus, a painful ½-second shock, delivered through an electrode on the shaved skin of the animal. The tone and shock were paired from 20 to 50 times.

The cats were kept awake overnight by placing them in shallow water, and then they were dried and allowed to sleep. The main measure was the EEG arousal pattern, recorded from previously placed electrodes. The conditioned stimulus was presented in an extinction procedure during sleep. The tone produced little evidence of behavioral waking, except an occasional ear twitch. However, the EEG did show a cortical arousal. Interestingly, the first few tones were characterized by long latencies (2-3 sec.). This was followed by shorter latencies, and a more sustained arousal response. Finally, the conditional response extinguished after 30 to 50 trials. When the animals awoke spontaneously, a flinch response could be evoked by the conditioned stimulus, but extinguished rapidly. This could be due to spontaneous recovery, or it might suggest some need for the extinction of the specific muscular response.

Both the formation and maintenance of discriminations involving quality and frequency were demonstrated. Neutral tones presented without shock during the original training did not produce an arousal response of any kind during sleep. Neutral stimuli presented for the first time during sleep, initially produced an arousal reaction which adapted out rapidly. In one cat, the required discrimination was between tones of 384 and 480 cps, showing a reasonably fine discrimination. This is analogous to the mother waking up at her baby's cry but ignoring other sounds. In another cat, Rowland used silence as the conditioned stimulus. During training the cat was exposed to a continuous clicking, but was shocked at the end of a 10-second period of silence. Later, this silence produced a regular EEG arousal pattern during sleep. This is analogous to the miller who could not sleep when his waterwheel stopped.

Later, Rowland removed most of the auditory cortex from three cats. The simple discrimination showed some retention both in flinching while awake and in arousal during sleep; these extinguished rapidly but could be relearned. More complex discriminations were not retained post-operatively and could not be taught anew. Unfortunately, Rowland does not say whether the cats were retrained just before the operation, so that it is difficult to evaluate the rapid extinction of the simpler discriminations. It is possible, however, that lower centers mediate simple discrimination during sleep.

Rowland's finding that familiar but neutral tones presented during sleep do not produce arousal, while new neutral tones, and of course the conditioned stimulus do produce arousal at least initially, suggests that the discrimination takes place independent of, and probably prior to, the arousal mechanism coming into play. Since the simpler discriminations are not dependent on the auditory cortex, as shown by the ablation study, the impression is that some sort of simple discrimination is made at a lower level, probably in the auditory mechanisms in the brain stem (see Neff, 1960), which then may or may not result in the activation of the reticular formation and the cortex. The existence of complex discrimination ability during sleep suggests that the cortex is involved at least some of the time and that, to some limited degree, it functions during sleep.

Segundo (1962) has presented further evidence that the performance of a response in the sleeping cat depends on a temporary EEG arousal. He found that an EEG arousal response precedes behavioral responsiveness. He also reports that the probability of evoking a response in a sleeping cat is lower than that for a cat which is awake.

A finer distinction can be made in the EEG levels of human subjects than of animals. It is possible, therefore, to investigate the quantitative relationship between behavioral efficiency and degree of EEG arousal on the human level. Coleman et al. (1959) correlated the reaction time in human subjects with an integrated measure of EEG amplitude. The performance measure was the time between the presentation of a mild auditory tone and the closing of a hand switch. The author reports a correlation of $+ .32$ ($p < .01$) between reaction time and EEG amplitude. In other words, the more synchronized the sleep the slower the performance. The correlation does not account for all the variance, obviously. The author reports that this was due largely to a slower reaction time in the dream stage of sleep. This is to be expected, as we have seen from earlier chapters, and could be due to the competing visual stimuli in the dream. During sleep onset, when dreams do not ordinarily occur, we would expect a higher correlation between EEG amplitude and reaction time. Other studies show, however, that responding is high even during the dream stage of sleep.

In another study, Zung and Wilson (1961) played a tape containing various sounds—some familiar and some unfamiliar to the sleeping subjects—and observed EEG shifts. They found that the percentage of subjects showing an EEG desynchronization was 8% in stage E, 32% in stage D, 45% in stage C, and 57% in stage B. They found no difference in the response to familiar and unfamiliar sounds. In a follow-up study, however, Zung and Wilson motivated subjects by promising extra payment if they woke up fully to specified sounds. These subjects were able to wake up to motivated stimuli in all sleep stages. During stage E the subjects woke up more frequently to all stimuli, but were less able to discriminate between them.

Another relevant experiment was performed by Oswald, Taylor, and Treisman (1961). A long list of names was read to human subjects who were asleep after a prior deprivation period. They had been instructed previously to respond by clenching their hand when their own name, or one other particular name, was read. The polygraph record included: EEG, the reading of a name, and the muscle potentials indicating clenching. Many of the clenchings were uncoordinated, and one would guess that they occurred more and more as the sleep synchronized. Nevertheless, there was a significant number of clenchings after the reading of the person's own name, and less clenchings after the others. Moreover, the frequency of K-complexes (somewhat analogous to arousal) on the EEG was greater after the person's own name than after the preceding names or some other name. Names read forward evoked the K-complex much more than when they were played backward, providing a control for some of the physical characteristics of the stimulus. One's own name may be more meaningful than the familiar sounds played by Zung and Wilson.

The authors point out that this kind of complex auditory pattern discrimination must involve cortical functioning (see Neff, 1960). They suggest that the sensory input is carried to the cortex, presumably through the classical sensory pathways, that a discrimination is made there, and that the cortex may or may not activate the reticular formation and thus arouse the brain as a whole.

The fate of a simple sensory-motor associational bond during sleep was studied by Fischgold and Schwartz (1961), and is of importance here. Human subjects were told to press a button, on a box attached to their hand, twice in response to a flash stimulus accompanied by a click. It was found that correct responding varied with the EEG stage of wakefulness. During the various subdivisions of stage A the subjects gave the correct double press 96% of the time. This fell to 78% in stage B, 32% in stage C, and to zero in stage D. Thus in the more synchronized stages of sleep, particularly as fewer and fewer alpha frenquencies are seen, the occurrence of a simple response decreases.

Of primary importance for the issue under consideration here is Fischgold and Schwartz's correlation of the behavioral data with specific qualitative EEG patterns, rather than stages as above. As Fischgold points out in the discussion following his paper, a good deal of confusion is produced by the fact that most investigators of the human electroencephalograph use the finely graded Loomis system of stages A through E, while most animal researchers use the rather vague terms *activated, aroused,* or *synchronized.* Thus, in order to get information more comparable to the animal studies, one must observe qualitative patterns outside the Loomis system. The authors observed several types of EEG reactivity comparable to the desynchronization pattern, including flattening of very slow waves and K-complexes. They found that during stages C and D, in a substantial number of instances when the double motor response was not given, there was an EEG reactivity of the type mentioned. They conclude that for the carrying out of instructions, alpha itself must be present. These other EEG reactions indicate the arrival of messages in the brain, probably in the cortex.

The possibility of new informational learning occurring during sleep has stirred up some popular interest recently. This is also of considerable significance to the theoretical questions under discussion here. Simon and Emmons (1955) reviewed the ten major studies in the area until 1955. They found several studies indicating that learning could occur during sleep, and others failing to show this effect. A number of technical flaws existed in the studies purporting to show learning during sleep, the most crucial of which was a failure to determine the sleep state of the subjects continuously during the presentation of the material to be learned. Thus a subject might have been in a drowsy state, or actually awake, when learning occurred. This is particularly likely

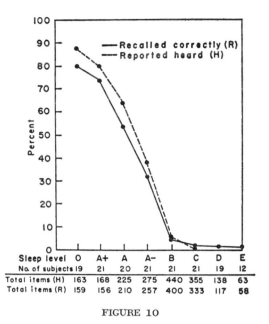

Sleep level	O	A+	A	A-	B	C	D	E
No. of subjects	19	21	20	21	21	21	19	12
Total items (H)	163	168	225	275	440	355	138	63
Total items (R)	159	156	210	257	400	333	117	58

FIGURE 10

in view of the fact that the degree of synchronization waxes and wanes in a wavelike fashion during the night. Simon and Emmons (1956) went on to study learning during sleep, with the aid of continuous EEG recording. They played a taped list of 96 questions and answers about somewhat obscure facts, at a rate of one every 5 minutes during 8 hours of sleep. The subjects, who were of average or above average intelligence, were asked to report immediately if they were awake and hear the answers. During the night continuous EEG recordings were taken, and the wave patterns classified into 8 categories ranging from the continuous alpha of wakefulness to the large delta waves of fully synchronized sleep. The main results are shown in Fig. 10, where it can be seen that the percentage of items correctly recalled in the morning is closely related to the percentage of answers reported heard during the night. Both of these percentages decrease as the brain wave patterns go from category O (continuous alpha —wakeful state) to category E (delta—fully synchronized sleep).

Category B is where alpha drops out, and is usually taken as the transition point from wakefulness to sleep. This is the point at which the learning drops off sharply. Categories A+, A, and A− are usually considered drowsy periods, and it can be seen that some learning takes place here but decreases as drowsiness merges into sleep. Since this study by its very nature had to limit the question-answer presentation to one time, Emmons and Simon (1956) did a follow-up study in which the material was presented as many times as possible. A list of 10 words was played to sleeping subjects over and over again during 8 hours of sleep. EEG recordings were taken, however, and whenever the alpha rhythm of wakefulness occurred the material was turned off. In the morning the subjects could recall or recognize the words no better than a control group.

Another cognitive activity which would be expected to be incompatible with sleep, is forgetting. This is particularly true in view of the current retroactive inhibition theory, which says that forgetting is a result of new learning replacing, and interfering with, old learning. If new learning cannot occur during sleep, then forgetting should be slowed down. This is exactly what happens. In the classic experiment in this area, Jenkins and Dallenbach (1924) compared the recall of tests of nonsense syllables after 1, 2, 4, and 8 hours of ordinary waking activity, with recall after similar periods of sleep. When asleep, the subjects were awakened for a brief period only once on any one night. The results show considerably better retention during the sleep period. While asleep, retention showed a decrease for the first two hours but none thereafter, as opposed to a sharper and greater drop during the wakeful state. The initial drop during sleep might have been due to the fantasy activity commonly occurring at bedtime. Woodworth (1938) reviews other evidence supporting these results; one study showed better retention the next day if the subject learned the material immediately before retiring, rather than two or three hours earlier. Newman (1939) found that the details of a story were retained better during sleep, but that there was no difference in retention of the basic plot during sleep or waking. However, as McGeoch (1942) points out, this can be explained by the finding that key ideas in prose passages and lines of poetry show little susceptibility to interference from other materials of a similar kind. The evidence, then, indicates that forgetting is slowed down during sleep, probably as a result of a lack of new learning. This is most likely due to the incompatibility of learning and related processes with sleeping.

What now of the basic issue of sleep in regard to learning, thinking, and similar cognitive processes? First of all, it is meaningful to grade various performance tasks according to degree of complexity. One can start with the simplest reflexive forms, progress to discrimination learning, and then to complex problem solving and creative thought. There is evidence suggesting that simple avoidance conditioning involves subcortical areas, while the more complex learning involves the cortex (see Neff, 1960; Galambos and Morgan, 1960). During sleep it is conceivable that the cortex may remain undisturbed while simple discriminations are made on the subcortical levels. These may be similar to Rowland's conditioned and neutral stimuli in which the discrimination is simply "danger yes or danger no." Similarly, other discriminations such as "stimulus familiar-stimulus unfamiliar" may be made. If the decision is "danger," or if the discrimination required is too complex, the message may be sent on to the cortex along the classical sensory pathways. So, for example, the discrimination between a designated name and another name may take place at a cortical level. But this does not necessarily mean a generalized arousal of the cortex. In fact, the evidence suggests that only if the decision is that the stimulus is significant, is there a general arousal involving the reticular formation. Probably a very limited part of the cortex is involved in making this kind of discrimination. However, if more than a discrimination between two patterns of stimulation is to be made—if new learning of verbal information, or general motor responding is to occur— then there must be a general arousal, evidence of alpha, and for all intents and purposes, wakefulness.

In an experiment which will be described in more detail in the next section, Granda and Hammack (1961) taught subjects to press a left-hand microswitch to avoid shock, and a right-hand microswitch to get a time out, during which they could sleep. They observed organized behavior during the time-out periods, and at other times when the EEG indicated synchronized sleep. They conclude that "higher mental states" operate even during synchronized sleep. They themselves report, however, that such behavior occurs mostly in the more desynchronized EEG sleep stages. Furthermore, such responding was generally infrequent and exhibited mostly during early training sessions. Thus it is similar to the usual EEG habituation to unfamiliar stimuli. It is also possible that a filter-type analysis of this phenomenon would show some alpha present during the periods of organized responding. In general, this study would fit in with the idea that simple responses can occur during the lighter stages of sleep, but that their probability of occurring decreases as sleep becomes more synchronized.

In the Granda-Hammack study it is also stretching a point to call miscroswitch-pressing, on a simple schedule, an example of the "higher mental processes." It looks more like the simple motor response most easily automatized. Supporting this is the finding that the almost purely motor task of ball-throwing showed no decrement with drowsy sleep-deprived subjects, while tasks such as mental arithmetic did show an effect (Weiskotten and Ferguson, 1930). There are also the anecdotes about soldiers sleeping during a march.

Thus, it would seem that the basic assumption that sleep and cognitive processes are incompatible is supported. However, it is necessary to state this as a quantative relationship: there is a reciprocal relationship between the degree of synchronization of sleep and the degree of cognitive functioning. With only a small or lower area of the brain active, only simple discriminations are possible. With the cortex partially aroused, more complex decisions are possible. For the highest forms of thinking, full wakefulness seems to be necessary.

SLEEP DEPRIVATION, LEARNING, AND PERFORMANCE

On the basis of the discussion so far, an attempt will be made to predict the kinds of results to be expected in studies on the relation of sleep deprivation to learning and performance.

In a natural situation one would expect some sort of rhythmic alternation between sleep and wakefulness determined by a multiplicity of motives. As hunger or some other motive mounted, the organism would exhibit various forms of overt behavior, as well as symbolic problem-solving activities in the service of this motive. As motivation to sleep increased as a result of this, the overt behavior and symbolic activities would wane as the state of sleep occurred spontaneously. This occurence would be a function of the relative strength of all the motives in the situation.

In a laboratory situation it is possible to manipulate the sleep motive and other significant motives. The consequences of various forms of behavior can also be controlled experimentally. The simplest prediction is in the case where a response leads to sleep in a sleep-deprived organism. Sleep deprivation is the major, but not exclusive, operation for increasing the sleep motive; sleeping is presumed to reduce this motivation. If after sleep deprivation a response is found to permit the possibility of sleep, this response will be reinforced. Learning will occur and the probability of the performance of the response in the future will be increased. Responses leading to better quality sleep through increased comfort or safety might also be reinforced.

Sleep deprivation would also be expected to facilitate the performance of irrelevant responses based on other drives, as long as there was no incompatibility of response involved. Thus, a sleepy person might show better performance of anxiety-reducing or fatigue-reducing responses.

In the foregoing situation sleep deprivation is assumed to lead to increased learning and performance, implying greater cognitive and brain activity in general. In brief, sleep deprivation leads to "arousal." Since, as we have seen in the previous section, sleep and cognitive activity are incompatible, this means that the operation of sleep deprivation leads away from sleeping behavior. However, this is only a temporary condition—a detour on the way to sleep itself. In other words, the sleep-deprived organism motivated toward the state of minimal cognitive and behavioral activity that is sleep will show a temporary increase in cognitive activity and even behavior, if this is necessary to get to the eventual goal of sleep. It is extremely important to keep in mind the contingent nature of this arousal.

When responses do not lead to sleep, the sleep-deprived organism will tend toward less and less cognitive and behavioral activity; at least the influence of the sleep motive will be in the direction of an increasing probability of sleep occurring. As we have seen, sleep is largely incompatible with learning, thinking, and performance. Thus, various tests of intellectual functioning, psychological performance, etc., will be expected to show impairment. The nature of this impairment will be that which would be expected from disturbances in attention. This is found with other motives and is particularly expected with the sleep motive because of incompatibility between sleep and intellectual functions. The degree of impairment in psychological learning and performance tests will generally increase with increased sleep deprivation.

However, the strength of competing motives will also affect performance. The social motives for approval, such as money, that brought the person into the experimental situation to begin with, can be viewed as the forces motivating the performance on the psychological tests. Thus, the degree to which the scores show a decrement is determined by the balance between the sleep motive and the task-oriented motives. Thus, sleep deprivation can impair performance but increased ego-involvement can compensate for this. An exact prediction requires careful quantitative measures of both of the conflicting motives.

Indications of wakefulness and signs of physiological arousal, as well as of organized performance, will be a function of the relative strength of the sleep motive and the task-oriented motives. Since the tasks do not lead to sleep, the only source of arousal is in the task-oriented motives. Thus, arousal occurs to the extent that task-oriented motives are preponderant over the sleep motive.

Learning and Performance Leading to Sleep

Throughout the ages men have learned many responses relevant to the reduction of the sleep motive. According to Kleitman (1939) the bed has evolved "from a pile of leaves, skins of beasts, framework interlaced with thongs, through the ornate beds of Cleopatra, and the Roman Emperors, the couch, the bedstead, the twelfth-century high-post, canopy-top beds, down to the iron beds of the eighteenth century and the modern folding cot." Today's crowning glory seems to be of extra large size, with a mattress designed by an orthopedist, surrounded by bookshelves, coffee percolator and phonographs, and covered with an automatically controlled electric blanket. (Of course all this requires the learning and perfection of instrumental responses and skills as well as a creative interest.) The when and where of sleep is learned, but will be discussed more fully in connection with socialization.

People can learn many different postural positions for sleeping, including either side, back, abdomen, with arms, legs, and heads in various positions. Observations have shown that most people have a dozen or so favorite positions and tend to use them pretty consistently night after night (Johnson et al., 1930). With sufficient sleep motivation, a person can learn to sleep in a hammock, a foxhole, or a classroom chair. Animals have also been observed to sleep in unusual positions when sufficiently motivated. For example, Fernberger (1929) reports that he found rats asleep hanging by their upper teeth from the wire mesh tops of their cages, when many of them were crowded together. In fact, this observation illustrates that sleep-deprived rats can learn a response to get some sleep—even an unusual response.

Nevertheless, the problem requires experimental analysis; unfortunately, there are few studies on sleep deprivation and relevant learning. The first experimental study was done by Bunch, Cole, and Frerichs (1937). They kept groups of rats awake for 24 hours by watching them closely, either touching them or picking them up whenever they appeared to go to sleep. The animals' ability to learn two water mazes under conditions of massed trials was subsequently tested. One was a four-unit T maze with eight inches of water requiring a swimming response; the second was a seven-unit T maze with two inches of water requiring a wading response. In both cases the sleep-deprived animals performed better than appropriate control groups in terms of: the number of trials to a criterion of learning, the time to traverse the maze, and the number of errors made. This difference was quite large and statistically significant in five out of six comparisons. The superiority of the sleep-deprived group was retained for two weeks, when they were tested again under identical conditions. The authors actually say that sleep was an irrelevant motive here, since the only reward was getting out of the water for a minute or so during which time the animals were not permitted to sleep. Of course motives do combine to facilitate performance, as mentioned earlier (see Brown, 1961). However, all of the evidence indicates an even closer tie between sleep deprivation and muscular fatigue. In the opinion of this writer, the sleep-deprived rats were learning to escape from the water faster in order to avoid the exhaustion of swimming, which was greater for them than for the controls because of the sleep deprivation. An observation made by the experimenters in the next article in this series supports this interpretation.

In the next study Bunch, Frerichs, and Licklider (1946) used the same general procedures in an attempt to observe the effects of varying periods of wakefulness on learning. They required rats to learn a difficult 14-unit T maze involving a swimming response, after periods of 8, 16, 24, and 48 hours of enforced wakefulness. These were compared with a normal group that had gone through the usual sleep cycles prior to learning the water maze. The results confirm the earlier study. All sleep-deprived groups did significantly better than controls in learning the maze, using trials to criterion, time, or errors as measures. The differences between the various sleep-deprived groups were not large, nor were they consistent. However, the authors made a significant observation about fatigue in the maze. They say that "during the early trials on the problem, it happened occasionally that an animal became exhausted from the vigorous activity demanded by the situation and had to be removed from the maze before it reached the goal . . . if an animal had more than two incomplete trials he was given no further training in the maze. . . . The number of animals eliminated in this manner was negligible for all the groups except the one in which the subjects were kept in a condition of apparent wakefulness for 48 hours prior to the learning test" (p. 503). Later, the authors say that 15% of the 80 rats in the 48-hour group were eliminated in this way. If escape from water was the only relevant motivation and the sleep deprivation was irrelevant, one would not expect this degree of exhaustion, and would particularly not expect it to occur primarily in the most severely sleep-deprived group. This observation indicates that the fatigue produced by the sleep deprivation was a strong motive in learning to escape from the water in the maze. While the reward was not sleep, it was at least a minute or two of muscular relaxation. Therefore, these studies are directly relevant to the effect of sleep motivation on learning and performance.

In a further experiment Licklider and Bunch (1946) studied the effects of chronic, rather than acute, sleep deprivation on maze learning. They also devised an ingenious method for keeping the rats awake. They observed that rats cannot be kept awake by putting them on a bed of nails, by a bright light, by disturbing sounds, by requiring them to balance on a precarious perch, or by revolving them in an activity wheel. They agree with Kleitman (1939) that muscular relaxation must be avoided. They therefore devised a water treadmill to keep the rats awake, using a wheel four and one-half inches in diameter and three and one-half inches wide, two-thirds submerged in water, slowly turning at a speed of about seven and one-half inches per minute, requiring the rat to keep moving back every 10 or 15 seconds to avoid being dumped in the water. Using this apparatus, the experimenters kept a group of rats awake for 20 hours a day for two to four months, and had them learn to swim a 14-unit T maze with one trial a day. The chronically sleep-deprived rats were superior, in comparison to controls, in all aspects of water maze performance measured: time, distance, errors, speed, and trials to criterion. There were three control groups: one was kept in the apparatus without the treadmill turning; another group, controlling for exercise, ran the same distance as the experimental group in about two hours a day; and a final group lived in regular lab cages. The experimental group was significantly better, statistically, than the last two controls on all five measures and the first control on two measures.

Webb (1957) used a modification of the Licklider and Bunch apparatus to study the effects of varying amounts of sleep deprivation on the time required to go to sleep in an observation cage. Each of 19 rats was observed, after periods of 0, 2.5, 5, 10, 15, 20, 25, and 30 hours of enforced wakefulness in a water tread-mill. The results can be seen in Fig. 11. The sleep latency in

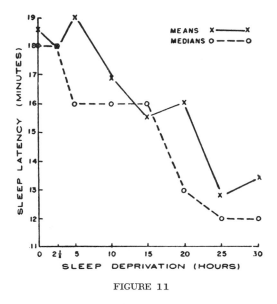

FIGURE 11

minutes shows an overall decrease as sleep deprivation increases. Before going to sleep the animals groomed themselves and seemed to need time to unwind. In a later study Webb (1962) found that sleep latency did not show any decrease over a period of 27 days of continuous wakefulness when the animals were tested once a day. The two studies suggest that sleep latency decreases to an asymptote in a day or so. Kleitman (1963, p. 219) cites several other studies showing that rats, kittens, and puppies have shorter sleep latencies after sleep deprivation.

Webb (1957) also tried to show that always going to sleep in a particular place would decrease sleep latency or, in other words, establish a sleep habit. The results were in the right direction but were not significant statistically.

The best way of demonstrating the learning relationship is to get an organism to learn an operant or instrumental response leading to a period of sleep as a reward. It is not too difficult to get a subject to learn to get rid of an external stimulus interfering with sleep. A man will get up at night to yell out the window at noisy adolescents, or he will learn to wear ear plugs if he is forced to sleep during the day. In an experiment to be described in more detail later, Lindsley (1957) was able to teach sleepy human subjects to press a microswitch to turn off a disturbing tone.

Another example of learning to adjust to a noxious stimulus enforcing sleep deprivation has been reported by Byck and Hearst (1962). Monkeys were trained to press a lever every five seconds to avoid shock and then were tested for continuous avoidance sessions for up to five days. Over this five-day sleep-deprivation period the monkeys showed a decrement in continuous performance and began to receive progressively worse shocks. The critical finding was that the monkeys showed a greater efficiency in performance when these five-day avoidance sessions were repeated eight times over a period of a month, with rest in between each five-day test. That is, after they had gone through the five-day test seven or eight times their performance did not deteriorate as much and they received fewer shocks. The authors suggest that the monkeys learned to press the lever with different hands, to close their eyes in between bar-presses, or to press the lever in a drowsy state.

However, in these situations there are two intertwined motives operating: the avoidance of the noxious stimulus and the wish to sleep. While these operate in the same direction, and are indistinguishable for all practical purposes, it is of some theoretical interest to separate them.

This was done by Granda and Hammack (1961), in an experiment that shows clearly that a period of sleep can serve as a reinforcement. Five human subjects were kept awake one full night and then tested the next evening, at their normal bedtime, for about two hours. Each subject was studied while reclining on a cot in a darkened room, with EEG recorded. A push-button microswitch was taped to each hand and electrodes were attached to a leg. Brief, mild electric shocks were administered through the electrodes every 3 seconds. These could be avoided, however, by pressing the microswitch on the *left* hand a little faster than every 3 seconds. This part of the study is the typical procedure of avoiding a noxious stimulus preventing sleep. However, very little sleep was possible during the 3-second periods.

The significant innovation in this study is that the other microswitch—the one on the *right* hand—led to a period of time sufficient for sleep. A fixed-ratio schedule of positive reinforcement was scheduled for this right-hand response. After 10 presses all the equipment was turned off for a "time-out" period of 5 or 8 minutes. This response was not motivated directly by shock-avoidance—the shock was being successfully avoided by the left-hand response—but rather by the desire for sleep, which was prevented by the necessity to keep the left-hand responding.

The results were in line with the sleep-motive theory. The subjects did learn to press the right-hand microswitch, and they did indeed sleep during the "time-out" periods. Moreover, the sleep became more synchronized and was achieved more quickly and frequently, the greater the number of weekly sessions. Unfortunately, no controls were run, so the possibility that a "time-out" from this sort of avoidance schedule is equally reinforcing to a non-sleep-deprived subject cannot be ruled out. It would also be of interest to vary the degree of sleep deprivation systematically.

In general, a fairly good case can be made for the notion that sleep deprivation can motivate learning and performance, if the learning is relevant to the reduction of the sleep motive or of closely related motives. In the case of the water maze studies, it is clear that a reduction of the fatigue produced by sleep deprivation is involved in learning. Sleep latency, a traditional measure of behavior strength, is a function of hours of sleep deprivation up to an asymptote. Observation shows that rats may learn an unusual response, such as hanging by the teeth, to get some sleep. The experimental studies have shown that a sleep-deprived human subject will learn an operant response not just to avoid a disturbing stimulus, but also to get a period of sleep. Much more needs to be done in this area to vary parameters of sleep-relevant learning systematically. Nevertheless, the evidence, even as it now stands, shows that sleep deprivation can motivate learning and performance if such behavior leads to sleep and the reduction of the sleep motive.

Decreased Attention to Irrelevant Tasks During Sleep Deprivation

In contrast to the preceding section, we will now consider the effect of sleep deprivation on all kinds of learning and performance tasks that have little direct relevance to the sleep motive. These tasks do not lead to sleep for the sleepy person. In fact, since the cognitive activities required by most of them are largely incompatible with sleep, these tasks actually interfere with sleep. These are the traditional sleep-deprivation studies.

Sleep deprivation may have quite a dramatic effect on these irrelevant tasks; an example is the marked decrement in intelligence test scores found by Edwards (1941). Many individuals have assumed implicitly that the effects of sleep deprivation are directly on cognitive processes; that there is a qualitative distortion of thought processes—possibly due to a toxic chemical effect on cortical functions by some sort of fatigue product. Such an assumption may be given credibility by reports of delusions and hallucinations occurring during sleep deprivation. (These will be discussed later.) Nevertheless, there is good reason to believe that sleep loss does not directly affect cognitive functions.

The fact of the matter is that the effects of sleep deprivation are variable and often contradictory. Thus, Edwards (1941) found a few subjects doing better after 96 hours of sleep deprivation than during a control period. Kleitman (1939) found a decrement, in a test of hand steadiness, with about 65 hours of deprivation, while Edwards (1941) found none with 100 hours. While Gilbert and Patrick (1897) found memory disturbances, memory tests used by Laslett (1924), Freeman (1932), and Edwards (1941) showed no decrements. These effects are due to a variety of factors that will be discussed in this chapter, foremost of which seems to be attention.

The most prominent symptoms of sleep deprivation in human subjects concern attentional difficulties. All observers report that sleep deprivation produces an almost overpowering drowsiness, listlessness, apathy, concentration difficulty, and inability to maintain continuous attention (Robinson and Herrmann, 1922; Katz and Landis, 1935; Kleitman, 1939; Edwards, 1941, and others). The studies reviewed in this section emphasize effects on attention. An attempt will be made to show that these effects account for the apparent cognitive disturbance.

The classic study of the effects of sleep deprivation on performance was done in 1897 by Gilbert and Patrick at the University of Iowa, and illustrates the approach most widely used by psychologists. Three subjects were kept awake for 90 hours and tested with a large variety of simple tasks, including reaction time, tapping, memory, addition, dynamometer, and perceptual sensitivity. Most of these tests showed moderate decreases, although visual acuity held up well and may even have improved. After a period of sleep lasting 12 hours, the subjects were restored to normal efficiency.

The Patrick and Gilbert study introduces a leitmotif that is heard again and again, in the various sleep-deprivation studies. The performance decrement appeared to be due to attention difficulties. The authors describe a subject who after 72 hours of sleep deprivation could not perform, in twenty minutes, a simple memory task that had previously taken only two or three minutes: "The attention could not be held on the work. A kind of mental lapse would constantly undo the work done" (p. 50).

Weiskotten (1925) studied his own behavior during a 62-hour vigil and found that his performance on tests stressing speed and attention suffered more than those focusing on accuracy. Subsequently, Weiskotten and Ferguson (1939) did an experiment involving three subjects deprived of sleep for 66 hours, and two controls. On an almost purely motor task—ball throwing—there was no noticeable effect on sleep loss. On the other hand, a coding test and a test of mental multiplication showed impairment but, as in the preliminary study, it was time scores and not error scores that suffered. In fact, the accuracy scores were a bit higher during the insomnia. The authors conclude that the effect is on attention and related factors, rather than on ability. They feel that sleep deprivation raises the threshold for the "work motives," except for "brief and sporadic intervals."

The importance of the degree of conscious effort or attention was demonstrated further by Kleitman and his associates, who engaged in sleep-deprivation experiments over several decades with some 35 subjects. Much of this work has not been published, but is available in summary form (Kleitman, 1939, Chapter XXI). Typically, a subject was kept awake for 62-65 hours, at which point he showed most of the major symptoms of sleep loss, such as visual blurring, overpowering drowsiness, and concentration difficulty. The latter symptom was shown, for example, by the fact that the subjects could not keep track of a simple count after reaching the numbers around 15 or 20.

In summarizing the results of the psychological tests, Kleitman divides them into those in which effort is significant and those in which it is not. The tests requiring little or no effort—knee-jerk, pupillary reaction to light, perceptual sensitivity, visual acuity, and GSR—showed no impairment during sleep loss. In fact, pain sensitivity increased. The EEG did show drifting into sleeping states. On the other hand, there was a decrease in performance on tests requiring effort, such as body steadiness, hand steadiness, opposite naming, color naming, mental arithmetic, and reaction time.

In addition to characteristics of the tasks that intrinsically demand more or less effort, the sleep-deprived subject can increase or decrease his own effort. An artificially high level of efficiency may be possible, but not over too long a time period. Several of the studies have suggested that the sleep-deprived subject can operate well for brief periods, but that prolonged attention is difficult. Therefore, it would be expected that the longer the test, the greater the effect. This is, in fact, precisely what does happen.

Kleitman (1939) has also varied task length. For example, in the color-naming test the subjects were required to name 100 colored squares, and were able to do so quite well even after prolonged sleeplessness. When the test was lengthened so that the subjects were required to respond to as many as 1,200 of the stimuli, their accuracy and speed scores went down.

Laslett (1924, 1928) criticized the earlier Robinson studies (Robinson and Herrmann, 1922; Robinson and Robinson, 1922), in which little effect of sleep loss was found, for using tests that were too short and thus enabling subjects to mobilize effort for a short period. He himself found effects on body sway, code writing, analogies, mental arithmetic, and the Thorndike intelligence test. He attributed his results to tests that were "long enough to negate the marked effect of compensatory effort." It should also be noted that Laslett took special care that his subjects did not learn their scores during the experiment, and asked them specifically not to take previous performance as a standard. Thus, he minimized the motivation to do well.

Laird (1926) also felt that the Robinson results were due to the use of short, novel tests. In order to demonstrate this, he took the mental arithmetic test and increased it to 30 minutes. He then found that an experimental group kept up for one night made more errors than a control group. Since the deprivation period was considerably shorter than that used by Robinson, it is likely that the result was due to the increased task length.

The operation of task length and related timing factors can be seen in Edwards' (1941) finding, mentioned earlier, that performance on the A.C.E. decreases with sleep deprivation. Using 17 experimental and 10 control subjects in a 100-hour deprivation study, Edwards found little consistent change in hand steadiness or grip, several visual acuity tests, and memory tests. As described elsewhere, there were some body-sway and reaction-time results. The significant finding, however, was the intelligence decrement. At first, this seems inconsistent with the negative results of Robinson and Robinson (1922), Katz and Landis (1935), and Moss (1925), all of whom used the Army Alpha test, as well as Katz and Landis' findings with the Otis test.

It is possible that the greater length of Edwards' deprivation period may have had an effect. But this hardly seems to account for it, since Katz and Landis' subject showed no appreciable decrement on either the Army Alpha or the Otis after six days of sleep loss.

Edwards himself points to the length—an hour or more—of the A.C.E. as the cause of the decrement. During this test, longer than any of the others, clinical observations showed that the subjects simply could not sustain their attention. They dozed and lost interest. At this level of sleep deprivation, and with this length of time, the test-oriented motivation was outweighed. It is interesting that as distinguished an authority in testing as J. P. Guilford remarks about the A.C.E. that in his opinion, most of the factors measured "should be assessed by means of power tests" (Buros, 1949, p. 218).

In general, the studies reviewed in this section suggest that the effect of sleep deprivation on performance is due to a disturbance of attention. Actually, all of the studies cited here were done many years ago and suffer from various deficiencies of design. As R. T. Wilkinson commented, "It may not be too much to say that there is not a single experiment before that of Edwards which could not be given a misleading result for one reason or another" (personal communication). Some of the reasons are: an insufficient number of subjects, a failure to control for diurnal rhythm, and inadequate control for practice. So, while these early results are suggestive, the issue requires more adequate experimental verification as well as a more powerful theoretical analysis than the vague idea of attentional difficulties. We shall describe a more sophisticated approach to this problem in the next section.

The Walter Reed Lapse Hypothesis

Preparatory to analyzing their own extensive performance data on sleep loss, Williams, Lubin, and Goodnow (1959) reviewed the literature which we have just covered. In order to account for the results the authors decided to extend a concept from studies of fatigue—the notion of "blocks" (Bills, 1931). Instead of assuming that fatigue results in a continuous and smooth decrement in performance—an assumption not in accord with observations of the increasing uneven quality of the process—Bills thought that the decrement was produced by brief periods of no response, or blocks, in a context of otherwise unimpaired behavior. These blocks were assumed to increase in frequency and duration with continued fatigue.

Bills (1935) went on to show that blocks are a function of the number of competing responses in a situation. Subjects were given the task of continuously naming colors on charts. The number and length of blocks increased with the number of colors to choose from. Thus, the block may be related to some sort of decisional conflict. The critical factor is not the number of elements involved, since Bills also showed that increasing the complexity of a letter sequence, in a monotonous copying task, decreased the number of blocks. In this case, there was no competition among elements, and increasing their number made the task a little more interesting. Bills thought that the disturbance in the blocking on the color naming was due to fatigue generated by the conflict. It is also possible that the block was filled with the decisional process required by the competing alternatives. Each of several color names may have been verbalized implictly, thus delaying the final spoken response. Recall the increase in decision reaction time over simple reaction time. For our purposes, we will assume that blocks are due to competing response tendencies.

This concept of "blocks" has been extended to account for most of the effects of oxygen deficiency (Maag, 1957). The time to work out a concept formation task increased with hypoxia, primarily because of the occurrence of periods of no response.

The idea of blocks has also been used by Broadbent (1958) to help explain the effects of noise on behavior. The history of this area bears some remarkable similarities to that of sleep deprivation. In the earlier studies (see Stevens, 1946) nearly 100 tests of motor coordination, hand steadiness, reaction time, visual functions, intelligence, and physiological processes were given to individuals subjected to intense noise day after day. Although the subjects became irritable, they showed no performance decrement. Subsequently, Broadbent designed a test requiring continuous vigilance—perceiving changes in a line of 20 steam pressure gauges—that showed impairment with noise. Again, periods of inattention seemed to account for the errors. Broadbent introduced the term *auditory blinks* to account for this—an analog of the concept of blocks.

The first application of Bills' theory of blocks to sleep deprivation was made by Warren and Clark (1937). They tried tests previously shown to have little decrement during sleep deprivation—addition and subtraction, color naming, and tapping. As in previous studies, they found little effect on error scores of up to 65 hours of wakefulness. In the addition and subtraction, however, as well as the color naming tests, they found a marked increase in the number of blocks. Blocks were defined as: a pause in responding at least twice the length of the average response. Tapping did not show this phenomenon. Bjerner (1949) also found periods of very long reaction time during sleep loss, which he called "lapses."

In their brilliant elaboration of the lapse hypothesis, Williams, Lubin, and Goodnow separate the problem of finding the sensitive aspects of a task from the motivational issue. This is not to deny the importance of motivation, but to determine where and how it will affect behavior. In order to predict the effect of a lapse on a test, it is necessary to make an extremely fine logical analysis of each situation and measure. Focusing on an aspect of tests found important by Broadbent, the Walter Reed group divided the tests into those controlled or paced by the S, and those controlled or paced by the E. For each type of task a lapse was thought to have a different effect on, for example, time and error scores. Thus, instead of grouping tests by the traditional areas of learning, perception, motor skills, etc., the Walter Reed group looked for the genotypically similar elements in terms of how a lapse would effect performance.

The first subject-paced task considered was reaction time. The E turns on the signal, but the S determines the reaction time. If the signal comes on during a lapse it will not be perceived, and no reaction will take place until the lapse is over. This reaction will be extremely long. If, however, the signal appears between lapses, a normal, rapid reaction will take place. Thus, the record will consist of very short and very long reaction times. If lapses increase in frequency and duration during sleep deprivation, the proportion of very long reactions will go up. This situation should be reflected statistically in a difference between median and mean scores. This is exactly what was found.

The median scores, less affected by the long reaction times, show only a slight rise during sleep deprivation. Mean scores, highly sensitive to long reaction times, show a marked, consistent, and significant increase. Task duration, which would presumably facilitate lapses, was also related to time scores. These reaction time results illustrate the care and precision required for adequate prediction.

Other S-controlled and paced tasks included in these studies —which involved from 72 to 98 hours of sleep loss—were an adding test, a communication experiment, and a difficult test of concept attainment. In all cases *time* scores were affected but not *accuracy* scores.

The E-controlled tasks characteristically involved the presentation of stimuli to the subject at fixed intervals. Thus, if a lapse occurs the subject could not pick up at a later time where he had left off. The Continuous Performance Test was most sensitive to sleep loss (see Fig. 12). Subjects watched a series

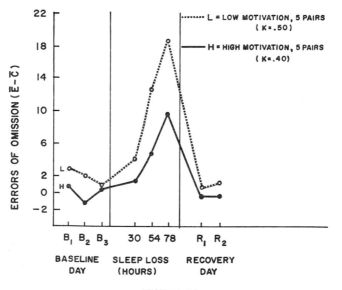

FIGURE 12

of random letters appear in a little apperture at a rate of one per second; they were to press a lever whenever an x appeared. As predicted by the lapse theory, it was errors of omission, more than errors of commission, that appeared during sleep deprivation. Auditory and vibratory versions of this task showed similar results, indicating that the effect was central. Other E-paced tasks, showing similar results, were a different part of the communication experiment and an information-learning procedure.

Williams, Lubin, and Goodnow suggest that their development of the lapse hypothesis can be used to explain many of the inconsistencies in the past literature. For example, they point to Weiskotten and Ferguson's finding that speed, but not accuracy, changes in a mental arithmetic task. In other cases it is difficult to tell just what measures were affected or what some of the characteristics of the task were, because of developments in apparatus, terminology, and communication styles over the years.

Nevertheless, the lapse hypothesis, in conjunction with a motivational analysis of the situation, offers the best explanation of the effects of sleep deprivation on performance. Lapses increase in frequency, duration, and depth with sleep loss. They are affected by task length and monotony. During a lapse, no response occurs and time scores are inflated. The degree to which, and the manner in which, performance is disturbed depend on the susceptibility of the test scores to periods of no information reception or response output. The physiological concomitants of lapses will be covered in the next chapter.

Confirmation of the work of the Walter Reed group has come from a study by Kornetsky, Mirsky, Kessler, and Dorff (1959) at the National Institute of Mental Health. Subjects were given the Continuous Performance Test and several other tasks, at about 45, and again at 69, hours of sleep deprivation. The tasks were grouped according to the impairment one would expect on the basis of the Walter Reed lapse theory: paced tasks with highly sensitive measures such as errors of omission; the less sensitive measures on paced tasks, e.g., errors of commission; and unpaced tasks. Impairment was related to this grouping. Furthermore, the degree to which the stimulating drug, dextroamphetamine, was able to compensate for sleep loss, was related to the type of task. The most impaired tasks were not restored, with the dosage used, to the pre-sleep loss level.

Several other recent studies are also consistent with the lapse hypothesis. Bowen, Ross, and Andrews (1956) found that response latencies in a tracking task were longer after one night's sleep loss, although vigorous bicycle riding just prior to the testing session had no effect. Chiles (1956) also used a one-night deprivation, and found a decrement, particularly with errors of omission, in a difficult color matching task. In both of these experiments the items were presented to the S's at a steady, fairly rapid rate over which they had no control. It would thus seem that these tasks were E-paced. It should be recalled that Chiles (1958) used this same task in studying heat, and found an adverse effect on performance only when the apparatus was operated as an E-paced task.

Performance and Variations in the Strength of the Sleep Motive

In the preceding two sections it was shown that performance of irrelevant tasks during sleep deprivation may be affected by disturbances in attention. The precise nature of the disturbance can be predicted by the lapse hypothesis. Whether a lapse occurs, however, would seem to depend on motivational factors.

In these sleep-deprivation experiments two sets of motives can be seen to operate: the sleep motive versus the task-oriented motives. Sleep deprivation motivates more and more lapses; actually, as we shall see later, the lapses may be periods of actual sleep. The lapses increase in frequency, duration, and depth, as hours of sleep deprivation increase. Motivating the cognitive responses incompatible with lapses are the various task-oriented motives: the desire to do well, the desire to please the experimenter, etc., or sometimes, an avoidance of noxious stimulation.

Thus the subject in a sleep-deprivation experiment is in a

conflict. The occurrence of the task performance, and its quality, would be expected to be a function of the relative strength of the two conflicting motives. Most studies, however, if they are concerned with motivation at all, concentrate on either the sleep motive or the task-oriented motives. In this section we will concentrate on the sleep motive. We will then consider task-oriented motives and finally the conflict between the two sets of motives.

The length of sleep deprivation should be negatively related to non-sleep-relevant task performance. It would be expected to operate in the opposite direction from task-relevant motives. As sleep deprivation increases, performance should decrease—all other things being equal. Many of the studies suggest this, but only a few demonstrate it clearly.

In the famous experiment by Katz and Landis (1935), a young man stayed awake for 231 hours, with surprisingly few physiological or performance effects. However, typing did show a marked decrease during the first few days, and subsequently had to be discontinued; the increasing difficulty in visual concentration made it impossible for the subject to continue.

Edwards' (1941) study shows the effect of degree of sleep deprivation even more clearly. For example, body sway was found to increase with sleep deprivation, as has also been shown by Kleitman (1939) and Laslett (1928). Seven subjects showed more body sway after 24 hours of sleep loss, seven after 48 hours, 11 at 72 hours, and 13 at 96 hours. Similar results were found with the American Council on Education Psychological Examination—an intelligence test. As is shown in Table II, more individuals do worse, rather than better, as sleep deprivation progresses.

However, as Kleitman (1939), Murray, Williams, and Lubin (1958), and Wilkinson (1963) have shown, it is not simply a matter of hours of deprivation. The relationship is complicated by the diurnal body temperature rhythm. Performance is better in midday, when the temperature is higher, even after several days of no sleep. Thus, performance efficiency may be greater on the third afternoon of sleep deprivation than on the second

TABLE II

INDIVIDUALS SHOWING CHANGES IN A.C.E.
PERFORMANCE DURING SLEEP DEPRIVATION

PERFORMANCE CHANGE RELATIVE TO CONTROL PERIOD	HOURS OF SLEEP DEPRIVATION			
	24	48	72	96
Individuals doing better	13	6	5	2
Individuals doing worse	3	11	11	14

Based on data in Edwards, 1941.

night. This is why it is so important, in sleep-deprivation studies, to conduct tests at exactly the same time of day from session to session.

A study of some clarity was done by Lindsley (1957). In this study the strength of the sleep motive was varied in two important ways: the subjects were studied during their sleep, after varying periods of prior sleep deprivation, and they were monitored continuously through the night so that the effects of the progressive satiation of the sleep motive could be observed. The performance of an operant response was recorded during sleep. A microswitch was taped to the hand of each of the subjects, and they were taught to press it with their thumb in order to control a 30 db tone administered through the earphones of a pilot's helmet. The intensity of the tone was controlled by the rate of thumb pressing: fast pressing avoided the tone, and the slower the rate the louder the tone. The subjects were kept awake for various periods, and then allowed to sleep in a comfortable bed.

A sample record from one subject is shown in Fig. 13. After 15 hours of sleep deprivation, at normal sleeping time, the subjects went to bed and showed about 24 minutes of fast responding, or what Lindsley calls the sleep latency. Then the rate decreased with the onset of sleep—about another 16 minutes. The rate of responding was very low for several hours, with a 2-hour period of no response during which the tone sounded at full intensity. After the onset of sleep the response rate during the first four hours was lower than during the second four hours. Responding during the night tends to be in short bursts, separated by no responding for a stretch, as would be expected from the wavelike nature of sleep. This result shows that when the subject's sleep motivation is highest he will reduce, and even cease, avoiding a somewhat noxious tone. As sleep motivation decreases through the night he will resume responding. When the subject is tested after 38 hours of sleep deprivation, the effect is more marked. The sleep latency is reduced to about 7 minutes. As shown in Fig. 13, the rate of responding is consider-

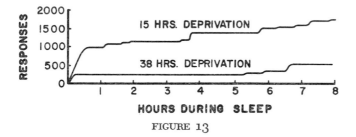

FIGURE 13

ably lower than for the 15-hour deprivation period. The 38 hours of sleep deprivation increased the period of no response to 5½ hours.

The results can be interpreted in terms of a conflict between the sleep motive and the motive to avoid the noxious tone. As the sleep motive was decreased during the night it became weaker relative to the aversive stimulus, and the probability of the response occurring increased. This responding came in bursts, suggesting an oscillation in the balance of the two motives. Such shifting could occur, for example, when the subject woke up to some degree to press the microswitch, and then became sleepier. The conflict theory also explains why the response rate is dramatically lowered by sleep deprivation. Any other factors increasing the sleep motive would presumably have a similar effect on the operant response. Conversely, the conflict theory would predict that the response rate would increase if the maximum loudness of the aversive tone was raised.

Performance and Variations in the Strength of the Task-Oriented Motives

The fact that an individual stays up in the face of overpowering sleepiness implies some competing motive—an inference ignored by most experimenters. What could this motive be? In a few instances it is money, but more often it is an elusive social or personal need. Youthful enthusiasm, the need to please the experimenter (often a professor), a chance to demonstrate one's virility, self-mastery, or courage, or many other social motives may enter the picture. In one case the subject wanted to prove that sleep was just a habit! These social motives are usually not measured or varied systematically. There is some evidence that they are of great significance. In many of the earlier studies sleep deprivation failed to impair performance. According to the investigators, this was due to an ability on the part of some or all of the subjects to "increase their effort," implying a powerful task-oriented motive. (Robinson and Herrmann, 1922; Robinson and Robinson, 1922; Moss et al., 1922; Laird and Wheeler, 1926; Freeman, 1932).

In addition to the motivation the subject brings into the laboratory with him, several factors in the situation may increase or decrease his task motivation. These include test interest, group morale, and experimenter behavior. The intrinsic interest of the tests themselves will be mentioned first.

Ax and his associates (1957) made a direct attempt to evaluate the importance of motivation by dividing a large array of tests into those of high and low interest. Those in the high group were administered individually by the experimenter, and provided knowledge of results; they included dexterity, serial learning, word fluency, several exercise measures, several steadiness tests, and a test of speed of falling asleep. None of the eleven tests showed a significant decrement after a night without sleep; in fact, five of them showed slight improvement and two others were significantly improved. The "test" showing the greatest increment is not surprising: it is the time needed to fall asleep!

Contrariwise, the low motivation tests were affected deleteriously by sleep deprivation. These tests included various forms of pursuit, reaction time, crossing out, word association, addition, coding, clocking, perceptual, Thematic Apperception, Critical Flicker Fusion, etc. They were either unmonitored by the experimenters, required sustained attention, or did not provide the subject with knowledge of results. Of the 16 measures, 14 showed a significant decrease with sleep deprivation. Thus, the degree to which the test arouses the motivation of the subject is important in determining his performance.

The stimulation of a social group may offset the effects of sleep deprivation. Laties (1961) used a mild deprivation of 37 hours (actually one night), and measured performance in group and individual tasks. At the beginning of the testing session, after sleep deprivation, the subjects reported lowered motivation and interest in the activities. By the end of the evening, however, the group appeared to have aroused interest to the extent that subjects reported as much motivation as in the control period. The author thinks that this may be the reason that the performance showed no decrement with sleep loss. The fact that the individual, as well as the group tasks, did not deteriorate may be due to the generalization of the group spirit to the whole situation, as is suggested by the self-reports.

There are various ways in which the experimenter can influence the task-oriented motivation. In some cases this may be done without full awareness of the significance of these motives. For instance, Laslett (1928) was able to show a decrement in coding, addition, intelligence, and body-sway tasks, to refute the Robinson findings. Laslett very carefully withheld knowledge of results, however, and specifically asked his subjects not to compare their performance with previous results. While Laslett believed he was eliminating an extraneous variable, he was probably reducing the task-oriented motive to the extent of contributing to the performance impairment.

A direct experimental manipulation of this variable was made by the Walter Reed group (see Williams et al., 1959).

Using a vibratory version of the Continuous Performance Task which he designed, Dr. George Crampton exhorted one group to do better, giving them information about their performance at the same time. Another group was given neither exhortation nor knowledge of results. In the simplest version of the task the high motivation group did significantly better than the control group. Other attempts to vary motivation were suggestive but not conclusive. Wilkinson (1961 a) has also clearly demonstrated in several studies the influence of knowledge of results.

Conflict Between Sleep Motivation and Task-Oriented Motivation

In the previous two sections we have seen that increasing the sleep motive leads to decreasing performance, while increasing task motivation has a beneficial effect. Now we will turn to studies in which the simultaneous operation of both sets of motives can be seen.

One study which throws some light on this problem is the work of Rowland (1961) that was described earlier, in a section showing that the delay-synchronization phenomenon varied with the relative strength of two competing motives. The EEG synchrony was increased if the intensity of the shock was lowered, and was eliminated entirely when the intensity was high enough. On the other hand, the phenomenon occurred consistently only if the cats were kept awake at night, thus increasing their motivation to sleep. Therefore, the appearance of the EEG synchrony response during a delayed stimulus is a function of the relative strength of the sleep and pain motives.

Also relevant to a conflict between the sleep motive and other motives, is an ingenious "Alertness Indicator," described by Kennedy and Travis in a number of studies (Kennedy and Travis, 1947, 1948; Travis and Kennedy, 1947, 1949). They found that subjects in monotonous, simulated lookout and tracking tasks, fell asleep periodically and showed an impairment of performance. These periods were associated with a drooping of the eyelids and a reduction in muscle action potentials from an electrode placed just above the eyebrow. Kennedy and Travis amplified these signals and placed them in a circuit with various stimuli—lights, buzzers, etc. Whenever the subject's muscle tension reached a predetermined level, he was awakened by the stimulus. In this sense the apparatus created a conflict between the motive to sleep and the alerting variable. In a real life situation, such as truck driving, the alerting variable might be anxiety.

Boren (1960) reports a study in which two monkeys were trained to avoid a shock by pressing a lever every few seconds. This was continued for seven days and nights. Response rate gradually declined, expecially after four days of sleep loss, and more shocks were delivered to the animal as a consequence. During the last few days a strong diurnal pattern was noted— the monkeys could keep responding during the day but fell off at night and received more shocks. The conflict here was between pain avoidance and the mounting sleep motive. A similar result was reported by Byck and Hearst (1962).

The study that most clearly shows the two conflicting sets of motives in operation during a sleep-deprivation experiment was done by Wilkinson (1961 b). This investigator used a choice reaction time task sensitive to sleep loss. Task motivation was varied by testing subjects with and without knowledge of results. Sleep motivation was varied by testing subjects with no sleep deprivation and again after one night's sleep loss.

The number of correct responses, the number of errors, and the number of gaps in performance showed similar results. The gap measure will be described in some detail because it has considerable theoretical interest. A gap was defined as a period of 1.5 seconds in which no response occurred. A gap seems to be the same as a lapse or a block and should vary with both sets of motivation according to conflict theory.

Wilkinson's results with the gap measure are shown in Table III. It can be seen that knowledge of results reduces the number of gaps even when there has been no sleep deprivation. Sleep deprivation without knowledge of results produces a marked increase in the number of gaps. Pitting knowledge of results against sleep deprivation reduces the number of gaps to a large extent, as can be seen in the lower right-hand cell. However, knowledge of results does not entirely overcome the effects of

Table III

NUMBER OF PERFORMANCE GAPS AS A FUNC-
TION OF SLEEP DEPRIVATION AND KNOWL-
EDGE OF RESULTS

	No knowledge of results	Knowledge of results
No sleep deprivation	14.3	7.1
Sleep deprivation	66.3	16.1

After Wilkinson 1961 b.

sleep deprivation. Both main variables and their interaction are significant.

Wilkinson's results offer strong support for the idea that performance efficiency is the resultant of a conflict between the sleep motive and a task motive, such as that related to knowledge of results. Furthermore, the results suggest that sleep deprivation motivates a response incompatible with task performance that results in performance lapses.

SUMMARY

A critical part of the definition of a motive is that it will motivate the learning and performance of a response. But sleep deprivation often leads to a decrement in psychological task performance. The important issue seems to be the relevance of the motive to the required performance. A motive may facilitate the learning and performance of a relevant response. A motive may also facilitate irrelevant responses if no incompatibility is involved. If two motives are eliciting incompatible responses then conflict occurs. The outcome is a function of the relative strength of the conflicting motives.

In many studies of the effects of such physiological motives as hunger, temperature, or noise, on psychological performance, a conflict between the task-relevant responses and competing responses exists. The decrement in performance which occurs under some conditions is a result of disturbed attention rather than a disturbance of capacity.

Sleep is largely incompatible with cognitive activities such as learning, the organization of performance, forgetting, or thinking. Anything more than simple discrimination requires arousal. Thus, it was predicted that sleep deprivation would lead to increased learning and performance, as well as to physiological arousal, only when the response eventually led to sleep. Otherwise the tendency for the heightened sleep motive is in the direction of decreased cognitive activities and thus impaired performance on psychological tests. Test behavior will also be influenced by whatever task-oriented social motives are involved. These antagonistic motives may produce arousal and compensate for the effects of sleep deprivation, Task performance will be a function of the relative strength of the conflicting motives.

Under the proper conditions the sleep motive can be shown to facilitate learning and performance. Sleep deprivation facilitates water maze performance in rats, where the reward is escape from the fatiguing conditions. Sleep latency is reciprocally related to hours of sleep deprivation. Most convincing is that sleepy human subjects will learn an operant response to get a period of sleep.

Sleep deprivation has complex effects on learning and performance that do not lead to sleep as a reward. Most of the tasks used require cognitive activity incomptable with sleep. Sleep deprivation operates to distract attention from the task, resulting in impaired performance. Tasks requiring more conscious effort or sustained concentration are most affected by sleep loss.

The Walter Reed lapse hypothesis is an attempt to explain and predict the precise effect of sleep deprivation, by an analysis of the task measures that would be altered by an increasing number of periods of inattention, or lapses. Thus, in subject-paced tasks, time scores would be most affected; in experimenter-paced tasks, error scores go up.

The effects of sleep deprivation on performance do seem to be a function of conflicting motives. Performance tends to deteriorate with increasing sleep deprivation, controlling for the nature of the task and diurnal rhythm. Task-oriented motives such as increased effort, task interest, group morale, and knowledge of results tend to facilitate performance. Performance has been shown to be dependent on an interaction of sleep deprivation and knowledge of results.

In general, the sleep motive appears to be related to learning and performance in the same manner as other motives, providing one takes into account the incompatibility between sleep and cognitive functions, the relevance of the reward to the sleep motive, and the role of competing motivations.

CHAPTER 6

Sleep Deprivation and Arousal

One of the properties usually attributed to a motive, as was mentioned in the introductory chapter, is a general energizing effect on the organism and on behavior in general. Some theorists equate motivation with energization. Brown (1961), a strong advocate of this position, describes a motive as a nondirectional, nonspecific energizing variable that interacts multiplicatively with all learned and innate habits to increase their reaction potential. Among other things a motivational state would be expected to increase general activity, energize all learned responses, and facilitate the performance of responses based on other motives.

A somewhat analogous conception has been called "arousal" or "activation" (see Malmo, 1959, for a review of these theories). Arousal theories are mainly physiological. Motives are assumed to produce an internal aroused state as shown by the EEG, GSR, or muscular tension. The relationship between the internal aroused state and overt behavior is not thought to be simple; performance first increases in efficiency and then decreases in a curvilinear fashion. There are several possible neurophysiological (see Malmo, 1959) or behavioral (see Brown, 1961) reasons for this nonlinear relationship, as well as the possibility of physical weakening (see Bindra, 1959). The main point is that motivation is synonymous with physiological arousal.

When we turn to phenomena associated with sleep deprivation in the context of arousal, the possibility of a sleep motive
seems remote. However, a careful analysis of sleep deprivation
and arousal may prove to be a testing ground for the energizing
concept of motivation. In this chapter we will first discuss the
possible connection between motivation and general activity, as
well as activity during sleep deprivation. Then we shall turn to
the more general problem of the relation between motivation
and arousal. Following this we will consider several aspects of
the effect of sleep deprivation on arousal.

MOTIVATION AND GENERAL ACTIVITY

General, spontaneous activity, as measured by tambour-mounted cages, activity wheels, mazes, etc., is often increased by motivational states. The pioneering studies of Richter
(1922-23), Wang (1923), and others showed that the activity of
the rat was influenced by hunger, illumination, hormones, and
similar variables. The best-known example is the dependence of
activity cycles on sex hormones in the female rat.

Recently, Bindra (1959, Chapter 9) summarized the hormonal effects: removal of thyroid, pancreatic, adrenal, gonadal,
or pituitary glands results in decreased activity which may be
reversed by hormone replacement under certain conditions. Seasonal and estrual activity cycles are also due to hormones. Hormones, of course, are closely related to drives such as sex, fear,
and aggression.

Hall (1961, Chapter 7) has a good review of the effect of
physiological motives on spontaneous activity. Most, but not
all studies, show an increase in activity measures with food or
water deprivation and a decrease with satiation. While there are
some clear examples of motives increasing activity, however,
there are too many exceptions to make a firm generalization.
There are three main arguments for not assuming a necessary
relationship between motivation and general activity.

First, in many instances increasing motivation past an optimal point results in decreased activity. Skinner (1938) found that hunger increased unreinforced bar-pressing up to about five days of deprivation, followed by a sharp decrease. Morgan and Stellar (1950), conclude after reviewing the literature that the nutritional deficiencies which lower activity are those that weaken the body physically. Similarly, Bindra (1959) concludes that hormone replacement therapy may increase or decrease activity; the larger doses appear to decrease activity. High levels of motivation may also result in decreased performance because of competing response tendencies (Spence, 1956). Induced tension may first facilitate performance but may then interfere with it (Freeman, 1948; Malmo, 1959). Not all of these results can be explained by physical debilitation; performance may deteriorate and activity slow down at very high motivational levels before actual weakening.

Second, environmental stimulation may have a great effect on activity and may even account for some of the effects of motivation. The length and type of bar interacts with hunger in determining spontaneous, unreinforced bar-pressing in Skinner boxes (Murray, 1953). Campbell and Sheffield (1953) and Hall (1956) found that hunger and a change in environmental stimulation interacted to increase general activity. Campbell and Sheffield explain their results in terms of lowered sensory thresholds as the main effect of motivation. On the basis of another experiment of theirs, however, one might also consider the role of learning. They found that environmental changes associated with food increased activity, but that no activity was elicited if the change was uncorrelated with food delivery (Sheffield and Campbell, 1954). Hall (1961, pp. 117-118) summarizes similar studies. Two major theorists, Estes (1958) and Miller (1959), conceive of "spontaneous" activity as a reflection of learned responses to the various stimuli in the testing situation, i.e., not "spontaneous" at all.

A third reason for limiting the motive-activity assumption is that activity may be intrinsically reinforcing. Animals will learn responses to get to an exploratory maze or to run in an activity wheel. Activity deprivation increases this. Opportunities to play, manipulate, or examine novel stimuli are intrinsically rewarding to animals and man (see Young, 1961, Chapter 2, for a summary). Naturally, these findings do not rule out the possible influence of an extrinsic motive on activity, but they do make it difficult to clearly identify observed activity as simply reflecting hunger, thirst, or other homeostatic motives.

In addition, there are the naturalistic observations on the immobilization reaction to stress: the withdrawal of the turtle in the shell or the freezing of a mammal (see Young, 1961, p. 389). Some organisms become quite still when hungry; for instance, some sea crabs camouflage themselves, cease activity, and flick out a tongue at an unsuspecting, edible organism floating by. Genetic differences in dogs have been shown to be related to level of activity in reaction to restraint (Scott and Charles, 1954). Similar examples could be found in a great variety of species, situations, and motivational states.

General activity level, then, is not necessarily related to motivation. Activity varies with type and level of motive, species and strain differences, and the environmental situation. Much of the observed "spontaneous" activity ascribed to motives may actually reflect learned responses to stimuli in the situation or may represent intrinsically reinforcing behavior. Thus, there is no good reason for measuring the appropriateness of classifying sleep deprivation as a motivational operation against the yardstick of its effect on activity. Nevertheless, it is of interest to examine this effect.

Sleep is, by definition, a lack of activity. As pointed out in the chapter on biological functions, this lack of activity is not absolute, but considerably less activity is shown during sleep than at any other time. The general direction of sleep deprivation is toward inactivity. Richter (1922-23) and others have simply used the absence of activity recording as an index of sleep. As mentioned earlier, Licklider and Bunch (1946) found that sleep-deprived rats fell asleep while being revolved around in an activity wheel—they would remain inactive as the wheel tumbled them over and over. Kleitman (1939) has articulated most clearly the incompatibility between muscular activity and sleep, in addition to the tendency toward inactivity with sleep deprivation.

Some people may interpret the water maze studies of Bunch

and his associates, described in the last chapter, as showing an increased activity with sleep loss. However, this increased maze activity was temporary and highly contingent upon the conditions preventing relaxation and sleep. The reinforcement was in part a chance to be inactive. In the study on chronic sleep deprivation in which rats were prevented from sleeping for twenty hours a day, Bunch and his associates observed that during the four-hour rest period the chronically sleep-deprived rats were inactive for 75% of the time, while the controls were inactive only 37% of the time.

One study that bears on this issue (Murray, Schein, Erikson, Hill, and Cohen, 1959), dealt with social behavior during the sleep-deprivation experiments at Walter Reed, mentioned in the last chapter. During certain periods, observations of the social, recreational, or general behavior of the subjects were made at 15-minute intervals. Categories included social conversation, games, TV viewing, hobbies, and passive nonparticipation. The most significant measure was that of activity change—the number of times the category of activity was different from that in the previous observation. In many ways this measure is analogous to the traditional tambour-mounted cage that really reflects a shift from, for example, sniffing at one end to looking out of the other end of the cage.

The results show that activity change increases with sleep deprivation. The results from the first group of subjects are shown in Fig. 14. The reversal at 55 to 64 hours is somewhat reminiscent of the decline in performance at high motivational levels. In the second group, shown in Fig. 15, however, activity change was even greater at 86 to 88 hours of sleep deprivation. The relevant differences were all significant.

Does this mean that sleep deprivation facilitates general activity? Not at all! Much of this shifting from one activity to another functioned to avoid the overpowering drowsiness that would frequently arise if the subject tried to maintain attention on one activity for any length of time. A subject would abruptly leave a card game as he began to nod, in order to get some different stimulation. One activity that increased was a listless sort of social conversation. Another was nonparticipation, which

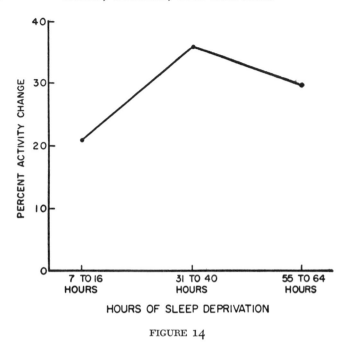

FIGURE 14

included wandering around aimlessly or leaning against the wall. On the other hand, the activities that made the subjects sleepier, e.g., hobbies and crafts, were avoided.

The conclusion was that the activity change reflected adaptive behavior designed to help keep the subject awake. This shifting of behavior, therefore, was motivated by the complex social motives involved in being a volunteer for a scientific experiment rather than the sleep motive itself. The direction of the sleep motive in this study, as elsewhere, was in the direction of drowsiness, relaxation, and inactivity.

Thus, the widely assumed relationship between motivation and general activity has severe limitations and may be explainable on other grounds. Sleep deprivation tends toward inactivity, although competing motivation arising from the experimental situation may sometimes give the appearance of an activity increase due to sleep motivation.

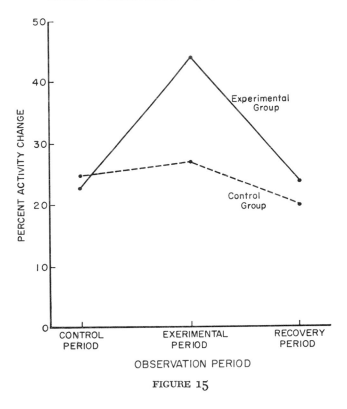

FIGURE 15

MOTIVATION AND AROUSAL

While general activity is not associated invariably with motive states, it is possible that motives do tend to energize the body in preparation for action. In other words, the effect of a motive is to make the organism more alert, arouse the brain and its cognitive processes, and prepare the internal organs and musculature for movement. This would not necessarily be translated into overt behavior unless, or until, the proper environmental conditions were met or competing factors were eliminated. Remember the sea crab who became inactive when hungry; yet he was alert and aroused for action, as shown by the rapid flicking out of the tongue when something edible came by.

This internal preparation for behavior, without overt performance, has been called arousal.

The concept of arousal or activation has been developed most adequately by Malmo (1958, 1959). Three threads of thought were woven together to form this concept: the early work of Freeman (1948) and his followers on the "energetics" of behavior, Hull's (1943) nonspecific drive state, and the recent work on physiological arousal (see Lindsley 1957, 1960). Briefly, the theory is that all motivational operations lead to a generalized state of arousal, providing the appropriate environmental stimulation is also present. This active state is first of all a central, physiological phenomenon, mediated by the reticular activating system, with consequent effects on peripheral systems such as muscle tension and circulation. Ordinarily this increased arousal will lead to more and more intense overt behavior, but not necessarily. For example, at great degrees of deprivation the organism may be alerted but may not display overt behavioral responses typically associated with the drive. This is sometimes called the *inverted U hypothesis*.

This is a useful concept and may help to explain many aspects of motivation and emotion, particularly in regard to the intensity dimension of behavior. Evidence for the hypothesized curvilinear relationship between central arousal and overt behavior has been gathered in the case, for example, of thirst. Bélanger and Feldman (1962) deprived rats of water at different times for periods of up to 72 hours. The physiological indicant of arousal—heart rate—increased consistently with hours of deprivation. On the other hand, the behavioral measure—bar-pressing for water reinforcement—increased in rate only up to 48 hours and then dropped off.

The increased heart rate is only found during the actual bar-pressing, so that environmental stimuli play a crucial role. Follow-up studies indicate that the results are not due to a physical weakening of the animal, nor do they appear to be dependent on the exertion of bar-pressing (Bélanger, personal communication).

Deprivation by itself does not produce the arousal, but deprivation plus the environmental situation leads to an arousal

(Malmo, 1959). Therefore, in identifying arousal with motivation, Malmo is led to the position that no motive exists until the stimulus is presented. Since it is also true that overt responses do not occur until the stimulus is presented, it seems to us that the critical distinction between motivation and behavior is lost. It would be simpler to identify motivation with time of deprivation and associated internal cues. Arousal, then, is part of the response pattern, although it need not be correlated perfectly with overt responding.

The point was made earlier that internal arousal can occur without overt responding. However, the reverse can also occur—motivated responding can occur without internal arousal. Miller (1951) has noted that, after prolonged avoidance conditioning, relaxation moves back in the chain until rats go through the whole behavior sequence nonchalantly. Solomon and Wynne (1954) have observed the same thing in dogs, and call it *anxiety conservation*. Perhaps the best example is given by Galambos and Morgan (1960), who say:

> A monkey learning to avoid shocks by pressing a lever at a signal appears to pass through a series of behavioral stages in the process. At first the signal arouses much "emotional" activity such as piloerection and vocalization. Later when learning has progressed to 50 percent correct responses, this emotional behavior can be partly replaced by an "alert or attentive" attitude. The fully trained animal, in final complete command of the situation, seems undisturbed by the signal and often delays making the correct response until the very last moment (p. 1492).

If the autonomic reaction is the motivation here, why does it drop out well before the overt behavior? Extinction is going on but it is difficult to explain the hundreds of perfectly performed trials without anxiety in the Solomon and Wynne study. Furthermore, Solomon and Brush (1956) report studies in which avoidance training was accomplished in organisms deprived of autonomic functioning, albeit not as rapidly.

It is possible that the conditioning in avoidance training is between the shock and the skeletal response. But other studies (Dollard and Miller, 1960) show that the skeletal response is not necessary. Another possibility is that the core of the fear "response" is, in essence, a central brain mechanism. Thus, the conditioning is between a stimulus and a central brain mechanism which may result subsequently in autonomic and skeletal muscular reactions.

The autonomic reaction adds stimulation to this, of course, but this is not the basic element. Rather the autonomic reaction seems to occur when a change in approach to a situation is required. In the early stages of avoidance when the animal is trying out many responses the autonomic reaction is intense. Miller (1951) also observes that making the escape door inoperative arouses the animal again, with increased vigor of responding, urination, defecation, etc. Note that this is not reconditioning.

On the neurophysiological level, the evidence from evoked potential research suggests that brain patterns in cortical, limbic, and reticular structures are variable during early avoidance conditioning, become more regularized during overlearning, but become variable again during extinction (Galambos and Morgan, 1960). Therefore, the lack of correspondence between the autonomic reaction and motivation is also true of the arousal mechanism in the brain.

The many observations on frustration and increased responding offer another example of autonomic reaction when experimental conditions make more aroused responding a more probably adaptive reaction (Dollard et al., 1939). Frustration depends on the strength of the original motive and the habit strength of the thwarted response (Brown, 1961). While the increased autonomic reaction may be viewed as a general motivational increment, there is really little evidence that reduction of such a motive is a powerful reinforcement if the original motive is not also reduced. In fact, if the original motive is not reduced the excited state and vigorous responding is extinguished, or habituated. Furthermore, frustration may produce quite different autonomic reactions in some individuals—depression, for example (Funkenstein et al., 1957). The effects of frustration on performance can be handled just as easily on the basis of past learning and association as by assuming a change in motivation (Child and Waterhouse, 1953).

Taken together, all of this evidence raises serious doubts about the equation of motivation with autonomic arousal. Arousal may continue to increase when behavioral measures indicate decreased motivation, and may disappear when behavioral measures show signs of continued motivation. It seems more reasonable to suppose that arousal is part of the response system of the organism that comes into play under a number of conditions requiring the full resources of the organism. The conditions might include new learning situations, extinction, frustration, and conflict. The aroused state of the organism would be expected not only to increase vigor of response but also perceptual, learning, memory, problem-solving, and motor skills, depending on the level of arousal and the nature of the situation.

Another problem with the concept of arousal is that arousal does not appear to be a simple unitary state. For example, different motives do not seem to summate in a simple way to increase arousal. Under some conditions summation occurs, and under others it does not. For example, Bélanger and Ducharme (1961) found that the heart rate of thirsty rats pressing a bar in a Skinner box was increased by electric shocks administered prior to testing. On the other hand, Bélanger and Tétreau (1961) found that an irrelevant hunger motive had an inhibiting effect on heart rate in thirsty rats pressing for water reward. Therefore, the state of arousal does not seem to be the same for all motivational states.

There is other evidence that the autonomic reactions involved in arousal do not constitute a single unitary phenomenon. Ax (1953) has reported an average intercorrelation of .12 between physiological measures of arousal. Even granting the importance of individual differences, mentioned by Malmo (1958), this hardly seems like a unitary thing. Individuals apparently have a unique stereotyped autonomic reaction to many different kinds of stress (Lacey and Lacey, 1958). Is it reasonable to suppose that these individual autonomic reactions would all have exactly the same effect on behavior?

Hebb (1958) has some doubts about the monism of arousal. He points out that testosterone does not equally facilitate rage and fear in male animals. He also mentions differences in fear and laughter. Arnold (1960) cites strong evidence for different patterns in fear and anger, as well as between sexual love and maternal love and between heat and cold. Other studies showed evidence of different autonomic patterns in disgust, fear, sexual arousal, and sexual consummatory activity.

Further evidence could be cited, but the main point is obvious: a number of conditions that are clearly motivational produce different patterns of autonomic arousal. The large individual differences may be genetic or may be due to learning (Bindra, 1959) and adaptation (Brown, 1955) in specific situations. The Russian experiments on the conditioning of various internal organs suggest that the arousal patterns may be even more influenced by learning experiences than we think.

It should also be mentioned that the Reticular Activating System, upon which so much of the theorizing is based, is not anatomically a unitary structure (Olszewski, 1954). Functionally, also, the RAS may act selectively as shown in the studies cited by Magoun (1958) in which attention is focused on one stimulus, while others are blocked out. It should also be kept in mind that the cortex controls both the activating and de-activating brain systems. This control could extend to patterns of partial arousal, inhibition, etc. One of the clearest examples is paradoxical sleep in which the cortex is aroused but body movement is inhibited. Lindsley (1961) also discusses the protective, inhibiting reaction of the RAS to sensory overload and distortion.

Of course, none of this should be taken to mean that there cannot be a general arousal at times. Many of the specific autonomic patterns overlap and would have similar effects on behavior. Total arousal might be elicited by certain motivational conditions. But the main point is that not all motives depend on a generalized arousal. Perhaps one way of putting it is to use Seyle's idea of a combination of local adaptation syndromes with the general adaptation syndrome.

One additional set of evidence casts doubt on the idea of arousal as synonymous with motivation. States of de-arousal may be associated with specific motives, specific species, and different levels of motivation. Bindra (1959) sees this point when he says that stresses such as anoxia and fatigue tend to decrease arousal.

Different species and strains also react with different patterns. Thus, animals like lions are very aggressive because of a high amount of nor-adrenalin. Adrenalin-type animals, such as the rabbit, show more fear (Funkenstein, 1957). One reaction of the rabbit in the face of danger is a death-feigning "still" reaction. So too, Hall (1941) was able to breed rats who reacted emotionally and others who reacted unemotionally to an open field test.

Even motives such as hunger may produce apathy, lethargy, and depression at high levels. High levels of hunger, thirst, heat, cold, confinement, and so forth did not typically produce arousal. This could be an evolutionary adaptation. Moderate levels of motivation might have a good chance of being reduced by active seeking. Extremely high levels of motivation would occur in unusual circumstances where survival chances might be enhanced by conserving energy and waiting for the conditions to change.

Therefore, it can be seen that the internal arousal version of the general energizing concept of motivation runs into many of the same difficulties as the older idea of motivation leading to an automatic increase in activity. Motivation—defined as time of deprivation or as a goal-directed sequence of behavior—is not correlated invariably with arousal. Arousal is not a unitary state. Arousal depends on the situation, the particular motive involved, the species, and many other factors. Arousal may be better defined as part of the overall response process. Nevertheless, arousal is also partly related to motivation and may be a useful concept at times. We would take the position that the state of arousal for each motive and each situation must be analyzed carefully. We shall now turn to the relationship between sleep deprivation and arousal.

SLEEP DEPRIVATION
AND AROUSAL

Malmo and Surwillo (1960) have attempted to extend the arousal analysis to sleep deprivation. Making the assumption that the deprivation of sleep operates like other physiological motives, the authors reason that such deprivation should result in physiological arousal and, if the environmental conditions are appropriate, in a facilitation of performance.

In the experiment, three subjects were tested ten times each during separate 60-hour vigils. The main task was an hour of auditory tracking during which EEG, EMG from various muscles, heart rate, respiration, and palmar conductance were recorded. Body sway and pain thresholds were measured at other times. A number of these measures showed changes which led the authors to conclude that the subjects were aroused by sleep deprivation. Thus, in all three subjects there were significant increases in respiration rate, palmar conductance, and muscle tension in an isolated muscle group (a different one for each subject). There was also a decrease in EEG alpha that the authors interpret not as a drifting toward sleep, but as arousal. To support their interpretations they showed that in two subjects, but quite the reverse in the other, there was a decrease in delta waves. Heart rate went up in two cases but down in a third. Pain thresholds went down in all three cases. Body sway showed variable results—one increase, one decrease, and one no change.

In fact, there is a good deal of variability in the results. While the subjects showed muscle tension increases in idiosyncratic muscle groups, they all showed decreases in a muscle of the left forearm. Then there is the subject who showed reversals in heart rate and delta waves. The variability is even more marked when the performance results are considered; one subject showed definite impairment, one slight impairment, and one an improvement. These performance results are related to those on body sway. It seems that there are important individual differences in the degree of arousal produced by a given amount of sleep deprivation.

It is reasonable to conclude from these results that some arousal took place, at least in some individuals. But what is questionable is the variable producing this activation. The authors conclude that ". . . sleep deprivation had the effect of increasing level of activation" (p. 22). There is good reason to believe that other motivations operating in the situation were the cause of the physiological arousal.

To show this, let us consider the situation facing the subject during his hour of testing: the subject was asked to turn a knob to keep a tone from appearing in the earphones he wore. In order to make the situation maximally alerting, the investigators used four motivational devices. First, the subject was required to press a foot pedal at each end of the excursion of the knob. Second, at the end of each trial he was given his results and a comparison with his best score. Third, heater coils connected to the subject's legs were wired into the tracking apparatus so that ". . . whenever the error score became disproportionately high, enough heat was generated by these coils to become actually painful" (p. 6). Fourth, the intensity of the tone in the earphones was proportional to the magnitude of the error.

There is little doubt that the subjects found this a tense situation. One subject was particularly disturbed by the blindfold and had to fight to stay awake. Another reported little catnaps. All the subjects reported increased effort, fatigue, and the usual sleep-deprivation hallucinations. Here, too, the subjects seemed to be in a conflict between the sleep motive and, not only the usual task-oriented motivations to stay awake, but possibly anxiety and frustration due to the methods used to arouse them. The physiological indicators of activation could be explained easily by this emotional factor. It is interesting that Malmo and Surwillo, in attempting to explain the one subject who showed a heart rate decrease, cite evidence that *anxiety* leads to heart rate increases in some people and to decreases in others (Gellhorn, 1953).

Still, one could argue that arousal was due in part to sleep deprivation. After all, the activation theory states specifically that arousal takes place only when the proper environmental stimuli are present. Thus, in the Malmo and Surwillo study, the situation—no matter how painful or anxiety arousing—only had an effect on the measures when the subject was sleep-deprived. Therefore there must be an interaction. But this argument is specious because it assumes a constant level of stimulation. Yes, if the stimulation was the same during high and low sleep deprivation then it would mean an interaction. There is indirect evidence, however, that the "alerting stimulation" increased during sleep deprivation. We know this because the heat stimulus and the tone in the ears were increased during the vigil. Therefore, our conclusion is that there is no evidence that sleep deprivation produces arousal or activation, but the means used to keep the subject alert may, in fact, do so.

A failure of sleep deprivation to produce physiological signs of arousal was reported recently by Ax and Luby (1961) in a study using less alerting conditions. During a vigil of 123 hours, five subjects showed decreases in hand conductance (GSR), muscle tension, body temperature, and hand temperature. Hand conductance and diastolic blood pressure reactions to a pain stimulus decreased in magnitude during sleep deprivation. An increase in respiration and the drop in hand temperature, which appear contradictory, were attributed to metabolic changes also observed and described earlier.

The authors conclude that sleep deprivation results in a marked decrease in arousal or activation. They suggest that there is a progressive fatigue of sympathetic centers. Since they found a reversal in blood pressure response to pain toward the end, they suggest that there is a parasympathetic dominance after about 100 hours. The authors interpret the differences between their study and that of Malmo and Surwillo as due primarily to the task. Their pain stimulus, an electric current to the toe, was probably less painful than Malmo and Surwillo's. Ax and Luby also conclude on the basis of their results that sleep deprivation is not analogous to hunger and thirst. They suggest not classifying sleep as a motive. We shall return to this later.

An experiment by Wilkinson (1961 a, 1962) offers support for the interpretation that activation effects during sleep deprivation are due to factors other than the operation of the sleep drive. Wilkinson gave subjects a task of adding sums for twenty minutes—once with normal sleep and again after 30 to 50 hours of sleep deprivation. During the first 15 minutes no information about results was given, but during the last five minutes the subject was told how long he had taken with each problem and whether the answer was right. In a previous study with a serial reaction task, Wilkinson (1958, 1961 b) showed that providing this sort of information had an incentive effect that counteracted the effects of sleep deprivation. Similarly, with these sums, giving knowledge of results had a beneficial effect; during the first 15 minutes performance after sleep deprivation was considerably poorer than normal, but when knowledge of results was given the difference disappeared. This again demonstrates the importance of motivation, but so far says nothing of arousal.

Wilkinson also measured the tension in a muscle of the arm not used for the addition, both in the sleep and in the no-sleep conditions. The main measure was the extent to which the muscle tension was higher after sleep loss during the performance. The subjects were divided into three groups of four each. Those showing intermediate and extreme difficulty with the sums had no discernible increase in muscle tension during the sleep loss period; the group having least impairment did show the increase. In other words, sleep loss does not result automatically in increased muscle tension, but those individuals capable of increasing their tension show less effects of sleep loss. It should be noted that the subjects maintaining good performance during sleep deprivation accomplished this by unusually high levels of arousal.

What all this means is that the occurrence of arousal during sleep deprivation is a product of motivations competing with the sleep motive. As we have seen, the activation theory does not necessarily predict an increase in various indices of arousal merely as a result of sleep deprivation, but that the increase is potential, or latent, and may be observed during the performance of a task. But Wilkinson's study fulfills the condition; the tension was measured during a performance task and yet two-thirds of the subjects showed no increase. Wilkinson concludes that the augmented muscle tension found in the group of subjects showing good performance is a result of increased effort. Once again, from the point of view presented here, it would seem that the critical motive behind both the physiological arousal and good performance is that strange desire to excel on which all psychological experimenters with human subjects rely. It is the same motive that enabled Wilkinson to get improved performance by giving knowledge of results. It is this motive to excel that is pitted against the sleep motive; if the motive to excel is high enough, as apparently it was in a third of the subjects, or if it can be aroused by knowledge of results, etc., then sleep deprivation will show no performance decrement; if the sleep motive is quantitatively greater than the motive to excel, as it was in two-thirds of the cases, there will be no arousal and an inferior performance.

Wilkinson also noted that when knowledge of results was given, muscle tension increased during both sleep deprivation and the control condition. However, during sleep deprivation the muscle tension increase led to an improvement, while after normal sleep it led to an impairment of performance. The increase in muscle tension increase was greater after normal sleep, so that this fits in with earlier work (Stennett, 1937) that too high a level of EMG may interfere with performance. The moderate rise in EMG during sleep deprivation helped performance. In fact, Wilkinson suggests that sleep deprivation improves efficiency; he found that during sleep deprivation, with knowledge of results, the subjects performed as well as after regular sleep, and with less muscular tension. With no knowledge of results, however, there was no difference in EMG but there was a superiority of performance after regular sleep. Thus, this line of reasoning would lead us to conclude that sleep deprivation leads to more efficiency with knowledge of results but that without knowledge of results subjects are more efficient after normal sleep. It seems to us that the real conclusion from this is that motivation and arousal are separate processes.

Along this line Wilkinson noted other instances when the tie between muscle tension and performance was broken. For instance, during sleep deprivation there was a decline in performance but no significant drop in muscle tension. Wilkinson suggests that the EMG measure (and this might apply to other measures) reflects not arousal in the usual motivational sense, but the effort of maintaining normal arousal and performance during sleep deprivation.

The general muscular changes occurring during sleep deprivation are in the direction of decreased arousal. Kleitman (1963, p. 229) says "Exhaustion and unconquerable sleepiness in man are always accompanied by extreme muscular weakness." Kleitman describes how a sleep-deprived subject drops pencils and spools because of low muscular tonus. This lowered level of muscular tonus is sometimes difficult to measure because of the familiar tendency of sleep-deprived subjects to pull themselves together for tests. However, there is one situation in which it was demonstrated in a complex but ingenious way.

Hand steadiness is a good index of muscular tonus and can be measured by a simple piece of apparatus. The subject is asked to hold a stylus in the holes of a metal plate for a period of time without touching the sides. Hand tremor causes the stylus to touch the sides and this is recorded automatically. Tension increases tremor and relaxation decreases it.

The research studies over the years have yielded apparently contradictory results on the effects of sleep deprivation on hand steadiness. Kleitman (1939) reports a decrease in hand steadiness with 60 hours of deprivation, Edwards (1941) found no change in 100 hours, while an improvement up to 28 hours of deprivation is reported in the *Handbook of Human Engineering Data* (1949). Furthermore Eagles, Halliday, and Redfearn (1953) report a decrease in finger tremor for two subjects during 48 hours of deprivation.

Williams and Lubin (1959) observed that there was muscular relaxation during sleep loss and suspected that it would result in a decrease in hand steadiness. They also noted, however, that later on in sleep loss, during long lapses, muscle tonus in the hand and finger disappeared and caused the hand or finger to drop suddenly. Therefore, they predicted that hand steadiness performance should first improve during sleep deprivation and then deteriorate.

The hypothesis was tested on a single subject undergoing a prolonged sleep-deprivation period. The results were analyzed separately for the smallest hole (2 mm in diameter) and the two largest holes (9 and 10 mm) in a standard hand steadiness apparatus. Contact time in the small hole *decreased* up to 72 hours of sleep deprivation and then *increased* sharply. Contact time on the larger holes was practically zero during the baseline days and the first two days of sleep loss, and then *increased* dramatically. The results confirm the prediction.

Lubin and Williams (1959) suggest that the first effect of sleep loss is to dampen muscular action, but that lapses later produce sudden losses of tonus. The first relaxing effect could be due to the de-activating system in the brain stem that we described earlier. The loss in muscle tonus during lapses is reminiscent of the periods of paradoxical sleep and could be controlled by the pontine mechanism. Or the whole effect could be described simply in terms of increasing muscular relaxation: mild sleep deprivation produces an optimal level of arousal for hand steadiness tests and prolonged sleep deprivation produces too much relaxation.

In any case, the Williams-Lubin hypothesis explains why errors start occurring on the large holes before errors on the small hole. It may also explain the improvement in hand steadiness in some studies and the deterioration in others.

There are two animal experiments relevant to the problem of arousal during sleep deprivation, and they offer contradictory results. The first study was done by Rust (1962) under the direction of Robert Malmo. Rust deprived rats of sleep in an activity wheel apparatus and tested them in a Skinner box bar-pressing apparatus. During testing the animals were mildly hungry and were rewarded for bar-pressing with food. Rats were tested after periods of 0, 12, 24, 36, and 48 hours of sleep deprivation and at another time without sleep deprivation but with a rapid run in the wheel to control for exercise. There was no difference in bar-pressing rate between the sleep-deprived and control conditions. However, variability was greater during sleep deprivation, apparently due to an alternation of activity and inactivity (Rust, personal communication). There is no evidence here that sleep deprivation energized a habit based on hunger.

Rust also measured heart rate during a five-minute rest period in the Skinner box before the bar was inserted, and for twenty minutes during bar-pressing itself. During the rest period heart rate increased with hours of sleep deprivation. During bar-pressing heart rate was also higher than the control for 36 hours of deprivation, and higher still after 48 hours. However, the curious thing is that heart rate during bar-pressing was lower than heart rate during the rest period. Since the animals were removed from the activity wheels just before the rest period it is possible that the heightened heart rate was due to the prolonged enforced wakefulness. Heart rate decreased from the rest period to the bar-pressing period and decreased still further, presumably, during the second half of the bar-pressing period when the animals tended to doze (Rust, personal communication). It is possible that prolonged exercise has a more arousing effect than brief exercise. It is also possible that frustration and irritability increased with sleep deprivation and contributed to the increase in heart rate. In any case, the reason for the arousal in this study is not clear.

Further evidence that sleep deprivation decreases internal tension comes from a study by Webb (1962) using a startle response. Startle is measured by the pressure exerted downward by a rat on a postage scale apparatus when a toy pistol is fired. The startle response is increased by conditioned fear or hunger. Fear also intensifies the GSR reaction to a neutral stimulus in human subjects (see Brown, 1961, pp. 148-155). In Webb's study rats were kept awake for 27 continuous days in the Licklider-Bunch water wheel apparatus. The startle response was measured each day. The sleep-deprived animals showed a significant *decrease* in the startle response over the 27 days; the experimental group was also significantly lower than a matched control group that showed an increasing startle. Thus sleep deprivation leads to a depression of the startle response or the underlying autonomic reactions. This is in line with a lowered arousal during sleep deprivation.

The results as a whole suggest that sleep deprivation leads to a lowered state of arousal—a de-arousal. This is seen in measures of autonomic functioning and muscular tension. An aroused state may be observed in a sleep-deprived subject under certain conditions, but this seems to be due to competing motivations and to the methods used to keep the sleep-deprived subject awake and alert.

THE NATURE OF PERFORMANCE
LAPSES DURING SLEEP
DEPRIVATION

So far we have seen that autonomic measures and muscular tension suggest a de-arousal effect of sleep deprivation, but we have said little about arousal in the brain. The EEG shows a tendency to drift into a synchronized pattern during sleep deprivation if the person is not disturbed. In fact, the subject tends to fall asleep (Kleitman, 1963). As usual, though, the person can pull himself together for tests. A more interesting question, then, is what changes take place during test periods as sleep deprivation progresses. Is the subject able to continue to be alert during examinations? For this reason we will discuss the EEG results in the context of the lapses that occur during sleep deprivation.

It will be recalled that lapses are periods of no response which increase in frequency and length during sleep loss. Depending on the characteristics of the task, lapses may interfere with performance. But what actually happens during the lapse? Is it a period of physiological arousal or not? The studies of Wilkinson, and Ax and Luby, described in the previous section, show that the effect of sleep deprivation is in the direction of de-arousal during performance. These investigators, however, did not examine the state of the organism during the lapses per se.

With sleep deprivation the most logical assumption is that de-arousal (actual sleep) occurs during a lapse. Several of the earlier studies on sleep deprivation report behavioral observations suggesting brief periods of sleep that might well correspond to lapses. For example, Katz and Landis (1935) report periods of inadvertent sleep during their subject's long vigil. Laslett (1928) talks of cycles of "sleep seizures." Edwards (1941) describes "waves of feeling very sleepy."

Changes in the electroencephalograph during sleep deprivation also suggest periods of synchronization. Kleitman (1939) describes studies in which subjects were monitored with an EEG after long periods of wakefulness. The records show a drifting in and out of sleep: when the subject made an effort to concentrate, the EEG included fast waves but the subject could not sustain his effort and as he lost his count, for example, the EEG showed a drifting back to slow delta waves. Of considerable interest is the observation that the subject was not aware of having slept.

Furthermore, EEG changes suggesting sleep are associated with disturbances of performance. In a study mentioned earlier, Bjerner (1949) found that extremely long reaction times during sleep loss were associated with drops in the EEG alpha rhythm. He called these *lapses* and felt that they represented brief periods of sleep.

The Walter Reed group found a consistent decline in the carefully measured amount of alpha frequencies with hours of sleep loss (Armington and Mitnick, 1959). Perusal of the records suggested that periods of little alpha showed wave forms suggestive of drowsiness. These periodic depressions of alpha were associated with errors of omission on the auditory version of the Continuous Performance Test (Williams, Lubin, and Goodnow, 1959). Using the same apparatus, Mirsky and Cardon (1962) confirmed their result, finding EEG waves to be slower and of higher amplitude during errors of omission than during correct responses.

Finally, Williams, Granda, Jones, Lubin, and Armington (1962) performed the definitive experiment in this area. An auditory discrimination reaction time test was used with soldiers deprived of sleep for up to 64 hours. The frequency of EEG waves was measured and proved to be an excellent predictor of performance. When the subjects were relaxed and not stimulated they showed a tendency to drift into a drowsy state with the EEG showing a B stage in the Loomis system. When this was continued the subjects became even sleepier and showed delta waves. On the other hand, during performance of the task the subjects hovered between A and B EEG stages. Most of the subjects showed a bi-modal distribution of EEG frequencies—alternate runs of alpha and theta (4-7 per second) waves. Performance errors occurred during the theta waves. Actual delta waves were rarely seen during the task. Thus, it appears that lapses consist of periods of drowsiness rather than highly synchronized sleep.

Mirsky and Cardon (1962) also used two other physiological measures—respiration and finger pulse. During natural sleep, cardiovascular changes result in increased finger pulse volume and volume change. Respiration becomes slower and shallower (see also Kleitman, 1939). Errors in the Continuous Performance Task were accompanied by these sleeplike vascular and respiratory changes. Williams et al. (1962) confirmed the finger pulse volume finding with their auditory discrimination reaction time task.

Thus, it seems that the lapses occurring during sleep deprivation consist of brief periods of some degree of sleep involving physiological de-activation. Fantasy material might also emerge, however. Thus Morris, Williams, and Lubin (1960) found that dreams, illusions, and hallucinations sometimes appeared during lapses. Williams, Lubin, and Goodnow (1959) are also reluctant to identify lapses with sleep because lapses also appear in conditions having little to do with sleep, such as hypoxia and psychosis. Wilkinson (1959) adds noise, heat, anoxia, drugs, and brain damage. Wilkinson points out, however, that the precise effects may be different: noise and heat, for example, have more effect on accuracy, while sleep loss has more effect on activity level.

The different kinds of behavior that can fill a lapse are most clearly illustrated by Pepler's (1959) study of sleep and heat. Both one night of sleep loss and a 100° F. temperature resulted in decrements in a tracking task and a serial choice task. These decrements involved time and were the sort easily explained by lapses. However, the two conditions did not show an interaction. Furthermore, the types of disturbed reactions differed. With sleep, pauses were associated with a failure to respond, but with warmth the pauses were followed by incorrect responses. In other words, sleep deprivation led to a decrease in activity or arousal, while heat had an energizing effect, albeit on incorrect responses as well as on correct ones. This is further evidence that sleep tends toward de-arousal.

Corcoran (1962) and Wilkinson (1963) have studied the effect of noise on performance of the serial reaction task during sleep deprivation. Corcoran found that noise reduces the number of performance gaps during sleep deprivation and Wilkinson found that the number of errors was reduced. The interesting thing is that individually both noise and sleep deprivation impair performance, but acting together they have a beneficial effect. The explanation seems to be that while sleep deprivation tends to reduce arousal, noise increases arousal. Together they produce a more optimal level of arousal for performance.

One way of understanding all these results is to assume that lapses consist of responses interfering with task performance. In the case of fatigue, Bills (1935, 1937) found that blocks were enhanced when competing responses were available. In fatigue, heat, noise, and similar conditions, the competing response most frequently is an incorrect reaction involving arousal; in hypoxia or psychosis, it may be delusional ideation. Some sort of escape fantasy may be involved in all of these frustrating conditions.

In contrast to these other motivating variables, the lapses of sleep deprivation consist of periods of drowsiness or de-arousal. Less frequently, dreamlike ideation may occur, but this is also a stage of sleep. Lapses are somewhat reminiscent of the findings on delayed response covered earlier. Many responses can fill the gap between stimulus and response; drowsiness occurs more frequently when the organism is sleep deprived or when no other response is available.

SUMMARY

Several theorists equate motivation with general energization. This may appear as an effect on general activity or on internal arousal.

Spontaneous activity is frequently assumed to be a function of motivation. Hunger, thirst, sex and other motivating conditions sometimes increase general activity. Nevertheless, the relationship is limited because activity tends to: decrease at high motivational levels; be influenced by learned environmental stimuli; be intrinsically rewarding and thus independent of other motives; and vary with particular species, strains, and motivational states. Thus a definition of motivation does not necessarily imply a facilitation of activity.

Sleep is relative inactivity, and the direction of sleep deprivation is toward general inactivity. Several experiments do show an increase in activity or social behavior during sleep deprivation. These results, however, reflect the motivation of the subjects to maintain wakefulness during the experiment.

While motives do not necessarily produce an increase in overt activity, they may still arouse the organism to a state of alert readiness for action. This has been called activation or arousal. There is an inverted U relationship with performance; activation increasingly facilitates overt behavior up to some optimal point and then interferes with it. This has been shown for a few motives. However, arousal and motivation are not perfectly correlated. Arousal depends on a number of other factors and may be thought of as part of the response process. In addition, arousal is not a simple unitary state. The relation with arousal has to be determined for each individual motive.

Some studies suggest that sleep deprivation results in arousal but the arousal found in these studies seems to be due to procedures designed to keep the subject awake and alert. Sleep deprivation itself leads to a lowered state of arousal or, in other words, a de-arousal. This has been shown for autonomic functions and muscular tension.

The performance lapses, which increase in frequency and duration during sleep loss, appear to be actually periods of drowsiness. Various signs of de-arousal—EEG slowing down, respiratory and vascular changes—are associated with these lapses and errors in performance. Other motives also produce performance lapses, but while the lapse may consist of incorrect responses in these other cases, during sleep deprivation there is a greater tendency to fail to respond. Thus, sleep-deprivation lapses consist of de-arousal pauses during which drowsiness or sleep occurs.

In general, one can say that motivation bears a complex relationship to arousal and activity. However, whereas most motivational variables tend to produce some degree of arousal, sleep deprivation leads to a de-arousal. We shall return to this point later.

CHAPTER 7

Personality Adjustment During Sleep Deprivation

The purpose of this chapter is to relate sleep deprivation to personality variables. Personality is a complex field of psychology, so that it is difficult to say exactly how a motive should relate to such variables. Nevertheless, enough is known to make it possible to determine whether or not sleep deprivation plays a role in the adjustment of the human personality that is at least roughly equivalent to that played by sex, hunger, thirst, and other physiological motives. One approach is to describe the effects of physiological motivation on personality and compare them with changes during sleep deprivation. The following will be covered: general social and emotional behavior, frustration-aggression, psychotic phenomena, repressive mechanisms, and individual personality differences.

GENERAL SOCIAL
AND EMOTIONAL BEHAVIOR

The general social and emotional consequences of a number of physiological motives have been studied experimentally and naturalistically. Thus, for example, prolonged famine, lasting months or years, has widespread effects on human behavior (Keys et al., 1950). If famine continues long enough, it

211

causes a loosening of social ties, a decrease in moral standards, and an increase in emotional disturbances. Families are abandoned, prostitution increases, and thievery becomes widespread. Migrations, riots, and rebellions occur. The individual at first feels irritable, quarrelsome, and fault-finding. Later he feels depressed, apathetic, and lethargic as he becomes weaker. On rare occasions cannibalism and murder have been reported. Most of these effects have been reported in natural famines. Limited laboratory experiments enable us to observe these changes more carefully.

The well-known Minnesota Semi-Starvation study (Keys et al., 1950) has provided a wealth of information on the psychological effects of prolonged partial deprivation of food. The performance results were mentioned earlier. Possibly, the most dramatic effect of semi-starvation was on the emotional reactions of the subjects. They became moody and apprehensive. The MMPI showed an increase in depression, anxiety, and concern over bodily functions. The general mode of reaction was severe apathy interspersed with outbursts of hostility. Subjects felt a loss of ambition, self-discipline, and social interest. Their conversation lost its sparkle and humor. Tests showed an increase in social introversion and a decrease in social leadership, which paralleled an increased dependence on the staff for group decisions.

The symptoms of apathy, depression, anxiety, and irritability have been observed, in one degree or another, with several other physiological motives. Specific dietary deficiencies—such as thiamine (Brozek, 1957), pantothenic acid (Bean et al., 1955), fat and protein (Brozek and Taylor, 1958), and others (Wohl and Goodhart, 1955)—produce the same sort of emotional change. Thirst is reported to exaggerate temperamental pecularities: serious people become "somber" and normally cheerful people exhibit a "hollow vivacity" (Marriott, 1950). Extremes of temperature also produce the familiar depression and irritability: something called tropical neurasthenia has been described (Reed, 1942), while a comparable syndrome is found in the arctic (Blair et al., 1947). In the tropics, naval personnel exhibit lethargy, poor concentration, memory difficulty, and a reduction in work capacity (Ellis, 1953). Emotional changes include anxiety, depression, irritability, and apathy, while on the social level a lowered sense of responsibility is noted. Oxygen deficiency results in marked alterations of mood: these include irritability, lassitude, and anger, or may go to the other extreme of exhilaration, euphoria, and boisterousness (McFarland, 1952).

Since all of these motivational conditions involve metabolic functions, it may appear that the reactions are due to physical weakness or a disturbance of brain chemistry. While these factors may be involved in severe deficiencies, they do not account for all of the results. For example, nonmetabolic motivational conditions—such as noise (Stevens, 1946; Plutchik, 1959), poor illumination (Tinker, 1949), glaring light (Tinker, 1949; Woodson, 1956), and sensory deprivation (Solomon et al., 1961)—result in tension, irritability, or anxiety. Apathy and irritability are frequent reactions to confinement in prisoner-of-war or concentration camps (Strassman et al., 1956; Bakis, 1952; Frankl, 1954). Therefore, affective disturbance may be thought of as related to strong motivational states of many kinds.

A question that arises is, how can there be so many different kinds of emotional reactions? For example, anxiety and apathy seem like opposites, while euphoria and depression are certainly incompatible. Individual personality differences account for some of these discrepancies and will be discussed later. Another determinant of some importance is the length of deprivation. For example, in the case of famine or experimental food deprivation, the aroused emotions—such as anger, rebelliousness, and apprehensiveness—seem to be greatest during the early stages, while the apathetic depression, interspersed with irritability, prevails later (Keys et al., 1950).

Now we turn to the social and emotional effects of sleep deprivation. The concentration difficulties experienced by sleep-deprived subjects have been described earlier in connection with learning and performance. Prolonged wakefulness produces many other affective disturbances, quite similar to those found with other motives. Anxiety, apprehensiveness, and nervousness have been reported (Robinson and Herrmann, 1922; Nichols, 1956; Morris and Singer, 1961). Furthermore, the increase in reported anxiety—in addition to changes in sleepiness, hostility, and task involvement—was related, in about half of the comparisons, to chronic anxiety level, as measured by the Taylor and Saslow anxiety scales (Nichols, 1956).

The Rochester study (Nichols, 1956; Laties, 1961) also showed that a combination of secobarbital and amphetamine had a beneficial effect on both affect and performance. The medication decreased hostility and depression, increased social interest and task involvement, and showed a trend toward decreasing anxiety. Furthermore, the effectiveness of the drug combination was greater with chronically anxious subjects. Nichols suggests that amphetamine decreased the need to sleep, while secobarbital reduced the anxiety in the situation. The other affective changes might be dependent on the anxiety level. Thus the results support the idea that sleep deprivation produces anxiety. It should be noted, however, that the anxiety evoked depends on the personality of the subject. This suggests that anxiety involves many personal concerns such as fear of failure, need to do well on the tasks, and fear of bodily harm.

According to Morris and Singer (1961), anxiety appeared only at the beginning of the deprivation and centered around fears of possible deleterious physiological effects of lack of sleep. Morris and Singer also found that the very first group of subjects studied at Walter Reed experienced the greatest degree of anxiety. This was probably related to the overconcern of a staff inexperienced with sleep deprivation. On the basis of the literature, the staff had been worried about psychotic reactions, circulatory effects, and even death. Thus, the anxiety seemed to be motivated by a concern over general health rather than an innate reaction to sleep deprivation *per se*. Some of the anxiety in semi-starvation may have been similarly motivated (Keys et al., 1950).

Therefore the arousal implied by the reports of anxiety during sleep deprivation may not be an integral part of the physiological reaction. It is possible that some goal-oriented arousal involving anxious feelings could arise, but this would be learned. Most of the arousal seems to be related to other motives—ego-involvement or concern over physical health. The prevailing mood during sleep deprivation is apathy and depression. This is akin to Selye's (1956) stage of resistance to stress. Like Selye's stage, the depressed mood may be punctured by moments of elation or irritability. Nevertheless, the prevailing mood fits in with the idea that sleep deprivation results in a general de-arousal.

Many studies report symptoms of depression (Weiskotten and Ferguson, 1930; Edwards, 1941; Tyler, 1947; Laties, 1961). The irritability, often associated with depression, is also observed frequently, but will be dealt with in more detail in the following section on frustration and aggression. On the other side of the affective coin, Edwards (1941) reports euphoria, Robinson and Herrmann (1922) describe a mildly intoxicated state in which subjects talked rapidly with an absurd emphasis. Tyler (1947) mentions irrelevant laughter and conversation; and Morris and Singer (1961) give a label of "autistic" to bursts of "prolonged uproarious laughter."

Sleep-deprived subjects are also described as apathetic (Tyler, 1947; Eagles, Halliday, and Redfearn, 1953) and lethargic (Weiskotten and Ferguson, 1930). The concentration difficulties prevent sustained interest in activities and lead to a listless shifting: "Typically, a sleep-deprived S would get into a card game, get tired of it after a while, get up and walk aimlessly about or sit for a few minutes, then join in another game or conversation, possibly with different Ss, and so on" (Murray et al., 1959, p. 234). While overt anxiety dropped out by the last day (Morris and Singer, 1961), apathy seemed to increase: one category of social behavior—passive non-participation—is clearly relevant to apathy; this increased consistently during sleep deprivation (Murray et al., 1959). In this regard, sleep deprivation parallels hunger.

Social interaction suffers during sleep loss. Carmichael, Kennedy, and Mead (1949) found a decline in activity, talkativeness, and sociability during card games scheduled on each day of a sleep-deprivation period. The game on the third day was canceled because of lack of interest. On the other hand, Murray, et al. (1959), found no decline in the games category; in fact, there was a tendency for this to increase. This writer, however, observed the card games in the Walter Reed study and found them qualitatively similar to the Carmichael et al. description.

One difference between the studies is that the Carmichael et al. games were scheduled regularly by the staff with some pressure to stay in the game; the Walter Reed free-choice situation enabled the subjects to leave and return to a game. It should also be re-called that social conversation increased in the Walter Reed studies, but this was listless and uninvolved. It would seem that games and listless conversation provided a minimal amount of stimulation that was helpful in staying awake, provided the person could shift activities whenever overwhelmed by a wave of sleepiness.

Other social processes are disturbed by sleep loss. A decrease in social initiative, as determined by self-ratings and objective observations, was found by Laties (1961). This was offset by the secobarbital-amphetamine medication. Schein (1957) found that the lapses of sleep deprivation interfered with a social communi-cation task. In line with the decreased social initiative, there are several reports of increased suggestibility in connection with sleep. Barber (1956) reports hypnotic-like reactions in subjects given commands during light sleep. Sleep deprivation is often used to aid "brain washing" (Sargant, 1957; Hinkle and Wolff, 1956). Unfortunately, several attempts to show increased sug-gestibility, made by Dr. Seymour Fisher during the Walter Reed sleep-loss studies, were unsuccessful. Finally, it should be kept in mind that social factors, such as group morale, can offset many of the effects of sleep deprivation (Laties, 1961).

The apathetic reaction can be viewed as an aspect of the de-arousal during sleep loss that was discussed earlier. Hunger and confinement seem to involve the same thing. Energy is con-served, fatigue reduced, and hostile conflict is avoided by a modulation of affect. In the prisoner-of-war situation the apathy was not accompanied by the guilt of a psychopathological depres-sion (Strassman et al., 1956). In the sleep- and food-deprivation studies, the depression was also probably not of the guilt-ridden type—an item analysis of the MMPI and Check List results should bear this out. Furthermore, it should be noted that, in the POW situation, really deep hopeless apathy was maladaptive, often leading to death. The apathy and depression of the sleep- and food-deprivation studies might be best characterized as a withdrawal and narrowing of interests, a partially successful damping of emotional reactions, and an emphasis on simply existing.

The social effects of sleep loss can be seen as an extension and consequence of the apathetic adjustment on the emotional level. Social interest and leadership make too many demands on the deprived individual and are avoided. Social spontaneity simply drops out. Only minimal forms of social interaction are possible and even these cannot be sustained. Everything is subordinated to the primary problem of getting through to the end of the study.

FRUSTRATION AND AGGRESSION

In the previous section, one of the emotional reactions to deprivation mentioned was aggression. Since this is specifically relevant to an important area of personality—frustration-aggression—it will be examined in more detail. The frustration-aggression hypothesis (Dollard et al., 1939; Miller, 1941) states that blocking a goal-response, in an on-going, motivated, behavioral sequence, results in an instigation to aggression. Such aggression may become overt or it may be inhibited by competing responses or punishment. Since most, although not all, deprivations result in the arousal of anticipatory goal-reactions that are not consummated, they can be assumed to involve frustration.

A great variety of physiological, situational, and social variables are involved in frustration and the expression of aggression (see Stacey and DeMartino, 1958, Section 5). Nevertheless, physiological motives serve as one possible source of frustration. In the studies mentioned in the preceding section, one form of aggression—irritability—has been associated with the deprivation of food (Keys et al., 1950), thiamine (Brozek, 1957), water (Wolf, 1956), oxygen (McFarland, 1952), and sensory stimulation (Solomon et al., 1961), as well as with adverse environmental conditions such as noise (Stevens, 1946), heat (Ellis, 1953), and cold Blair et al., 1947). Thus we may conclude that irritability is a frequent consequence of these motivating conditions.

The specific frustration is probably related to the experimental or natural conditions preventing gratification or escape.

Overt aggression is rarely reported in experimental situations; the irritability is usually limited to verbal reactions, pushing in line, or unreasonableness. This is most likely due to the social constraints and basic trust in the experimenters. In natural situations, however, the aggression may become clearly manifest. As mentioned earlier, for example, famine may lead to riots, rebellions, and an increase in crime (Keys et al., 1950). Hunger may have greater effects than fear. For example, social disorganization and anti-social behavior was not shown in Germany at the end of World War II, during the most devastating and prolonged bombing attacks, until the transportation system was so disrupted that famine set in (Janis, 1951). Under the right social conditions, overt aggression and anti-social behavior can occur. It should be kept in mind, however, that the aggression is goal-directed—the riots and rebellions are against a government in whom the people have lost faith; the prostitution and thievery, which are the main crimes involved, are a desperate means of adapting to the situation.

Sleep deprivation might be expected to lead to aggression. Sleep deprivation would be expected to elicit the goal response of sleeping or an anticipatory drowsiness and nodding, depending on the hours of sleep deprivation and the time of day. Conditions preventing the goal response or the anticipatory response would constitute frustrations. According to Dollard et al., this should produce some form of aggression. Since there are strong social sanctions against overt physical aggression, verbal hostility and irritability might be expected to occur.

Sleep deprivation traditionally produces an increase in irritability; it is a classic symptom. Irritability during sleep deprivation, in some degree, has been reported by Weiskotten and Ferguson (1930), Freeman (1932), Katz and Landis (1935), Kleitman (1939, p. 304), Sears, Hovland, and Miller (1940), Edwards (1941), Tyler (1947, 1955), Nowlis (1953, p. 129), Nichols (1956), Murray et al. (1959), Laties (1961), and several others. Evidence of increased hostility in drawings has been found in the Yale group (Sears, Hovland, and Miller, 1940). Overt aggression is not common—only Tyler (1947) reports this.

While there is general agreement that some form of aggression is found with sleep deprivation, there is enough inconsistency in the degree and type to warrant a close examination of the data. It is possible that hours of sleep deprivation determines the quantity and quality of aggression. On the other hand, other factors may be more important. For example, Eagles, Halliday, and Redfearn (1953) report no signs of irritability in two subjects kept awake for 48 hours. They believe that this was "because our subjects were not pushed or cajoled in any way" (p. 48). In many of these studies so many social factors are uncontrolled and unreported that it may be impossible to evaluate them. Nevertheless, it seems worthwhile to try to make some sense out of these observations. Let us look at the four studies containing the most relevant information. They range from severe to very mild in degree of aggression reported.

The first study is the one done at the California Institute of Technology by Tyler (1947, 1955), involving several hundred young soldiers, marines, and civilians kept awake for as long as 112 hours. Most of the men showed extreme irritability. In addition, several subjects became aggressive, provoked fights, and had to be restrained. These cases appeared to suffer a transient psychosis with paranoid content. Was this all due to the loss of sleep? The methods used by Tyler to keep the men awake were severe and may have provided additional sources of frustration. The program of constant activity used was that ordinarily reserved for parachutists and other elite troops. It included sports, tactical problems, and night marches as long as 35 miles. The over-all frustration of the study is, perhaps, best illustrated by the 22% drop-out rate.

The well-known Yale study of sleep deprivation (Sears, Hovland, and Miller, 1940) involved just 24 hours of sleep deprivation with six college students. The aggression remained mostly on the verbal level, but was quite strong and directed at the experimenters. One subject produced spontaneous drawings of violently dismembered "psychologists." In this study, other frustrations were deliberately added to sleep deprivation: smoking was forbidden for Ss but not for Es, an E "forgot" to bring promised games, and an E who went out to get a hot breakfast "failed" to return. After the study, the Ss reported that the broken promises were the most severe frustrations, while the sleep deprivation made them more susceptible to such irritations.

The Rochester study (Nichols, 1956; Laties, 1961) employed 16 undergraduates tested on two normal evenings and again on two evenings after a night without sleep—about 37 hours of sleep deprivation. No significant increase in overt aggression or hostility during sleep deprivation was reported by reliable observers sitting behind a one-way vision screen. On the other hand, an adjective check list and a rating scale, filled out by each subject, showed an increase in subjectively experienced hostile feelings. A preliminary study (Nowlis, 1953) suggested an increase in hostility on the Rosenzweig Picture Frustration Test, but subsequent analysis attributed this to a re-test phenomenon (Nichols, 1956). The methods used to keep the subjects awake were mild: they were allowed to read, talk, or play games, as well as attend classes during the day. Some of the group tasks (ball and spiral, ring and wire) were frustrating, but group morale was high. In this milder situation covert hostility was aroused, but no overt aggression appeared.

Finally, the Walter Reed study (Williams et al., 1959; Murray et al., 1959; Morris and Singer, 1961) represents a low point in aggression. Twenty-five young soldiers were kept awake for 98 hours with very little hostility observed. What little irritability occurred was in response to nudging when a subject appeared to be dozing off. A specially selected series of TAT cards, representing different degrees of hostile pull, showed no differences between the experimental group and their matched controls in hostile content after 86 hours of sleep deprivation (Murray, 1959). A battery of projective tests (the Rosenzweig, Iflund, Glad, and Rorschach tests) was given three times during the deprivation period with no indication of increased hostility (Loveland and Singer, 1959). The nearly total lack of aggression is probably related to the gentle methods used to keep the men awake: games and snacks were available; nurses rubbed swollen feet; staff members, including officers, helped the men stay awake by walking, playing games, and talking to them; except for the occasional nudges, no coercive or hostile techniques were employed. In addition, Morris and Singer (1961) think that the staff sensed aggression coming up and headed it off by diversion. The general morale of the group was high, with no one dropping out.

The results of these four studies are summarized in Table IV. The frustration from sleep deprivation alone does not seem to account for the aggression observed: the 24-hour Yale deprivation produced more aggression than the 37 hours at Rochester or the 98 hours at Walter Reed; the degree of deprivation is roughly comparable in the CIT and Walter Reed studies, but with markedly different results. Other sources of frustration in the experimental situation—social as well as physical—seem to be more closely related to aggression. General frustration seems to be greatest in the CIT study, next in the Yale one, then the Rochester, with the Walter Reed experiment as a low point; degree of aggression follows this.

It is more difficult to evaluate the possible operation of social inhibition or facilitation of aggression from the written reports. No actual punishment of aggression was used by any of the experimenters. Nevertheless, it would seem that positive social feelings would operate to balance out hostile feelings and produce inhibition. There was little warmth apparent in the CIT or Yale studies; in fact, the behavior of the staff in maintaining strict discipline or introducing frustrations may have justified a certain amount of direct hostility. Furthermore, men who became overtly aggressive in the CIT study were allowed to sleep—this may have encouraged instrumental aggression in a few subjects. In contrast to these facilitory effects, the high morale and friendly atmosphere in the Rochester and Walter Reed studies probably counteracted open aggression. The need for group cooperation in the Rochester study made inhibition of hostility almost mandatory. In the Walter Reed experiment, the staff tended to anticipate and divert hostility. These variables would tend to inhibit the overt expression of hostility.

In general, the degree of aggression observed in sleep-deprivation studies can be seen as a function of three interacting variables: frustration due to the blocking of sleep responses;

TABLE IV DEGREE OF FRUSTRATION AND AGGRESSION DURING SLEEP-DEPRIVATION STUDIES

STUDY AT	SLEEP FRUSTRATION (HOURS DEPRIVED)	OTHER SOURCES OF FRUSTRATION	SOCIAL INHIBITION OR FACILITATION OF AGGRESSION	RESULTING AGGRESSION
California Institute of Technology	112	Paratroop-type training, military discipline, 35-mile night marches	Authoritarian methods focus aggression on staff with some justification, aggression usually led to removal from study: effect was facilitory	Widespread irritability, overt aggression, unprovoked fights, paranoid symptoms, 22% drop-out
Yale	24	No smoking by Ss, broken promises	Experimenters elicited direct aggression by consciously frustrating actions, experimenters studiously avoided counter-aggression: effect was facilitory	Verbal attacks on Es, drawing of mutilated psychologists
Rochester	37	Frustrating tasks, otherwise gentle	High group morale, need for group cooperation in performing tasks: effect was inhibitory	No overt signs of aggression, but subjective feelings of hostility
Walter Reed	98	Effort made to eliminate frustration, but Ss nudged at times	Friendly equalitarian atmosphere, staff diverted impending aggression: effect was inhibitory	Irritability only to nudging, no overt aggression, no hostility on projective tests, no drop-out

frustration due to experimental procedures; and situational factors inhibiting or facilitating the overt manifestations of aggression. Much of the hostility reported in earlier studies, and attributed to sleep deprivation itself, may have been produced by other sources of frustration or facilitated by the social situation.

It would be erroneous, however, to conclude that sleep deprivation contributes nothing to the frustration. For example, in animal studies, where the operation of social factors would be less marked, aggression still occurs during sleep deprivation. Kleitman (1939) reports irritability and viciousness in sleep-deprived dogs. An attempt to keep groups of rats awake on a community treadmill by Licklider and Bunch (1946) resulted in extreme irritability leading to fighting and death. This was largely because the rats tended to bunch together and climb on one another's backs, making it even more difficult to nap. Most of the rats on a 24-hour-a-day, terminal schedule died from fighting. Attacks were precipitated by slight physical contacts but were not always directed against the actual offender. In his study of 27 days of complete sleep deprivation, Webb (1962) conducted an aggression test in which pairs of experimental or control animals were observed for 10 minutes. During the last few days immediate and sustained fighting broke out in the experimental pairs, but not in the controls. This was not without some stimulus control, however. After one experimental animal died, his partner —who had been aggressive—was paired with a control and thereafter ceased fighting. It should also be noted that the aggression test followed the measure of startle reaction to pistol shots and a sleep latency determination, both of which may have produced some frustration.

The results in the animal studies bear certain similarities to the kind of irritability noted in the Walter Reed studies. While every effort was made to reduce social sources of frustration, mild irritability was provoked by the nudges used to arouse the subject when he appeared to be on the verge of falling asleep. Nevertheless, even this frustration, which seems so closely related to the simple desire to go to sleep, gets involved with the individual's personal and social motives. For example, the irritability often took the form of an indignant denial that sleep had occurred. Kleitman (1939, p. 304) reports similar results, mentioning resentment on the part of the subject at being distrusted. Still, at least part of the frustration could reasonably be attributed to an interference with the responses leading to sleep.

The literature sometimes gives the impression that the increase in irritability during sleep deprivation is diffuse and totally generalized, but our analysis suggests that the irritability is not quite that indiscriminate. For example, for most of the subjects in the Walter Reed study, the irritability was confined to the nudging. Complaints about food, water, etc., were not widespread. Sometimes complaints seemingly unrelated turned out to be connected with sleep: one man complained about people peering to see what book he was reading; actually, he was using the book to prevent others from seeing him close his eyes, so they approached to make sure he was awake (Morris and Singer, 1961). Sleep-deprived animals, in the Licklider and Bunch study, showed aggression to other animals climbing on top of them and preventing sleep; the fact that the wrong rat was sometimes attacked was probably due to the crowded conditions. In the Webb study, a non-sleep-deprived rat did not elicit fighting, nor was the pistol shot reported as having aroused aggression. While aggression may not be effective in the situation, it is relevant to the motive.

Therefore we see that irritability, hostility, and sometimes overt aggression during sleep deprivation is due to a combination of the frustration of various social motives and the frustration of goal responses and anticipatory goal responses related to sleeping.

PSYCHOTIC PHENOMENA

Delusions, hallucinations, and other severe psychopathological symptoms have been observed in many states of extreme physiological need. In some cases, a confusional psychosis appears to be due to a direct impairment of brain metabolism; the delusions and hallucinations resulting from severe niacin deficiency would be an example of this (Wohl and Goodhart, 1955). In other cases, the psychological conflict and frustration may play a large role; for instance, the subject in the Minnesota Semi-Starvation experiment who developed a transitory manic psychosis (Keys et al., 1950).

Physiological conditions that may produce psychotic symptoms include famine (Keys et al., 1950), thirst (Wolf, 1956), salt depletion (Marriott, 1950), a decrease in oxygen (McFarland, 1952), and sensory deprivation (Bexton et al., 1954; Freedman and Greenblatt, 1960). The symptoms include the wish-fulfilling hallucinations, such as the mirage in severe thirst, and delusions, such as the fear of being executed of the salt-depleted soldier in India. While the lack of food, vitamins, water, salt, and oxygen are very much tied up with metabolism, sensory deprivation does not seem to fit this category. Thus, it would be inappropriate to conclude that only those conditions interfering with brain metabolism produce psychosis.

The sensory deprivation studies are particularly relevant to sleep deprivation. In the classical study (Bexton et al., 1954), subjects were put in a room in which stimuli were absent or constant. Among other things, the subjects reported visual disturbances that were at first innocuous, but at times appeared to be on the level of hallucinations. They would "see" dots of light, white lines, etc. Later, the patterns seemed like designs on wallpaper. Finally, in some subjects there were integrated scenes, e.g., a procession of squirrels. They included sound and touch at times. One man had a feeling of being hit in the arm by little pellets from a miniature rocket ship he saw. Some of the milder perceptual difficulties persisted after the experiment.

There are a number of explanations for these phenomena (Solomon et al., 1961; Fiske and Maddi, 1961). A change in brain function may be involved, but not necessarily a biochemical malfunctioning. A change in the balance between the Reticular Activating System and the cortex has been suggested (Lindsley, 1961). This change in balance might also take place between the Reticular Activating and Sleep Systems. Diffuse light produces more imagery than total darkness. Hallucinations are not under the control of the Ss; they appear and reappear. Sensory deprivation subjects seem to "slip into a dream-like transitional state between sleeping and waking which makes coherent thinking difficult . . ." (Freedman et al., 1961). This sounds similar to the lapses of sleep deprivation.

Phenomena of a psychotic type have been reported in a large number of sleep-deprivation studies. To begin with, Gilbert and Patrick, in the original sleep-deprivation study in 1897, describe several hallucinations. These were mostly of a neutral emotional tone (e.g., swarms of particles), but one S had a dream-like experience in which a man was being hung. Visual illusions—perhaps a more accurate term for most of the experiences—have been reported by a number of experimenters over the years (Laslett, 1928; Weiskotten and Ferguson, 1930; Katz and Landis, 1935; Kleitman, 1939; Edwards, 1941; and Tyler, 1947).

In addition to the visual disturbances, several authors describe their subjects as being in a state of general confusion, with disorientation, incoherent speech, and illogical thought (especially Robinson and Herrmann, 1922; Weiskotten and Ferguson, 1930; and Edwards, 1941). Several cases in which paranoid delusions occurred have been reported: the Katz and Landis (1935) subject felt that the experimenter was persecuting him; Tyler (1947) mentions a subject who developed the idea that he was on a secret mission for the President. In an experimental study of a fall-out shelter (Altman et al., 1960), a man assumed a leadership role, and in his zeal, went without sleep for most of three days. He then became suspicious and developed the idea that he was being radiated. The staff felt that the lack of sleep contributed to this adjustment difficulty. Such fully developed delusions are rare, however.

Incidental observations have been made in connection with talkathons, marathons, and similar contests in which disc jockeys and others try to stay awake to break a record or get a prize. Brauchi and West (1959) describe two competitors who stayed awake for 168 hours. Both exhibited bizarre behavior, but one in particular became overtly psychotic and was hospitalized for four months. Cappon and Banks (1960) studied 20 individuals who had to keep awake for 88 hours to win a cash prize. As the hours went by, more and more subjects reported changes in perception of time, space, and their own bodies. After about 64 hours, their perceptual distortions began to be emotionally disturbing. Of course, many individuals volunteering for this sort of thing often have some adjustment difficulties in their regular lives.

In a recent sleep-deprivation study, Bliss, Clark, and West (1959) obtained further information about hallucinations. They report visual effects ranging from minor disturbances to hallucinations, such as seeing jets of water rising from the floor. Time judgments also changed in the wish-fulfilling direction. During informal conversation the subjects showed some mental confusion. The authors also report on two clinical cases in which full psychotic episodes were preceded by a prolonged period of sleeplessness. Of particular interest was their finding that 48 hours of sleep deprivation enhanced the hallucinatory effects of lysergic acid (LSD-25). With sleep deprivation, characteristic hallucinations were obtained with only half the dosage level required in the normal condition.

The results from this study suggest that there may be some interaction of sleep deprivation with on-going psychotic processes. The only study in which psychotic patients were experimentally sleep-deprived was done by Koranyi and Lehmann (1960), who kept six chronic hospitalized schizophrenic patients awake for 100 hours. The patients showed high morale and held up well for about three days. The typical drowsiness, irritability, withdrawal, and apathy of sleep deprivation were shown. After three days, however, they started a progressive physiological, behavioral, and personality deterioration. Most important, they began to exhibit the symptoms of acute schizophrenia which, as chronic patients, they had not had for years. Hallucinations (mostly auditory), delusions, posturing, incontinence, and other regressive behavior appeared; for five of the patients, the symptoms closely resembled those they had at the time of hospital admission 5 to 15 years earlier. Thus it seems that sleep deprivation induced the acute phase of the psychosis.

Psychotic phenomena associated with sleep deprivation were studied systematically for the first time during the Walter Reed studies (Morris, Williams, and Lubin, 1960). Subjects were given a series of standardized psychiatric interviews during the experiment. A great variety of interesting subjective experiences were reported suggesting difficulties in thinking, perception, and feelings about the self. The interviews were taped and later rated by a psychiatrist and a psychologist with a number of five-point scales for: visual misperception, temporal disorientation, cognitive disorganization, tactile misperception, and disorientation for space, objects, and persons.

The visual misperception scale is relevant to hallucinations. As shown in Table V, visual disturbances varied from simple

TABLE V

VISUAL MISPERCEPTION SCALE

1. Eyes itching, burning, or tired: difficulty in seeing, blurred or diplopia
2. Visual illusions: changes in or loss of shape, size, movement, color, or texture constancies; disturbed depth perception
   Examples: "The floor seems wavy."
               "The light seems to flicker."
               "The size and color of the chairs seems to change."
3. Labeling of illusions, but with no doubt concerning their illusory character
   Examples: "Looks like fog around the light."
               "That black mark looked like it was changing into different rock formations."
4. Labeling of illusions with some doubt concerning their reality
   Examples: "I thought there was a fuzz around the bottle."
               "I thought steam was rising from the floor; so I tested my eyes to check whether it was real."
5. Labeling of illusions (hallucinations) with, for a time at least, belief in their reality
   Examples: "I saw hair in my milk. The others said there wasn't any, but I still felt there was and would not drink it."
               "That (Rorschach card) looked like an envelope; I turned it over to check, and it had my name and address on it."

After Morris, Williams & Lubin, 1960.

double vision to actual hallucinations. Twelve of 26 subjects reached stages 4 or 5. An over-all increase in visual misperception was found for both the 1956 and 1957 groups, as is shown in Fig. 16. The hallucinating did not occur until 60 to 90 hours of sleep loss.

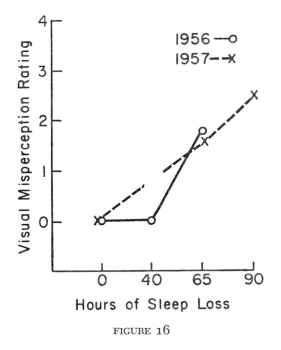

FIGURE 16

The temporal disorientation scale also showed an increase during sleep deprivation; the errors in time estimate placed the subject closer to the end of the study. The cognitive disorganization scale was also significantly related to hours of deprivation: the subject would lose his train of thought; become confused with fantasies, dreams, and intrusive thoughts; and show brief periods of incoherence. The other scales were not significant. However, it was noted that speech became slurred, flat, and mumbling at certain times. Some subjects reported feelings of depersonalization.

How can these phenomena be explained? First of all, they appear to be closely related to the lapses described earlier. Typically, during the interview, a subject's speech would become slow and mumbling, followed by a major lapse. During this drowsy period, the subject might shift topics suddenly or allow intruding thoughts to enter the conversation. Dreams, illusions, and hallucinations were closely associated with these lapses. Therefore nearly all the psychotic phenomena—hallucinations, confusion, and incoherence—can be traced to these drowsy interruptions in the flow of consciousness.

Since most of the illusions and hallucinations were visual, some disturbance must be present in this function. Standard tests of visual acuity, depth perception, etc., show no change during sleep deprivation—the subject pulls himself together for these brief tasks. At other times, however, they do drift into drowsy periods involving eye movements. Miles and Laslett (1931) showed that sleep-deprived subjects had difficulty maintaining a visual fixation. Subjects sometimes fall asleep, with slow rolling eye movements, while the eyes are still open. The two eyes are uncoordinated so that before sleep actually sets in double vision occurs, in spite of the subject's efforts to fixate.

Given the actual difficulty in fixating because of an approaching lapse, the simple visual misperception is understandable. The hallucinations grow out of this, but require additional misinterpretation. This is facilitated by the lapses which, according to Morris et al. (1960), disturb the individual's frame of reference, thought continuity, and cognitive processes. Such discontinuities make it difficult for the subject to make his usual distinctions between dreams, illusions, thoughts, and reality.

It is surprising that there are not more reported instances of hallucinations with dynamic significance but without total personality disorganization. Actually, the present reviewer does recall an incident in the Walter Reed studies not mentioned by Morris, Williams, and Lubin (1959): one subject thought he heard his mother calling him. Interestingly, Edwards (1941) reports two similar instances: A girl thought she heard her mother and another girl heard her housemother call her when the latter was not there. Tyler (1955) reports that the most common visual hallucinations concerned seeing a girl or female relative and feeling that fellow subjects resembled girls. These hallucinations were not excessively emotional in most cases, yet they bear an appropriate relationship to the experimental situation these normal people were in. The feminine figures may have represented a regressive, dependency wish, or the calling voices may have recapitulated the childhood situation of being awakened by the mother. Laslett (1928) reports a subject who thought he heard the university chimes. This may be related to the wish-fulfilling temporal distortions found by Bliss et al. (1959) and Morris et al. (1960).

These examples also show that, although they are not as prevalent as visual misperception, auditory disturbances can occur with normal as well as psychotic individuals. Kinesthetic hallucinations, such as a feeling of a tight band around the head or feeling an arm rest moving, have also been reported by Edwards (1941), Eagles, Halliday, and Redfearn (1953), and Morris, Williams, and Lubin (1960).

It is possible that some of the hallucinations were influenced by social suggestion. According to Morris and Singer (1961), symptoms sometimes spread to suggestible subjects. One hysteric picked up another's dream-like experience of seeing two dogs in the hall. An illusion of a "tight band around the head" spread in one group. In the Koranyi and Lehmann study, the idiosyncratic symptoms of five of the patients waxed and waned according to the ups and downs of the most dominant patient, who had assumed a leadership role. Nevertheless, most of the specific illusions or symptoms in both normal and disturbed subjects did not show a contagion. Furthermore, the 1956 and 1957 Walter Reed experiments, using totally different samples, showed similar results. Finally, Morris et al. (1960) marshall evidence to show that the psychiatric interviewer did not subtly suggest symptoms. Therefore, while social factors *may* influence this material, the results as a whole cannot be explained on this basis.

It is possible that more systematic and precise experimentation will be able to show that the psychotic symptoms observed during sleep deprivation can be explained more closely in terms of the person's attempts to adjust to the conflict between sleeping and staying awake. The symptoms do appear in conjunction with lapses, which probably represent the point of conflict balance. On the neurophysiological level this would be reflected in the balance between activating and de-activating mechanisms. The occurrence of symptoms ranging from mild perceptual illusions to delusions and hallucinations can be interpreted as consistent with an interpretation of sleep as a motive, since other motivational conditions are similar.

The psychotic phenomena, for the most part, are associated with lapses. Since, as we have seen earlier, these lapses represent a drifting towards sleep and EEG synchronization, many of the results seem to be due to the hypnogogic and dissociated state associated with falling asleep. This would be a drifting into regular synchronized sleep as shown by the EEG. Other aspects of the phenomena look more as if they are occurring in aroused sleep. The rhythmic occurrence of the lapses, the sudden loss of muscle tonus and the more dream-like experiences suggest paradoxical sleep. The loss of muscle tonus and the dream-like experiences do not occur in all lapses; they occur mostly during the longer ones in the later stages of sleep deprivation. Still, the EEG shows synchronization. We suggest that the lapses represent waves of actual sleep, that at first these lapses represent synchronized sleep, but at a later stage the subject passes through a synchronized phase and then a period of paradoxical sleep before awakening. The hypnogogic experiences occur during the onset of synchronized sleep and the more dream-like experiences occur during aroused or paradoxical sleep.

In this connection, there is a striking similarity in the hallucinations of sensory deprivation and sleep loss. The perceptual disturbance in sensory deprivation starts with shimmering, undulating surfaces, etc., and proceeds to interpreted scenes. Perhaps a lapse-related process is at work. Sensory deprivation subjects also appear to have drowsy periods that border on dreams.

The hypothesis about lapses during sleep deprivation seems to account for much of the misperception, disorientation, disorganization, and incoherent speech. However, some of the observations on delusion do not appear to fit such a simple scheme.

One possibility is that the delusions and some of the better developed hallucinations occur in pre-psychotic personalities during the stress of sleep loss. The study on chronic schizophrenics would support this. Another possibility, not incompatible with the first, is that these symptoms represent an attempt at resolving a conflict between the desire to sleep and the wish to complete the study. Completing the study takes on a good deal of personal significance for some subjects so that an overwhelming desire to sleep would be viewed as a personal threat.

REPRESSIVE MECHANISMS

How do subjects try to adjust to the overwhelming urge to sleep that must increase during the prolonged periods of sleep deprivation employed in various experiments? A clue is given by the observation that men tend to deny that they are really sleepy. This suggests the personality adjustment mechanisms of suppression, or even of repression. If an individual can do nothing to gratify a need in a given situation and is unable to change the situation, he may attempt to modify the internal demand. This is the repressive type of adjustment mechanism.

First, a word about repression. Freud (1936) used the concept to explain difficulties in recalling anxiety-arousing sexual and hostile material. However, the general applicability of the concept of repression to any motive was pointed out by Freud in his last book. He says, "Theoretically, there is no objection to supposing that any sort of instinctual demand whatever could occasion these same repressions and their consequences . . ." (1949, p. 85). Freud did go on to say that he thought the sexual instinct was of greatest importance in neuroses, but the statement above certainly liberalizes the use of the idea of repression. Later, Dollard and Miller (1950) redefined the concept in behavioral terms and extended it to additional classes of motives and responses. They distinguished three types of repression of a motive: the inhibition of responses labeling the motive, the inhibition of responses producing the motive, and the inhibition of responses mediating the motive.

Repressive defenses are sometimes shown in the adjustment of subjects to various physiological deprivations. For example, while most measures of hunger increase with degree and length of food deprivation, this may only hold up to moderate motivational levels—at very high levels of deprivation, subjective feelings of hunger may be attenuated or decreased. One study on acute starvation at the University of Minnesota is relevant (Brozek, 1955). Young men were totally deprived of food for four and one-half days. Self-ratings showed that the desire for food *decreased* significantly during the four days. On the fourth day of starvation, the "desire for food" received an average low rating of 1.4 (on a scale from 0 to 10) as compared with a rating of 2.9 for "desire for water" (water was available at all times) and 4.8 for "tiredness in walking." In the larger semi-starvation study (Keys et al., 1950), self-ratings of hunger showed an increase but the curve was negatively accelerated and did not reach the level the staff expected. In other words, they *underestimated* their hunger. The men were consciously preoccupied with food-related topics but it is not clear from the report whether this increased or decreased during the six-month period. There were few food themes in dreams, and projective tests showed no effects.

Motivation has often been measured with the aid of fantasy productions. There is a considerable body of data showing that the arousal of a motive leads to an increase in relevant themes in response to TAT pictures (Atkinson, 1958). Of course, direct behavioral expression of the need may be inhibited by anxiety (Mussen and Naylor, 1954; Kagan, 1956). Furthermore, the expression of a need in fantasy itself may be avoided because of anxiety attached to the need-relevant verbal responses (Eriksen and Brown, 1956). Therefore, fantasy may be influenced by repressive mechanisms, as well as by motivation.

In experiments involving the physiological need for food, many factors interact to influence fantasy (see Hall, 1961, pp. 256-261 for a summary). In the classical study by Atkinson and McClelland (1948) fantasy productions of mildly hungry men showed an increase in responses involving forks, plates, etc., but a marked decrease in descriptions of eating itself. Hunger themes may increase with cards least suggesting food and decrease on those most suggestive (Epstein and Smith, 1956). The Minnesota study, of course, showed no effect on projective tests (Brozek et al., 1951), while others show the decline in food-relevant themes at high motivational levels (Lazarus, 1961). All this suggests some sort of repressive mechanism.

The role of anxiety in inhibiting the expression of a primary motive, in an experimental situation, has been shown most clearly by Clark (1952). Two groups of college students were asked to write stories. In one group, sexual motivation was aroused by pictures of nudes, or an attractive, perfumed female experimenter. In contrast to expectations, the sexually aroused group had fewer sexual themes than the controls writing about neutral scenes. Embarrassment, guilt, or anxiety had been aroused along with sexual motivation. Furthermore, when the study was repeated in the context of a fraternity beer party, the stories did show the expected increase in sexual themes; alcohol reduces inhibition!

The men undergoing prolonged sleep deprivation in the Walter Reed studies can be seen as facing a difficult adjustment problem. They were caught in a conflict between an overpowering urge to go to sleep and various social and personal pressures to stay awake. The exact nature of these social and personal pressures to stay awake is not known, but they would appear on the basis of general observation to include the subjects' needs to appear strong, masculine, and grown-up in comparison with their fellows and in the eyes of the staff. Similarly, they wished to avoid failure, shame, and humiliation. Sleep can be construed as a physiological motive with a number of learned components such as verbal, instrumental, and mediating responses. In order to resolve the conflict between the sleep motive and the various social motives the subjects denied, avoided, or inhibited the learned responses whenever possible. According to the Dollard-Miller analysis of repression, responses labeling, evoking, or mediating sleep would produce cues that would add to the already strong stimuli for going to sleep. Inhibiting these responses would be adaptive. While it is difficult to say to what extent this was conscious or unconscious, the structure of the process seems to be of the repressive type.

The inhibition of responses labeling the sleep drive can be seen in the finding by Murray, Williams, and Lubin (1958) that sleep deprived subjects tended to deny feelings of sleepiness. During 98 hours of sleep loss these subjects rated themselves significantly lower on a sleepiness scale than did staff observers. The discrepancy increased significantly from day to day up until

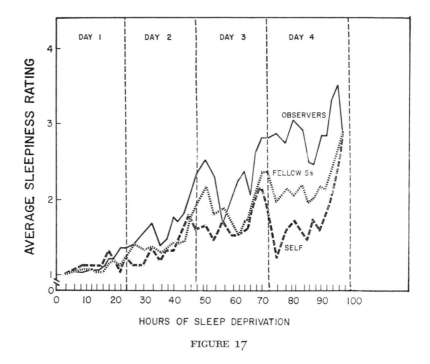

FIGURE 17

the last few hours of the experiment, when the subjects' ratings suddenly increased dramatically. Possibly the need for denial had disappeared by then. The subjects' ratings of one another were intermediate between their self-ratings and the observer ratings. These results are shown in Fig. 17. Self-ratings of fatigue, which appeared to be less ego-involving, were higher than the self-

ratings of sleepiness. The denial was interpreted as an adjustment mechanism for maintaining wakefulness.

Another finding in the Walter Reed experiments provides an
example of the inhibition of responses producing the sleep motive. As mentioned earlier, Murray, Schein, Erikson, Hill, and
Cohen (1959) made direct observations on the social, recreational, and general behavior of sleep-deprived and control subjects. The striking finding was that the subjects tended to change
restlessly from one form of social and recreational behavior to
another. The subjects seemed to change activities most abruptly
when they were suddenly faced with almost overpowering
drowsiness, which occurred with increasing frequency during
the sleep-deprivation period. Persisting in any one activity for
any length of time increased the drowsiness and made it more
difficult to stay awake. In other words, responses that would
increase the sleep motive were inhibited.

The Dollard and Miller theory of repression would also
suggest that responses mediating the sleep motive would be
inhibited. Such mediating responses might include the overt and
covert verbalizations that are involved in Thematic Apperception
Test fantasy productions. Thinking about sleep might increase
the tendency to go to sleep, while avoiding sleep thoughts would
help maintain wakefulness. Therefore, according to this theory
of repression, TAT sleep themes should decrease during sleep
deprivation. A study was designed specifically to test this hypothesis (Murray, 1959). A series of TAT cards was carefully selected
and pretested to represent a continuum of sleep suggestion. The
test was administered to experimental subjects after 86 to 90
hours of sleep loss as well as to controls. Reliable ratings made
by clinical psychologists showed that there were significantly
more sleep themes in the stories by the control subjects than the
sleep-deprived experimentals. The difference was greater with
increasing degree of sleep suggestion on the cards. This is shown
in Fig. 18. Sub-themes such as instrumental and goal responses
related to sleep showed similar results. The groups were not
differentiated on the basis of fatigue themes, length of stories, or
tension ratings. A comparison with normative data showed that
the control subjects did not have an unusually high number of

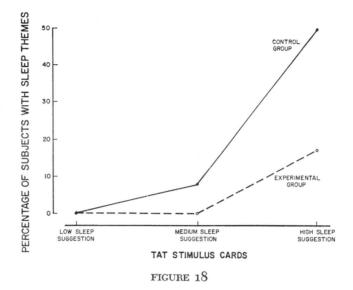

FIGURE 18

sleep themes. Thus the results confirm the hypothesis that during prolonged sleep deprivation there is an inhibition of responses mediating the sleep drive such as the overt and covert verbal responses involved in TAT fantasy productions.

The results of the Walter Reed study have been confirmed by C. L. Nelson (reported in Epstein, 1962). In one part of the study, body temperature, sleepiness and fatigue ratings, and TAT stories were obtained at midnight before and after one night's sleep loss. Fatigue ratings were found to vary more directly with sleep deprivation than were sleepiness ratings. Telling half the group that they would have to undergo another night of sleep loss lowered the fatigue ratings somewhat but lowered the sleepiness ratings even more so. Nelson also found that TAT stories showed a decrease in emphasis on sleep from the first night to the second. Furthermore, sleep emphasis was lower in the group expecting further deprivation than in the group expecting to terminate.

The results from the Walter Reed studies fit in with the earlier studies suggesting that repressive mechanisms may influence subjective, fantasy, and behavioral manifestations of motives. In fact, Lazarus (1961) cites this TAT study to buttress his argument that fantasy productions may be strongly influenced by ego-defensive processes. In his discussion of Lazarus' paper, Atkinson (1961) takes issue with this interpretation. Rather than interpreting the lack of sleep themes as a repressive mechanism, he says that a true sleep motive—in the sense of a goal-directed tendency—was not operating at the 86 to 90 hours of sleep deprivation. He bases his argument on Hebb's (1949) idea that the cues of extremely long deprivational states may never have been associated with a goal response and are so dissimilar from typical motivational cues that little generalization takes place. Thus a man who has never been deprived of food for more than a few hours may not experience hunger during real starvation. Atkinson points out that there has never been an association between 90 hours of sleep deprivation and sleeping. Therefore, no sleep-directed tendency is present.

Atkinson's explanation, however, does not hold up under close scrutiny. First of all, there are the lapses, or microsleeps, that increase monotonically with each of four days of sleep deprivation—far beyond the length of sleep deprivation previously experienced by the subjects. These microsleeps resemble anticipatory goal responses closely. Another fact against Atkinson's explanation is the sudden and dramatic upswing in sleepiness ratings at the very end of the experiment (Murray et al., 1958). Subjects rated themselves consistently less sleepy than did objective observers; this discrepancy increased significantly on days 1, 2, 3, and 4. During the last night, on ratings made at midnight, 2:00, 4:00, and 6:00 a.m., the average discrepancy remained large—the subjects rated themselves more than a full scale unit lower in sleepiness than did the objective observers. Then, suddenly, at 8:00 a.m.—just before the deprivation period terminated and the men went to bed—they rated themselves as quite sleepy, showing no difference with the ratings of the observers at that time. These results suggest that the subjects were sleepy, showed an increasing tendency to drop off to sleep, but denied their sleepiness right up to the last few hours of the deprivation period, when there was no longer a need for an adjustment mechanism, so that they reported their motivational state more accurately. This analysis makes Atkinson's explanation less plausible and supports Lazarus' ego-defense interpretation.

An important question remaining is why repressive adjustment mechanisms were so widely used in the sleep-deprivation activation—why not obsessional, conversion, or some other defense mechanism. Actually, not every subject used a repressive mechanism, as we shall see in the next section on individual differences. In addition, the psychotic episodes described in the previous section suggest that in extreme conditions paranoid and projective mechanisms may come into play. Still, repressive mechanisms were widespread. Why?

One reason may be set—the degree to which the situation is structured to encourage one form of behavior more than another. For example, in assessing the effect of hunger on a word-completion test, Postman and Crutchfield (1952) arranged the first few word stems on the list so that they suggested food in varying degrees. Either 0, 1, 2, 3, or 5 food responses would be elicited in the several groups. The more of these words at the beginning, the greater the number of food words the subjects gave later on. This kind of set had a greater effect than did several hours of food deprivation. Set may encourage or inhibit behavior.

A more general social set may have been operating in the Walter Reed studies to facilitate the use of repressive mechanisms. Morris and Singer (1961) made general observations on the social transactions between the staff and the subjects. As mentioned, it was noted that the first group of subjects studied had the greatest amount of anxiety, which may have been aroused by the overconcern of the inexperienced staff. Morris and Singer believe that the use of denial of sleepiness, on the part of the subjects, was encouraged by the fact that the experimenters themselves avoided this topic. Nevertheless, not all subjects were discouraged in describing their feelings. In fact, the ones who used denial the most, according to Morris and Singer, were those with the greatest anxiety and the most difficulty in staying awake.

It is interesting to note, in connection with the denial of

sleepiness, that fatigue themes on the TAT were not inhibited. Indeed, there was some evidence that fatigue-like "exhaustion" themes were more frequent in the experimental group. This may have been a displacement from the sleep needs. Actually, there is no reason why sleep should be so inhibited while fatigue is not. Both feelings are present during sleep deprivation—a desire to sleep and muscular fatigue. In retrospect, it seems to the present author, that the staff was a little more permissive about fatigue; a man who complained of muscular aches was often invited to sit down and take it easy. Perhaps, if the study had been labeled a "Fatigue Experiment," sleepiness would have been expressed openly and fatigue denied.

The influence of set was studied systematically by Nelson (Epstein, 1962). In one experiment, subjects were not actually deprived but were tested several times during the day and at midnight. Set was varied by telling half the group the study was related to sleep. Those who did not know the study was related to sleep showed an increase in sleepiness ratings but those who were told showed a decrease. Fatigue ratings showed a tendency to increase in both groups but were higher in the group that had been told about the study. Thus set is an important factor in the process of adjustment to physiological sleep deprivation.

INDIVIDUAL PERSONALITY DIFFERENCES

It is almost axiomatic, in the field of personality, that individuals will react to the same stress in widely different ways. The nature of the stress may determine reactions to some extent, but individual differences due to variations in innate temperament and early learning experiences can always be seen. So, although we have seen that the general emotional pattern during sleep deprivation includes anxiety, depression, irritability, perceptual distortion, and repression, it is also of interest to see how individuals differ in this.

Personality differences are seen in reaction to many physiological deprivations. As mentioned earlier, thirst tends to exaggerate temperamental peculiarities (Marriott, 1950). Keys et al. (1950) report that semi-starvation brings out different individual weaknesses. Acceptance of pemmican during a survival exercise was related to the maturity and adjustment of individual soldiers (Torrance and Mason, 1957). Deviant MMPI scores, for anxiety and internalization of problems, were related to physiological adaptation to a cold room (Fine and Gaydos, 1959). Subjects with psychoneurotic fatigue did not hold up well with an oxygen decrease (McFarland and Barach, 1937). Finally, individual personality differences determine to a large extent how long a person can stand sensory deprivation and the kind of behavior he will show during the experiment (Solomon, 1961).

Individual differences in performance, mood, irritability, adjustment level, and tendency toward hallucinations have been observed, in a casual way, by nearly all the sleep-deprivation experimenters. Edwards (1941), for example, reports that women did as well as or better than men, while slightly built individuals held up better than the stronger, athletic types. Of the six schizophrenic patients studied by Koranyi and Lehmann (1960), two were paranoid, two catatonic, and two hebephrenic. The symptoms that emerged during sleep deprivation were consistent with the diagnosis: the paranoids became more paranoid, the catatonics more catatonic, and the hebephrenics more hebephrenic. Very little was done, however, to relate individual variables to behavior during sleep deprivation systematically before the work of Loveland and Singer (1959) and Morris and Singer (1961).

The reader may perhaps recall that Loveland and Singer administered the Rosenzweig, Iflund, Glad, and Rorschach tests to each of 25 sleep-deprived and 25 control Ss before, during, and after the deprivation period. As mentioned earlier, no consistent group results were obtained. The authors concluded that basic personality structure is not affected by sleep loss.

Nevertheless, some individual changes in style and content of communication were observed, with more of these changes in the experimental group. Such changes seemed to be determined by the S's standing personality adjustment interacting with the whole experimental situation. Interviews confirmed this

(Morris and Singer, 1961. For example, basically well-adjusted individuals met the situation well, while those with existing personality problems had more difficulty. These problems may have been latent; thus, a man who ordinarily maintained a polite facade was transformed into a chronic complainer. The psychological tests given before the deprivation period indicated that this person was characterized by "overt stoic control" and "preconscious critical and hostile attitudes." Morris and Singer conclude that sleep deprivation may require defensive shifts, but that these shifts are congruent with the basic personality structure of the individual.

Which individuals showed the greatest defensive shifts? Morris and Singer studied 27 subjects intensively. They classified the subjects according to mode of adjustment: 3 realistically admitted being sleepy; 8 denied being sleepy but would admit, for instance, difficulty in keeping their eyes open; 10 also showed partial denial but in addition complained a great deal about things in general; and, finally, 6 showed a complete, severe denial of any sleepiness. Most of the subjects who showed the greatest anxiety and defensive shifts came from this last group —those showing complete denial. The rest came from the next to last group: the partial denial plus complaining.

It can be seen, therefore, that the use of general denial is inversely related to successful adaptation to sleep deprivation. Morris and Singer believe that the experiment aroused more anxiety in some individuals than in others. Loveland and Singer suggest that it is the "loosely defended neurotics" who showed most test-retest change. It is not clear from all this, however, whether the use of denial caused the difficulty in adjustment or whether the least adapted individuals are those who rely habitually on denial. It would seem to be the latter since basic personality did not change. Either way, though, it highlights the limitations of repressive defenses. As Dollard and Miller (1950) point out, repression may give temporary relief, but it prevents the use of the higher mental processes in finding better modes of adjustment to the situation.

It was possible, Loveland and Singer found, to predict efficiency in performance tasks on the basis of the baseline

Rorschach Test alone. The main item in this prediction was R, the total number of Rorschach responses. This was taken as a measure of the general motivation of the person. A person with high motivation would be able to compensate for sleep loss by increasing his effort during the performance tasks. It should be noted that this variable also predicted the performance level of the control Ss, so that it is not specific to sleep deprivation per se.

The twenty talkathon contestants studied by Cappon and Banks (1960) showed wide variations in ability to endure sleep deprivation. The more anxious or neurotic a person was, the shorter the deprivation he could stand. This was shown by significant results with several objective tests: the Maudsley Medical Questionnaire, the Nervous Scale of the Cornell Medical Index, and the Taylor Anxiety Scale. Low intelligence, measured by the Raven Progressive Matrices, was also associated with difficulty in continuing in the contest.

In the Walter Reed study, Loveland and Singer used the Rorschach to predict which subjects reported hallucinations. These were not necessarily those who showed performance deterioration or personality shifts. Recall that those who had the most difficulty were those who denied the most; they may also have denied hallucinations. The people who did report clearly classified hallucinations (Step 5 in the Morris-Williams-Lubin scale) fell into two groups: loosely defended hysterical personalities and personalities with schizophrenic traits. Both of these groups are known, clinically, to exhibit hallucinations under sufficient stress.

SUMMARY

Strong physiological motives have many effects on emotion, personality, and social behavior. Anxiety, depression, irritability, euphoria, and apathy have been observed. Hostility is seen in experimental laboratories; overt aggression may occur in natural situations. Hallucinations and other psychotic phenomena have been reported. Repressive defenses are sometimes used.

Behavior under high motivational conditions also reflects individual differences.

Sleep deprivation produces similar affective disturbances: anxiety, depression, irritability, euphoria, and apathy. The prevailing mood is an apathetic depression suggesting a de-arousal reaction. This increases with the amount of sleep deprivation. Anxiety occurs mostly at the beginning and is related to subject and staff concern over physical health, as well as to the existing personality of the subject. Irritability and elation occur in short outbursts. The depression is not the guilt-ridden type. Rather, the emotional changes seem to be part of an adjustment process in which interest is withdrawn from the environment and affect modulated. Social behavior also reflects this.

The presence of irritability suggests the frustration-aggression hypothesis. The amount of covert or overt hostility seems to be influenced strongly by other frustrations in the experimental situation as well as by social influences inhibiting or facilitating the expression of aggression. Nevertheless, frustration of the sleep response itself still produces some aggression, as shown in animal studies and in human subjects' reactions to nudges when on the verge of sleep.

After prolonged sleep deprivation, subjects may become confused, disoriented, and unable to sustain thought. Delusions occur in exceptional cases. Visual misperceptions ranging from mild illusions to hallucinations increase with sleep loss. Chronic psychotic patients show a return of their acute symptoms after prolonged sleep loss. These psychotic phenomena are associated with lapses and probably are like the hypnogogic experiences associated with falling asleep or with the dream experiences of aroused sleep. Some of the psychotic phenomena may represent attempts at conflict resolution.

The Walter Reed study suggested that suppression and other repressive adjustment mechanisms are widely used to maintain wakefulness. This is shown in sleepiness ratings, general behavior, and TAT fantasy. It is unlikely that this is due to a lack of experience with such prolonged sleep deprivation. Staff attitudes may have fostered the use of repressive defenses.

Although sleep deprivation does not alter basic personality

structure, certain individuals will show defensive shifts congruent with their basic personality. Denial may not be particularly adaptive, since those with the most denial had the greatest anxiety and showed the most defensive shifts.

The data as a whole suggest that sleep-deprived subjects are in an intense conflict between the sleep motive and the motivation for continuing in the experiment. When it reaches the point where the subject is lapsing frequently into partial sleep, the psychotic phenomena appear. The subject typically attempts to adjust to the conflict by a narrowing of interests, a muting of emotional reaction, and a denial of sleepiness. These are not fully successful, so that the subject runs into frustration which may produce outbursts of irritability. The entire experimental and social situation determines how much overt aggression and hostility will emerge.

It can be seen that sleep deprivation poses the same problems for personality adjustment as do other motivating conditions. The affective, cognitive, and defensive adaptations are similar to those shown in other conflict situations. On the personality level, sleep deprivation operates as a motivational variable.

CHAPTER 8

The Pathology of Sleep

The study of anomalies has contributed significantly to the development of many scientific fields. Interest is aroused when something does not go according to our prescribed theoretical plan. It is much more than morbid curiosity over the idiosyncrasies of a bizarre case or the fascinated repulsion of the abnormal and the different. The disturbance in functioning, which pathology implies, often enlightens us on the normal functioning of the process in question. In the anomaly, two correlated functions may be separated in a way that makes it clear which one is causal. The abnormal case may make possible an observation beyond the reach of experimental procedures in a democratic society.

In psychology the abnormal case has been particularly important (Murray, 1961). For example, John Dalton's introspective account of his own red-green color blindness formed the foundation for color vision theory for over a century. The entire field of personality is really based on the half-dozen clinical cases published by Freud. As Allport (1953) has pointed out, this is not without its dangers. Nevertheless, in conjunction with experimental research and comparative studies of normal man, systematic clinical observation or even a dramatic single case can be of great importance.

The phenomena of sleep embrace many abnormalities. People suffer from excessive sleep, inability to sleep, restless

247

sleep, nightmares, sleepwalking, bedwetting, and so forth. One has only to mention one's interest in sleep at a cocktail party to hear tales of long, endless nights of torture. Spouses will add complaints of teeth-grinding, snoring, pillow-punching and incessant tossing. Many a man has offered his soul to the devil for a good night's sleep.

As fascinating as these phenomena are in themselves, they will be analyzed here for another reason. How do sleep disturbances fit in with the present theoretical development of the sleep motive? Are they consistent with the abnormalities found in other physiological motives or do they constitute a different realm of phenomena setting sleep apart? Are the disturbances caused by organic or psychological factors? If organic, do they involve the physiological mechanisms which are known to control sleep and waking? If psychogenic, do they develop and function in a fashion analogous to other psychopathological processes?

In order to answer these questions we will first examine the pathology of similar physiological motives such as hunger. Then the organic pathologies will be compared with the sleep mechanisms described in Chapter 4. Psychological influences in sleep disturbances will occupy most of our time. First, excessive sleeping will be treated as a defense mechanism; then the way in which emotions may produce insomnia will be described; and, finally, behavioral anomalies during sleep, such as sleepwalking, will be scrutinized. Hypnotism will be mentioned briefly.

One note of caution before starting: in spite of the importance of clinical data, its usefulness can be limited by methodological weakness. Unfortunately, many of the studies in this area are methodologically weak. While a clear clinical case may be sufficient to establish the existence of a phenomenon, a proliferation of single, unrelated case studies, each with its strong theoretical assertions, does not add a great deal. Very little systematic research or testing of hypotheses has been attempted. Controls are nearly always absent. Objective measures, even when available, have been used rarely. There are exceptions of course, such as Anthony's fine study, but the bulk of the research does not give one confidence in the validity of the conclusions drawn.

In two studies in which a control group was used, generalizations made by earlier researchers—on the basis of sleep-disturbed patients only—were refuted. Thus Anthony (1959), using matched neurotic controls, did not find more frequent sibling birth trauma or interparental aggression with sleep-disturbed children. Similarly, Tapia et al. (1958) found about the same incidence of sleepwalking in matched neurotic and normal groups. One wonders how many other findings would be supported by research using adequate controls.

We will not belabor this point unnecessarily, but the analysis will have to be regarded as tentative. Within these limitations we will try to bring what data are available to bear on the main issue of the feasibility of regarding sleep as a motivational variable.

PHYSIOLOGICAL MOTIVES AND PSYCHOPATHOLOGY

In what way can a physiological motive become involved in psychopathology? What are the causal factors? Evidence suggests that physiological motives such as hunger, thirst, breathing, micturation, defecation, fatigue, sex, and pain can become involved in a neurosis or psychosis in many complex ways. We are treating these motives here in their narrow physiological sense, not as expressions of a general libido or other psychological formulations. Thus, we are not beginning with a concept of hunger that includes maternal affection or a concept of sex that includes all interpersonal attraction. We will mention this later, but for the moment we are simply asking what role these basic biological urges play in personality adjustment. The three best understood functions—hunger, elimination, and sex —will be discussed. Instead of trying to cite this vast literature, we will rely mostly on the excellent summaries in the *Handbook of American Psychiatry* edited by Silvano Arieti (1959).

Hunger may be increased or decreased by emotional factors. When hunger is increased the appetite becomes ravenous, overeating occurs, and obesity is the result (Deri, 1955). The obese individual is usually insecure and immature. The basic source of insecurity is probably a deep-rooted fear of separation from the mother. The case histories suggest that the maternal figure was dominant in the home with the overeater dependent upon her. When the person feels anxious, eating is a solace and a means of reducing the anxiety.

The conditions under which overeating becomes the main mode of reducing anxiety are not known. On the physiological level, eating and digesting food are incompatible with the sympathetic activity involved in anxiety. It is said that food is a symbol for maternal love. However, this is more or less true for everyone. Ordinarily anxiety in the child is inhibited by the equally incompatible security or relaxation response that is produced by the direct expression of affection on the part of the mother (Murray, 1964 a). One may conjecture that the mother of the obese individual is lacking in affection and uses feeding as the main anxiety reducer. Eating and obesity may also have idiosyncratic meanings to the person, such as oral impregnation or self-punishment (Deri, 1955).

It should be noted that obesity may also be produced by purely organic factors (Jervis, 1959). Thus, a deficiency in pituitary or other endocrine gland functioning can result in weight gains. Similarly, clinical cases involving lesions in the hunger area of the hypothalamus may show obesity. This has also been demonstrated experimentally (Morgan and Stellar, 1950).

Hunger is inhibited by emotional reactions in many cases. As mentioned above, hunger and anxiety are physiologically incompatible. Thus, nausea and vomiting are frequent symptoms of anxiety because of sympathetic interference with digestion (Portnoy, 1959). The refusal of food on an emotional basis is called *anorexia nervosa*. This is seen in disturbed youngsters (Gardner, 1959), hysterical personalities (Abse, 1959), and depressed patients (Gutheil, 1959 a). Not very much is known about the development of this symptom except that anxiety plays a central role. Since the interference with the digestive process is an innate, automatic part of the bodily reaction to stress, it would seem that *anorexia nervosa* requires a much simpler explanation than overeating. Anxiety involved in any number of conflicts—sex, independence, aggression—could produce this symptom. Hypothalamic lesions may also result in an inhibition of hunger (Stellar, 1954).

A more complex interaction between hunger and emotional factors may produce the gastrointestinal lesions known as ulcers. While acute anxiety inhibits the flow of digestive fluids, chronic anxiety appears to increase the flow as a sort of compensatory reaction. Prolonged flow may result in ulcers. The actual production of ulcers depends on an interaction between organic, personality, and situational variables. Soldiers in the stress of basic training got ulcers only if they had a high level of pepsinogen and also had dependency conflicts (Lidz and Rubenstein, 1959).

The motive to defecate will be mentioned only briefly. This eliminative function may be increased or decreased by emotion. The increase, diarrhea, is frequently a symptom of anxiety (Portnoy, 1959). A related psychosomatic ailment, colitis, is found in dependent, depressed individuals, particularly after the loss of a loved one (Lidz and Rubenstein, 1959). On the other hand, constipation is frequently seen in depressed (Gutheil, 1959 a) and neurasthenic (Chrzanowski, 1959) patients. Of course, constipation and diarrhea are also symptoms of a wide variety of organic conditions.

Sexual functions are quite sensitive to emotional influences. Here, too, sexual activity may be heightened or inhibited. Sexual activity may be greatly increased, although disturbed in some ways, in manic states (Arieti, 1959). Borderline psychotic individuals frequently exhibit excessive sexual activity, apparently as a means of breaking out of their feelings of depersonalization and to compensate for their lack of affectionate relationships (Schmideberg, 1959). Organic conditions such as hypothalamic tumors and paresis also result in hypersexuality (Gutheil, 1959 b).

Sexual activity may be inhibited by anxiety. The male form of this, impotence, may be the result of a great variety of anxieties including the fear of losing one's independence through interpersonal involvement, castration fears dating back to childhood, and simple fear of death in cardiac and respiratory patients.

The person may have a more or less unconscious "vow of chastity" dating back to the adolescent struggle over masturbation (Gutheil, 1959 b). Frigidity is the corresponding condition in women, but other inhibitory symptoms may include dysmenorrhea, vaginismus, problems in conceiving, bearing, and delivering a child, and lactating afterwards. This inhibition is usually related to a fear of death or injury, competitive feelings toward men (penis envy), and hostility toward the husband (Benedek, 1959).

Infections, tumors, and hormonal deficiency may lead to impotence by disrupting the sexual reflex chain at any one of a number of points (Gutheil, 1959 a). In particular, hypothalamic tumors may reduce sexuality. This has also been shown experimentally (Stellar, 1954).

Several general statements can be made. First of all, disturbances of primary motives may be produced by many organic conditions, especially injury to the known neural mechanisms mediating the motive. However, emotional factors may produce the same disturbance independently. In many cases, a combination of organic predisposition and emotional interference best explains the outcome. Therefore, both physiological and psychological factors must be examined in evaluating the pathology of any motivational variable.

Another point that is suggested by this review is that three kinds of psychological variables must be considered. First, the emotion that may be involved—for example anxiety, depression, mania. Second, the conflict involved—such as affection, sex, independence. Third, the type of personality involved—passive, dependent, immature, active, etc.

A finding that will be of major importance in evaluating sleep disturbances is that emotion may either increase or decrease the physiological motive. Anxiety may inhibit hunger, defecation, or sexual activity. But the reverse is also true. Overeating and excessive sexual activity may be a way of reducing anxiety. Diarrhea may be a symptom of emotional distress.

The reasons for the development of one or another symptom are not clear. Why does one person develop a hunger symptom and another a sexual one? This is probably related to the social learning in the family group during childhood. The mother who relates to her child only through feeding and the father who bases self-esteem only on sexual prowess probably focus anxiety in these areas. Why is the function increased in one case and decreased in another? Here, too, the specific learning situation would have to be known for an adequate explanation. The inhibiting of eating and sexual functioning by anxiety probably requires no complex explanation since this appears to be innate. The parents may teach the child that sex is dangerous and the anxiety reaction will do the rest. The use of eating, or other activity, for reducing anxiety probably depends on a more complex acquisition procedure in which the child learns that security comes from these activities.

NEUROPATHOLOGY OF SLEEP

Many disorders of sleep can be attributed to disturbances of brain function. Disturbance may be produced by inflammation, trauma, tumors, metabolic dysfunction, or epileptic discharge. These are clearly physical factors, often with demonstrable anatomical, biochemical, or physiological changes. The resulting sleep disturbances can be grouped loosely as hypersomnia, insomnia, and nocturnal behavioral symptoms.

Hypersomnia, or excessive sleeping, follows as a symptom from a variety of neurological diseases. *Encephalitis lethargica,* mentioned earlier in Chapter 4, is a disease that runs through an acute psychotic stage, a stage of insomnia, and finally, a stage of excessive sleepiness (von Economo, 1930; Alpers, 1938). The symptoms of the last stage may range from occasional drowsiness to a profound stupor lasting for weeks. Patients can be aroused temporarily. Sometimes there is a reversal in the day-night sleep pattern although Kleitman (1939) believes that this is simply a side-effect of nocturnal insomnia. Patients sometimes go for several days without sleep and then sleep for several days. Von Economo (1930) also describes a dissociation between cerebral and body sleep—during the day patients were mentally alert but muscularly drowsy, while at night they were asleep mentally but their bodies were restless. This latter condition often resulted in somnambulism.

The disease is probably due to a virus which has an affinity for the hypothalamic sleep and wakeful mechanisms. Von Economo (1930) found inflammatory lesions in these areas. Davidson and Demuth (1945, 1946) also found that brain-damaged patients with sleep disturbances had lesions at the cortical-diencephalic level or in the hypothalamic area. Both of these studies suggest that disruption of the Reticular Activating System is responsible for hypersomnia.

Narcolepsy is a more specific syndrome than general hypersomnia. Narcolepsy usually consists of sudden sleep—occurring at periodic intervals throughout the day. Muscular symptoms such as cataplexy and sleep paralysis and visual symptoms such as hypnogogic illusions or dream-like states may occur in conjunction with hypnogogic attacks. The attacks last from five to thirty minutes. They may be precipitated by physical or emotional excitement but also occur spontaneously (Daly and Yoss, 1957; Imlab, 1961; Bowling and Richards, 1961).

The cause of narcolepsy is a matter of dispute. Some authors believe that epilepsy may be involved in at least some cases (Bjerk and Hornisher, 1958). However, Yoss and Daly (1960 a, b, c) found that narcolepsy appeared in as many as four succesive generations in the same family and suggest that it is an inherited condition. The nature of the inherited defect is not clear. Yoss and Daly (1960 c) found no evidence of metabolic dysfunction. There may be a neural defect.

In any case, the narcoleptic state seems to be related to sleep. GSR resistance increases (Cave, 1931) and BMR is lower than normal (Daniels, 1934) during the day with narcoleptics. This suggests a drowsy state, and the EEG records do show a preponderance of drowsy waves (Daly and Yoss, 1957; Imlab, 1961; Bowling and Richards, 1961). Recently Rechtschaffen et al. (1963) reported that narcoleptics show an unusual nocturnal sleep pattern. While normal subjects practically never show the Stage 1-REM dream period at sleep onset, narcoleptics frequently begin this period within minutes of falling asleep. Rechtschaffen et al. marshall additional evidence suggesting that the daytime sleep seizure of the narcoleptic consists of Stage 1-REM periods. They also point out the similarity in the loss of muscular tonus in cataplexy and paradoxical sleep. Rechtschaffen et al. suggest that narcolepsy is caused by an abnormal triggering of the pontine mechanism for aroused sleep.

Insomnia is the opposite form of sleep disturbance and it too may be associated with a variety of pathological conditions including neural lesions, toxic, infectious, or metabolic diseases; and arteriosclerosis. The inflammatory lesions of the anterior hypothalamus in *encephalitis lethargica* produce insomnia (von Economo, 1930). Litvin (1950) reports insomnia in many medical conditions involving increased metabolism, including hyperthyroidism. Parkinsonism also produces insomnia, with a subsequent sleep reversal. High blood pressure and other circulatory disorders may also cause insomnia (Jacobson, 1929).

Insomnia is a common complaint in the aged (Liberson, 1945; Ginzberg, 1955). Falling asleep is not too difficult but the person keeps waking up throughout the night (intermittent insomnia) or wakes up early in the morning and cannot get back to sleep (terminal insomnia). Tiller (1964), however, reports a severe insomnia complaint in only about a quarter of his outpatient geriatric group with most of the insomnia complaints dating back at least a decade. It is clear, then, that insomnia is not associated invariably with aging. It seems to be more common in those geriatric patients with arteriosclerosis and senility (McGraw and Oliven, 1959). These conditions may interfere with brain function.

In general, insomnia may be produced by any disease that interferes with the functioning of the brain, whether through systemic effects on metabolism or the structural changes in arteriosclerosis (Muncie, 1934). It is not clear if the effect is generalized or acts specifically on sleep mechanisms. However, lesions in the sleep mechanisms of the thalamus and hypothalamus can produce insomnia by themselves.

Several special sleep disturbances have been grouped together as nocturnal behavioral symptoms. Several of these appear to have an organic basis. First of all, there is the condition known as *pavor nocturnus,* or night terrors. Night terrors occur in children from about ages 3 to 8, but are uncommon. They are quite different from ordinary nightmares, consisting of terrorized crouching, screaming, and agitated running (Kleitman, 1939; Sperling, 1958; Anthony, 1959). Night terrors have been related to epilepsy, migraine, infection, neural lesions, and a family history of neuropathology (Kanner, 1957; Anthony, 1959).

Somnambulism, or sleepwalking, consists of the acting out of a behavioral sequence during the night without awareness or recall. Kanner (1957) has drawn a comparison between sleepwalking and *pavor nocturnus* in that both involve actions without consciousness. Somnambulists in military service have been found to have more abnormal EEG's, enuresis, epilepsy, and family histories of sleepwalking and enuresis than normal controls (Pierce and Lipcon, 1956 a).

Finally, enuresis is a behavioral disturbance that originates in synchronized sleep and may substitute for a dream (Pierce, Whitman, Maas, and Gay, personal communication). About 15% of children from 4 to 14 years of age are persistent bed-wetters (Baller and Schalock, 1956). As might be expected, abnormal bladder tone accounts for some cases (Braithwaite, 1950; Hallman, 1950). Neurological factors may also be involved. Enuretics frequently have more abnormal EEG's (Gunnarson and Melin, 1951), with as many as 70% showing epileptic patterns (Temmes and Towakka, 1954).

The interesting thing about all these behavioral disturbances during sleep is that they appear to have some connection with an aberration of normal dreaming. *Pavor nocturnus* and somnambulism involve dream-like actions with no consciousness. Enuresis may substitute for dreaming. In all three cases, visual dreams either do not occur or are not recalled. The hint of epilepsy and other neurological disorders in these disturbances suggest failure in any one of a number of neural mechanisms. The balance of arousal and inhibition in normal dreaming seems to be reversed in these pathological conditions. Instead of hallucinatory arousal and motor inhibition, there is motor arousal and hallucinatory inhibition. Nevertheless, in both normal dreams and these behavioral disturbances full wakeful consciousness is not aroused. Coordinated study of the neurophysiology of dreaming and the neuropathology of behavioral disturbances might be rewarding.

Now that many cases of excessive sleeping, insomnia, and behavioral disturbances of sleep have been shown to be due to neurological conditions, many people would rule out psychogenic causes. This is the old battle between "biotropic" and "sociotropic" traditions in psychology and psychiatry. Does everything have to be black and white? Has not the experience in psychosomatic medicine shown that most disturbances depend on an interplay between somatic predisposition, emotional development, and the current social situation? The abnormal neurological findings do not explain all the pathology of sleep. Although 20% of sleepwalkers have abnormal EEG's, 80% apparently do not. In addition, the 20% may be close to the baseline for abnormal EEG's found in normal populations—especially in children.

It is a classical logical fallacy to conclude that because A has been shown to cause B, then C cannot also be a cause. At the risk of being called a mealy-mouthed eclectic, we shall take the position that both neurological and psychological factors may produce sleep disturbances. This is not a return to the "soul concept"; psychological processes operate through neurophysiological mechanisms. The distinction is really between malfunction due to anatomical or biochemical abnormalities versus malfunction due to conflicting, inappropriate, or distorted information from the environment, past or present.

SLEEP AS A DEFENSE MECHANISM

Sleep is, by definition, a means of detaching the person from the environment. While this usually serves the biological need for restoration, the process may also come to serve psychological motives for avoiding painful aspects of the social environment or avoiding anxiety-arousing responding to a situation. The idea that sleep may become involved in emotional conflict is a simple extension of known psychogenic factors in fatigue and neurasthenia (Bartley and Chute, 1947; Cameron, 1947). Sleep may be even more effective in avoiding reality and the necessity for action.

A number of psychoanalytic writers have described sleep as a mechanism for defending against anxiety. According to Sullivan (1953), an infant threatened by the prolonged anxiety of his mother may escape into sleep; he calls this the dynamism of "somnolent detachment." Horney (1937) says that excessive sleeping is one way of "narcotizing" anxiety. Sleep may represent a denial of feelings, an escape from reality, or a regressive form of gratification (Willey, 1924; Willey and Rice, 1924; Jones, 1935; O'Connor, 1951; Deutsch and Murphy, 1955; Switzer and Berman, 1956; Goldstein and Griffin, 1959). As with most defenses, sleep serves a double purpose—anxiety is avoided and partial gratification is obtained (Alexander, 1948).

A case illustrating sleep as a defense mechanism is provided by Markowitz (1957). A 15-year-old Negro boy had attacks of sleep nearly every day. He described the situations precipitating these attacks as follows: "I used to fall asleep easily, especially when I had an argument with my mother or had a grudge against anyone or was mad. . . . I fall asleep when I am frustrated or want to get away from dull conversation . . . I had to stay home and take care of my little brother; I sat down and fell asleep. . . ." The patient had a good deal of anxiety about aggressive feelings. When the situation demanded some sort of hostility or aggression, anxiety was aroused and he fell asleep.

Markowitz' patient sometimes fell asleep in the waiting room just before the therapy hour. Sleepiness and sleeping before or during the therapy hour has been observed in a number of patients with a variety of explanations. Sleeping is said to be motivated by anxiety over dependent (Stone, 1947; Lewin, 1954) or aggressive (Davison, 1945; Barker, 1948) feelings toward the therapist. Oral, anal, and phallic wishes have been described (Parkin, 1955). Sleeping during therapy may represent resistance (Ferenczi, 1950; Scott, 1952). On the other side of the couch, sleeping on the part of the therapist may represent countertransference, especially impatience with the uncommunicativeness of the patient (Cohen, 1952).

In one case, sleeping during therapy was traced back to its origins in childhood (Bird, 1954). Whenever the patient had shown anger as a boy, the parents had suggested that he was tired and sent him to bed. In addition, the childhood anger was sometimes preceded by masturbation. As an adult in therapy, the patient slept excessively—once for almost six weeks of interviews —whenever angry or sexual feelings toward the therapist arose.

This case also shows that sleep as a defense may be acquired on the basis of social learning in the family. It is not necessary to remain within a psychoanalytic or psychopathological context to see how sleeping can be learned as an adjustment. Instead of viewing excessive sleep as a symptom of a disease, it is more profitable to examine its acquisition by trial and error anxiety reduction, active parental teaching, or imitative learning in childhood. Recall that sleeping occurs as an adaptive response in the sensory-deprivation experiments. The more mature and integrated subjects made the greatest use of sleeping in this situation (Goldberger and Holt, 1958, 1961). Thus excessive sleeping may be adaptive or maladaptive, depending on the current situation.

Case histories suggest a wide variety of family situations, personality types, and emotional conflicts associated with excessive sleeping. Unfortunately, there is little systematic research and what there is tends to be inconsistent and conflicting. Some authors see excessive sleeping as an hysterical symptom (Langworthy and Betz, 1944; Pai, 1950). Other reports associate it with an obsessive-compulsive neurosis (Drake, 1949; Pond, 1952). Some find it present in several varieties of neurosis (Smith and Hamilton, 1959; Goldstein and Griffin, 1959). It is sometimes, although infrequently, found in depressed patients, especially those who are shy and passive (Drake, 1949; Kraines, 1957). Still others find a link with paranoid schizophrenia (Learman and Weiss, 1943; Smith, 1958). In this connection, Janet (1921) reports a psychotic case in which sleep lasted for five years, although one wonders if this was a coma.

The basic conflicts attributed to excessive sleepers also vary and probably reflect the theoretical biases of the authors. Aggression and hostility are the most frequently mentioned inhibited impulses (Davison, 1945; Drake, 1949; Schneck, 1952; Smith,

1958; Smith and Hamilton, 1959; Goldstein and Griffin, 1959). Sexual conflicts are also described (Davison, 1945; Spiegel and Oberndorf, 1946; Pond, 1952; Smith, 1958; Goldstein and Griffin, 1959). Guilt motivating a need for punishment, or even death, is emphasized by Davison (1945). Independence-dependence conflicts are found by Barker (1948) and Langworthy and Betz (1944).

In contrast to this bewildering variety of diagnostic labels and conflicts, nearly all writers agree on the observable personality characteristics of the excessive sleeper. He is described as passive, dependent, shy, constricted, withdrawn or immature. No one reports an aggressive personality. A student of the present writer, Dr. Carol Lucas, has made a careful and exhaustive analysis of the case material in this area. She concludes that, although the data are inadequate in many ways, they suggest the hypothesis that the excessive sleeper is a passive individual who has learned to use sleep as a defense against aggressive feelings.

The relationship between schizophrenia and excessive sleeping is of special interest because several theorists have described schizophrenia as a twilight or dream state (Ewen, 1934; Rosen, 1953). Oswald (1962) has described the similarities between schizophrenic and dream thought. Although an acute schizophrenic episode may be associated with insomnia, the early stages of a schizophrenic process, for example in adolescence, may find the individual spending 10 to 16 hours a day in bed (Sullivan, 1956). Just because the individual spends time in bed, however, does not mean that he is asleep. Sullivan (1950, p. 190) says that in the prolonged periods spent in bed by the preschizophrenic ". . . one sleeps deeply as little as possible; one remains alert and dozes as much as possible . . ." The time in bed may represent a withdrawal from reality and a concentration on inner fantasies. The drowsiness may facilitate actual dreaming but this does not mean the schizophrenic is in a continuous dream state during the day.

The possibility that the schizophrenic is asleep or in a dream state during the day was tested specifically by Rechtschaffen et al. (1964). Five schizophrenic patients were examined for EEG, REM, and EMG changes during the day. No evidence of dream periods were observed even when the patients were hallucinating or preoccupied by delusions. One patient had a brief period of actual sleep, but otherwise the EEG indicated full wakefulness. Other investigators also report that the cortical EEG does not differentiate schizophrenics from normals (Lyketos, Belinson, and Gibbs, 1953). On the other hand, Hodes, Heath, and Hendley (1954) report a sleep EEG from the sub-cortex and Corwin and Barry (1940) report breathing patterns suggesting daydreams in awake schizophrenics. On balance, the evidence does not support the idea that schizophrenia consists of living in a dream state. However, various conditions may produce normal drowsiness in the schizophrenic person.

A question has also been raised about the nocturnal sleep of schizophrenics—do they dream more than normal subjects? Dement (1955) compared normal and schizophrenic subjects. Rapid eye movements associated with dreams appeared in both groups. There was no difference in the type, incidence, or duration of REM's. Schizophrenics reported dreams about 60% of REM awakenings as opposed to 88% in the medical student control group. But Dement felt that much of this difference was due to schizophrenic negativism. Dream content was similar between the two groups, except that the schizophrenics dreamt more of isolated, inanimate objects—such as a shelf floating in mid-air. Even this may be due to distortion in the reports because qualitative observations of the eye movements did not indicate a lack of dreamer participation. Koresko et al. (1963) found no difference in dream time between hallucinating and nonhallucinating schizophrenics. On the other hand, there is the Fisher and Dement (1963) report on the patient increasing dream time during an acute psychotic episode. It is possible that acute anxiety increases dreaming, but this may not be specific to schizophrenia. At the present time, the evidence forces us to conclude that the sleep of schizophrenics does not differ in significant ways from other populations.

If sleep is used by a neurotic patient to "narcotize" anxiety, might it not also be used for therapeutic purposes? Sleep therapy was first tried in Switzerland in 1922 (see Wikler, 1957) and has gained some popularity, especially in the Soviet Union (Andreev, 1960). Sleep is induced by sedatives, electronarcosis, or suggestion for about 20 hours a day over a period of 10 to 20 days. It is said to be most effective in cases showing affective disturbances— catatonic excitement, manic states, depressions, and acute anxiety (Parfitt, 1946; Andreev, 1960; McGraw and Oliven, 1959). Obsessional cases do not seem to respond well. The overall therapeutic results are no more spectacular than those for other forms of therapy. No control groups have been used. Depending on the criteria, about a third to half the cases are said to be helped significantly, with the milder cases responding best (Azima, 1955; Andreev, 1960; McGraw and Oliven, 1959). Relapses are not uncommon (McGraw and Oliven, 1959).

Tiller (1964) instituted a program of "regimented rest" for about 20 elderly patients complaining of insomnia and sleeping less than 7 hours a night. They were required to rest in bed for 9 to 10 hours a night and 1 to 2 hours in mid-day. Not only did the patients report an increase in the duration of actual sleep, but they also reported a decrease in tension, anxiety, and somatic symptoms.

Aside from therapeutic claims, sleep therapy is of theoretical interest. McGraw and Oliven (1959) conclude that the best results are reported whenever a great deal of anxiety is present. This supports the idea that sleep and arousal are incompatible. But why would the mere temporary suppression of anxiety be helpful in adjustment? The Russian explanation is that prolonged sleep allows Pavlovian protective inhibition to build up (Andreev, 1960). In this sense, sleep is seen as a healing process, but there is no indication of what specific changes take place. To the extent that the anxious patient has lost sleep, sleep therapy would probably be helpful, just as the malnourished alcoholic is helped by an adequate diet. Others have thought that the regressive aspects of sleep therapy might be important (Azima, 1955). The entire therapeutic milieu seems to play a role (Andreev, 1960). It may also be that the extra "dream time" permits a discharge of tension. At the present time, there is no clear rationale for sleep therapy and no convincing evidence of its general effectiveness, but it seems to offer some research possibilities with regard to the nature of sleep and adjustment.

EMOTIONAL INTERFERENCE
WITH SLEEP

Just as sleep can be used to block out anxiety under some conditions, anxiety can prevent the occurrence of sleep. Sleep and anxiety are largely incompatible responses. Why does sleep win out in some cases and anxiety in others? This probably depends on the individual personality, the differential habit strength of the two responses, and the relative strength of the two motives at any given time. To say that anxiety sometimes prevents sleep and sleep sometimes reduces anxiety is not avoiding an issue; prediction requires a precise knowledge of the relevant factors.

According to Freud (1961) the biological wish to sleep can be impeded by strong emotions attached to unfulfilled needs. This can lead to anxiety dreams or insomnia. Fenichel (1945) reports that patients suffering from strong anxiety cannot relax enough to sleep. An inverse relationship between sleep and anxiety is also assumed by Sullivan (1953). He goes on to say that when powerful motivations are operating, deep and restful sleep is not possible. Children's sleep becomes more restless after being shown evening movies (Renshaw, Miller and Marquis, 1933). Physiologically, emotion may interfere with sleep by increasing blood pressure and muscular tension (Jacobson, 1929), hyperventilation (Conn, 1950), arousing the cortex (Riesenman, 1950), and bringing the sympathetic nervous system into play (Wexberg, 1949).

The disruption of sleep by anxiety is, perhaps, most clearly seen in the combat situation (Grinker and Spiegel, 1945). On the night before a mission, combat fliers have insomnia almost routinely. If they do sleep, they have nightmares. Frequently, sleep is impossible the night after a mission because of persevering emotional tension. The combat neuroses growing out of this situation are often accompanied by difficulty in falling asleep, nightmares, and fatigue upon arising.

Relevant here is a study on anxiety by Hamilton (1959).

Psychiatric ratings on a large number of symptoms were made on a group of neurotic anxiety patients. The results were factor-analyzed and a general anxiety dimension was obtained. Symptoms of insomnia (including nightmares and night terrors, as well as various kinds of broken sleep) had the highest loading on this factor. The second factor was bipolar and differentiated somatic from psychological forms of anxiety. The insomnia symptoms appear more related to the psychological forms of the anxiety—tension, anxious mood, depression, etc.

Insomnia is prominent in many neurotic and psychotic individuals (Sperling, 1955; Weiss, 1962). It is viewed as largely a psychogenic or psychosomatic symptom by Wexberg (1949), Caprio (1949), Kanner (1950), Weiss and English (1950), Karpman (1950), and many others. The proximate cause is anxiety, but the anxiety in turn is related to a variety of factors in different persons.

First of all, the insomniac may be afraid of an external source of danger. During sleeplessness the organism is alerted to external as well as internal stimuli (Freeman and Watts, 1942). Schizophrenic patients with insomnia frequently have the fear that others are watching them and, fearing malicious intent, they are unable to sleep (Burton and Harris, 1955). These unrealistic fears are, of course, related to the patients' inner motives, but appear in the form of external dangers. Realistic external dangers and worries may also produce sleeplessness (Fenichel, 1945, p. 189).

Psychoanalytic writers have emphasized the increased internal perception and general letdown of defenses associated with sleep (Rothenberg, 1947; Conn, 1950; Sullivan, 1953). This increases the danger of prohibited impulses coming into awareness and thus may produce insomnia (Fenichel, 1942; London, 1950, etc.). The favorite feared impulse of psychoanalytic writers is the sexual one, naturally. The temptation to masturbate may prevent sleep through feelings of guilt (Windholz, 1942; Karpman, 1950). Deeper Oedipal conflicts may be involved (Ujhely, 1950). Gutheil (1960, p. 333) reports a case of an elderly unmarried woman suffering from insomnia who said "I was very sleepy but I was afraid to fall asleep because when I dozed off I saw a pair of arms embracing me. I cried, 'no, no!'"

Nonsexual conflicts may also provide a source of anxiety preventing sleep. Hostile feelings and guilt may be involved (Davison, 1945; London, 1950; Sullivan, 1956). An example of this is the man who was avoiding the guilt of dreaming about the death of his wife (Gutheil, 1960). The loss of sleep may serve as the punishment for the guilt (Davison, 1945; Gilman, 1950). Sullivan (1956) believed that feelings of envy and jealousy are particularly sleep disturbing. Similarly, Wexberg (1949) sees ambition as a factor. Kingman (1930) thought that insomnia is an urban psychosis resulting from an "addiction to business." All these studies suggest that social strivings can provide a source of tension and thus insomnia.

A case illustrating neurotic insomnia is presented by Shaffer and Shoben (1956). A young coed developed a number of symptoms during her senior year, including depression, loss of appetite, constipation, and insomnia. She was unable to get to sleep until 2 or 3 in the morning, frequently slept through her classes until noon, and woke up feeling dull and tired. She was an only child and had been overprotected. She did well at school but was socially shy and withdrawn. Six months before the neurotic symptoms developed she fell in love with an older man, but was extremely conflicted and vacillating in the sexual part of their relationship. He broke it off eventually, and this was the major precipating factor, along with some career indecisiveness, in the insomnia and other symptoms. A little while later when she made some important career decisions and attracted another young man, the symptoms disappeared. One can see in this case the operation of sexual and independence conflicts, particularly as they relate to basic needs for love and self-esteem.

Sleep may also be feared for its symbolic value. Some individuals equate sleep with death (Kingman, 1930; Shneidman, 1964). There are examples in literature and religion of the intertwining of sleep and death. Feifel (1961) reports that many people prefer to die "peacefully in their sleep" as opposed to some other mode. The topic of sleep can also become integrated into delusional symptoms so that sleep or sleep rituals have complex symbolic meanings.

Going to a totally different tradition, the Hindus believed

that sleeplessness was to be found in four groups of people: 1) those persecuted by their superiors; 2) those deprived of wealth and property; 3) those consumed by a passion for unattainable women; and 4) professional thieves and housebreakers (Sarma, 1933). The picture is not too different from that painted by the psychoanalysts.

Finally, insomnia may be worsened by a fear of insomnia itself (Conn, 1950). Insomniacs are prone to exaggerate their loss of sleep (Gilman, 1950; Imboden and Lasagna, 1956). They worry about the effects on their health and sanity. A vicious circle is set up leading to chronic insomnia and daily fatigue.

The occurrence of insomnia may be traced back to learning experiences in childhood. Actually, true insomnia is rare in children (Kanner, 1957), but the label has been used to describe children who fight off sleep (Anderson, 1951). The term "sleep phobia" has also been used to describe the child who cannot go to sleep without the presence of the mother (Kanner, 1957). The child cannot go to sleep without her or if he awakens he cries for her. The fear of being separated from or losing the mother seems to be the basic anxiety (Anderson, 1951). The presence of the mother may also reduce the child's fear of losing control over aggressive impulses during sleep (Sperling, 1955).

Insomnia, along with other sleep disturbances, develops in a home in which there is some general emotional problem (Anderson, 1951). Sperling (1955) reports that children's insomnia is caused by a "neurotic" mother. Various parental anxieties revolving about adequacy, aggression, and competition may influence sleep disturbances in children (Hirschberg, 1957). Rejected delinquent boys have been found to sleep restlessly (Clardy and Hill, 1949-1950). Adult insomnia may be traced back to childhood experiences such as being punished for not sleeping (Weiss and English, 1950). Some children are punished by being sent to bed, which may associate sleep with loss of love. Other aspects of family socialization in the area of sleep will be discussed in the next chapter.

In which diagnostic groups does insomnia occur most frequently? According to Millet (1938), insomnia occurs in almost every neurosis. Nevertheless, there is a great deal of variability in the degree of disturbance from one individual to the next. Sullivan (1956) believed that persons with hypochondriacal, obsessional, and dissociational symptoms usually sleep well because the tensions are drained off adequately. However, when the threat to the personality is too great, these neurotic mechanisms do not function as well. Those with active envy, jealousy, and hate have more disturbed sleep. Thus, it depends on the degree to which active emotion has not been drained off. Conn (1950) reports that 80% of neurotics complain of anxiety and 50% of insomnia. Perhaps the insomnia occurs in the most anxious neurotics. Weiss et al. (1962) reports that insomnia in a psychiatric outpatient group is due almost exclusively to emotional factors rather than physical or environmental ones.

The incidence of insomnia in schizophrenia is a matter of some dispute. There is no doubt that there is a great deal of variability in sleep disturbance in this diagnostic category. To a large extent this is due to a difference between acute and chronic schizophrenic states. As mentioned earlier, Sullivan (1956) reports long periods spent in a drowsy state in the preschizophrenic period. During the acute phase, however, insomnia may appear dramatically. Sullivan (1956, pp. 158-160) reports that before the development of the paranoid mechanism, the sleep function in the paranoid schizophrenic is badly disturbed. A major psychotic break is sometimes accompanied by a prolonged period of insomnia (McGraw and Oliven, 1959; Bliss, Clark, and West, 1959). Excited paranoid patients require large doses of drugs to quiet them (Magnussen, 1953).

Recall from the chapter on personality adjustment during sleep deprivation, that prolonged wakefulness produces perceptual, emotional, and thinking changes, which while not truly psychotic in themselves may facilitate psychotic symptoms. Of particular interest here, is the study by Koranyi and Lehmann (1960) in which the acute psychotic symptoms returned during a sleep-deprivation experiment with six chronic schizophrenic patients who had been free of acute symptoms for years.

Stuporous catatonic patients show a peculiar sleep disturbance that is not true insomnia, but neither is it restful sleep. Both the EEG (Deglin, 1958) and motility measures show little difference between the wakeful and sleeping states. On the other hand, nonstuporous catatonics show sleep-wakeful patterns similar to normals (Forbes, 1934; Magnussen, 1953; Deglin, 1958). The catatonic stupor represents a more acute phase of this particular disorder and possibly more emotional turmoil.

In contrast to the sleep disturbance during the acute phase, chronic schizophrenics tend to sleep well. Sullivan (1956), who probably knew more about schizophrenics than anyone, said that after the acute stage the sleep of the schizophrenic is profound because of the general regression of the self-system. The paranoid patient may continue to complain of difficulty in sleeping, but objective evidence, such as lines in the face, show he is sleeping much better than during the acute phase. The sleep of the paranoid may be interrupted, however, by persecutory dreams. Objective evidence generally supports Sullivan. While some insomnia is seen in chronic schizophrenics, it is considerably less than in depression (Ewen, 1934; Cason, 1935; Liberson, 1945; Deglin, 1958; Kraines, 1957). The general schizophrenic regression is shown in the area of sleep by a breakdown in the usual diurnal rhythm, with sleeping occurring irregularly throughout the day in many patients (Schulte, 1955). This is reminiscent of the infant's polyphasic sleep pattern. Nowadays, it is difficult to observe many of these patterns because of the effects of drugs, total push milieu therapy, etc. With respect to the persecutory dreams Sullivan mentioned, Cason (1935) found that although a smaller percentage of a psychotic group reported nightmares, those who did experienced them more frequently than normals. Schulte (1955) concludes that ". . . during the night there is much more calm in the wards of schizophrenic patients than in those of the depressives . . ."

The differentiation between acute and chronic schizophrenia provides a good working hypothesis in understanding the relationship between schizophrenia and sleep disturbances. The acute phase, which may represent an attempt to regain social contact, may lead to insomnia. The acute phase is by definition a time of emotional turmoil, whether this is the persecutory anxiety of the paranoid or the affective stupor of the catatonic. In other words, the insomnia is produced by active emotional arousal. The chronic schizophrenic, or the insidiously developing schizophrenic, is dealing with active emotional stress by a massive regression. In the area of sleep this regression often appears as more profound sleep, infantile sleep patterns, or a drowsy withdrawal from reality.

Insomnia is one of the classical symptoms of depression. Excessive crying in neurotic, psychotic, and involutional insomniacs has been noted frequently (Burton and Harris, 1955; Weiss and English, 1950). Within this diagnostic grouping, however, there is considerable variability. Part of this is due to the cyclical nature of depression; it waxes and wanes in depth. Kraines (1957) found that the worst insomnia occurs at the depth of the depression—the person has difficulty falling asleep and wakes up after a few hours. Before and after the deepest depression, insomnia is only moderate. Furthermore, during the very early stages in the development of the depression and upon the return to normality, hypersomnia may appear with the patient sleeping 10 to 14 hours a night. EEG evidence supports this (Diaz-Guerrero et al., 1946). In a statistical study of depression, Grinker et al. (1961) found that 55% of the patients had difficulty in getting to sleep. Thirty-five percent awoke during the night, 47% woke up very early in the morning, and 87% required sedation for sleep.

Anxiety seems to interfere mostly with going to sleep and produces so-called initial insomnia, while depression is more closely associated with early waking or terminal insomnia (McGraw and Oliven, 1959). Anxiety is usually mixed with the depression—as many as 67% of depressed patients show overt signs of anxiety (Grinker et al., 1961). Kraines (1957) reports that over 60% of deeply depressed patients have anxious, terrifying dreams, even though they were not aware of their dreams previously. The dreams of the depressed have a good deal of masochistic content according to Beck and Hurvich (1959). The scale used to measure masochistic dream content included unpleasant affect, crying, and unpleasant experiences. This is probably why both initial and terminal insomnia are found in a depressed population. Muncie (1934) describes a transition from initial to terminal insomnia in some depressions—the patient at first is worried and anxious so that he does not fall asleep easily, but later as he becomes more depressed he wakes up early. There is no simple explanation for these different types of insomnia with anxiety and depression, although they seem empirically true.

The sleep of depressed patients has been studied with the new EEG-REM technique (Oswald et al., 1963). Six depressed patients and six matched normal controls were observed. The depressed patients spent significantly more of the night awake, with the records showing initial, intermittent, and terminal types of insomnia. When the depressed patients did sleep, however, they showed a normal percentage of time in REM periods. A barbiturate reduced the time awake, as well as motility, EEG shifts, and duration of REM's.

Patients in a manic state do not sleep much. At the beginning of a manic episode sleep may be deep and refreshing; then sleep is reduced to 2 to 4 hours, although it is refreshing and comes easily; finally, in the acute phase sleep is almost completely absent and activity is constant (Kraines, 1957). Day and night motility is high in manic patients (Kammerer et al., 1957, p. 1935). While this state results in a decrease in sleep, the subjective feeling of fatigue is not present. Nevertheless, if the manic is allowed to prolong his incessant activity during the acute phase, he frequently dies of a heart attack. Since mania is thought of as a reaction to depression, the situation can be thought of as a defensive arousal interfering with sleep.

As mentioned earlier, insomnia is a fairly common complaint among the aged (Liberson, 1945; Ginzberg, 1955; Tiller, 1964). At least some of this seems to be due to emotional disturbance. More sleep disturbances are found in older people who have some form of psychopathology (Ginzberg, 1955; Busse, 1960). The type of insomnia most common in geriatric patients is terminal, suggesting depression (McGraw and Oliven, 1960). Tiller (1964) reports that older people sleeping less than 7 hours a night complain of tension, fatigue, apprehension, and somatic symptoms. The cause and effect relationship is not clear here but there is some reason to believe that the emotional factors produce the insomnia. Many elderly people, particularly those in institutions, feel rejected and unwanted. Ginzberg found that those patients who had fewest social contacts and most difficulty in adjusting to the hospital also had the most sleep disturbance.

Treatment of insomnia revolves around the reduction of anxiety by one means or another. Various sedative drugs are used although they often have undesirable side effects (McGraw and Oliven, 1959). Progressive relaxation is the method Jacobson (1929) insists is most effective. Favorable results have been reported after pre-frontal lobotomy (Freeman and Watts, 1942; Cohn, 1950; McGraw and Oliven, 1959), although this seems a bit radical. According to Weiss and English (1950) a harmful way of treating insomnia is telling the patient that he really did sleep well. The main thing seems to be to reduce anxiety. This could also occur as a result of psychotherapy if the sources of the anxiety were eliminated.

BEHAVIORAL DISTURBANCES DURING SLEEP

In the previous sections it was shown that sleep can be used to reduce anxiety or anxiety can prevent sleep. This section will deal with the kind of sleep disturbance that involves some overt behavioral manifestation during sleep. The major behavioral disturbances are: night terrors, nightmares, sleepwalking, and bedwetting.

We will begin with a discussion of the behavioral sleep disturbances in childhood because these have been studied most systematically. Clardy and Hill (1949-1950) list the major sleep disorders in childhood with the frequency of their occurrence as follows: night terrors or *pavor nocturnus* 3%, nightmares 7%, sleep walking 1%, enuresis 26%. Minor disturbances, such as restlessness, mumbling, talking, teeth-grinding, early or frequent waking, and difficulty in falling asleep are found in about 46% of the population. Anthony (1959) has determined the incidence of three of these symptoms in different age groups, as is shown in Table VI. Night terrors occur in the youngest group most frequently, nightmares in an older group, and sleepwalking around puberty.

Table VI

AGE PATTERNING IN A SAMPLE OF CHILDREN
WITH SLEEP DISTURBANCES

	Age groups		
	4 - 7	8 - 10	11 - 14
Night terrors	18	7	5
Nightmares	3	11	2
Sleepwalking	1	6	13

After Anthony, 1959.

A chi square analysis of Anthony's descriptive data shows a significant relationship between age and type of disturbance (p<.001). Kleitman (1939) also reports that night terrors are most frequent between the ages of 3 and 8. Pierce and Lipcon (1956 b) report the onset of sleepwalking from 7 to 15 years, although many subjects reported "lifelong" somnambulism.

In 1897, de Menacèiene (described in Anthony, 1959) produced night terrors in children experimentally by waking them out of a sound sleep and producing fear by suggesting different things—for example, that the house was on fire. The child was in a kind of hypnogogic state at this point and showed terror along with cataleptic posturing. The night terror was produced most easily with children from 3 to 8, when awakened from a deep sleep, who also showed a "nervous disposition" and "suggestibility." The attacks were comparable to those occurring spontaneously. Wendt (1952) observed that children with night terrors are hyperactive and emotionally sensitive. So, although night terrors may have an organic basis as we mentioned earlier in this chapter, they may be precipitated by anxiety.

Nightmares have also been produced experimentally (Murray, 1933). After five 11-year old girls played a game of "murder," one girl had a fearful nightmare in which she was convinced that burglars had entered her room. Two of the other girls who had also been frightened at the "murder" game, believed her and refused to sleep in the same room, but the remaining fearless pair were unaffected. The first girl continued to have nightmares with burglar content for several months.

Sleepwalking in children has been compared with night terrors by Kanner (1957) because in both anomalies there is amnesia for the events, consciousness is clouded, and waking does not occur. Sleepwalkers, however, sometimes remember the episode as a dream. Nightmares, on the other hand, are vividly recalled and typically awaken the child with a feeling of suffocation and helplessness.

Anthony was struck by the age specificity of night terrors, nightmares, and sleepwalking as it relates to developmental level. Thus, night terrors occur during the time when the child is extremely "realistic" according to Piaget (1960). This is when the normal child thinks of the dream as a real object in the room. Nightmares occur after the child normally distinguishes between illusion and reality to some extent. By puberty the child usually has identified the source of the dream as internal, although it is not clear how this would relate to sleepwalking.

Anthony goes further and distinguishes two syndromes: a visual and a motor one. There is also a mixed type. The visual syndrome includes both nightmares and night terror groups. During the day these children tend to develop day terrors and phobias. They are more visually oriented on several laboratory tests than are age-matched neurotic controls to a statistically significant degree. Similarly, they tend to have more eidetic imagery. Their interests are in the visual arts, frequently.

On the other hand, the motor syndrome consists of the sleepwalkers who during the daytime show symptoms such as tics, stammer, and restlessness. They are not good visualizers and have significantly less intense dream imagery than neurotic controls. Their interests are more in the area of crafts and athletics, although this may be due to the fact that most of them are boys. This group shows a significantly higher performance than verbal I.Q. on the WISC. Sandler (1945) also believes that sleepwalkers have strong kinesthetic imagery, although his data suggest that their imagery is strong in all modalities.

Anthony believes that the choice of sleep disturbance is dependent upon these innate visual or motor tendencies rather than environmental or psychological factors. Anthony also believes, however, that the content of the sleep disturbance comes from the emotional problems of the child. We have no quarrel with the importance of constitutional and maturational factors in determining the specific symptom. A young child is more likely to have a night terror than an older one. But from a psychological point of view the interesting question is why a sleep disturbance of any kind occurs and what emotional factors might be involved.

Anthony also compared the group of children with major sleep disturbances and the control group of equally neurotic but non-sleep-disturbed children on the basis of emotional background factors. The critical differentiating item in the history of the sleep-disturbed children was the presence of a "highly anxious, phobic, and fear-communicating mother." This occurred 73% of the time in the sleep of the disturbed group and only 34% of the time in the neurotic controls and was statistically significant at the .01 level. Also differentiating the groups was the presence of emotional or physical trauma and separation from the mother. The length of time the child slept in the parents' bedroom—and thus may have been exposed to parental sexual relations—also differentiated the groups but may have occurred after the development of the sleep symptoms. On the other hand, interparental aggression, suppression of daytime activities, birth of a sibling, family history of mental illness, and undue parental pressures failed to show statistically significant differences between the groups.

Anthony had the parents fill out check lists having to do with anxiety. The mother and sleep-disturbed child showed a positive correlation on a "fear" check list, especially on items related to sexuality and pregnancy. This was also the clinical impression of interviewers. The ratings of the parents further showed that the sleep-disturbed children were more fearful than the neurotic controls, as well as being more suggestible.

Night terrors, nightmares, and sleepwalking are considered to be psychogenic by Sperling (1949-1950). Anxiety connected with sexual and aggressive motives is the motivating force (Sperling, 1955; Sperling, 1959). Fraiberg (1950) points specifically to trauma such as separation from the mother, which was confirmed by Anthony's study. Sperling (1958) distinguishes between psychotic, neurotic, and traumatic forms of *pavor nocturnus*. The psychotic type seems closest to the syndrome described by Anthony.

The strong suspicion that this psychotic type of *pavor nocturnus* is organic is reminiscent of the difficulty in separating organic and autistic children. The milder forms of *pavor nocturnus* and nightmares are more clearly psychogenic. (See the chapter on dreams for an additional discussion of nightmares.)

The role of anxiety in children's sleep disorders seems clear. The severity of the anxiety seems to be important in producing disturbances of sleep, rather than the specific family dynamics (Anthony, 1959). However, once severe anxiety is roused in a child by a phobic mother, separation anxiety, etc., then the choice of specific sleep symptom may depend on constitutional and maturational factors.

Sleepwalking may persist into young adulthood, or even beyond. This comes to light most frequently in situations involving communal sleeping such as military service. Pai (1946, 1950) found that 6% of a neurotic population in the Army suffered from somnambulism. About 5% of normal college freshmen report sleepwalking (Jenness and Jorgensen, 1954).

Sleepwalking has been described as an hysterical dissociative symptom (Janet, 1920). Most authors see it as the acting out of a dream (Maslow and Mittelmann, 1951; Gutheil, 1960; Anthony, 1959). Sleep-talking, gnashing of teeth, or hitting the pillow would be minor actions in accordance with the dream imagery. Sleep-talking can occur in nondream periods but seems related to awakening in the experimental situation. Sleep-talking during REM periods is related to dream content (Rechtschaffen et al., 1962). In sleepwalking the entire behavioral sequence emerges. The person may hike through the woods while still sleeping. Eyes are open and obstacles are usually avoided, but the individual is not awake and often has amnesia for the whole episode. Suggestibility is usually heightened. There is a startling case of an entire family going out for a sleepwalk (Anthony, 1959).

The most recent evidence throws doubt on the traditional

view that sleepwalking is the acting out of a dream (Luce, 1965). Sleepwalkers, studied in a laboratory at U.C.L.A., became somnambulistic only from EEG stage 4. As the episode progressed, they showed an awake alpha rhythm. It is possible that the sleepwalking substitutes for dreams as an enuresis.

The meaning of the action is sometimes apparent. One therapy patient would get up at night and walk toward his brother's bed clenching his fist as if to choke someone. Another patient would walk toward his mother's room to make sure she was not having relations with a strange man (Gutheil, 1960). Soldiers sometimes relive battle experiences in the somnambulistic episode (Pai, 1946). There are several recorded cases of homicide committed during a period of somnambulism (Podolsky, 1959).

Sleepwalking is not believed to appear as a totally isolated symptom. Usually the somnambulist is thought to be a maladjusted individual with a host of problems and other symptoms (Sandler, 1945; Pai, 1950; Maslow and Mittelmann, 1951). Pai (1940) found psychogenic causes for about 83% of his sleepwalkers. However, another study showed no difference in the incidence of sleepwalking in a neurotic group and carefully matched normal control group (Tapia et al., 1958). About 13% of the normals reported sleepwalking and only 11% of the neurotics. Nevertheless, as the authors point out, their data were historical, i.e., the sleepwalking in the controls might have occurred during a tense period in childhood. Certainly more data are needed, but this evidence is enough to doubt that sleepwalking necessarily represents a disrupting lifelong neurosis. It could be that the relatively common conflict over masturbation at puberty generates enough tension to produce sleepwalking without massive psychopathology (Maslow and Mittelmann, 1951).

Although sleepwalking may not require a well-developed neurosis, some tension or anxiety does seem to be the motivating factor. Pai (1946) reports that severe anxiety was the most common psychogenic cause in his group of somnambulists. In another study, about 50% of a group of Navy recruits with somnambulism believed that apprehension about the future, rumination about past grievances, or preoccupation with financial difficulties would bring on an episode of sleepwalking (Pierce and Lipcon,

1956 b). In line with the importance of anxiety is the observation that sleepwalking responds well to sodium amytal interviews (Sandler, 1945). However, other anxiety symptoms may take the place of the sleepwalking.

Descriptions of the personality of the sleepwalker suggest an immature, insecure, and dependent pattern. They tend to have poor heterosexual adjustment and have little interest in children, possibly viewing them as rivals (Sandler, 1945). Sleepwalkers tend to be conforming and noncompetitive. Under stress they withdraw and feel humiliated, with sleepwalking episodes likely after such an experience (Pierce and Lipcon, 1956 b). The overall pattern is similar to that of the excessive sleeper.

In childhood the somnambulist is said to have been typically immature, frequently the youngest child, and dependent on the father and older brother. The mother is often domineering, anxious, and punitive (Sandler, 1945). In many cases, the home situation was extremely insecure because of ill health of one of the parents. By age 10, 30% of the sleepwalkers had been separated from their parents in one way or another. Sometimes the sleepwalking begins immediately after the separation from the mother (Pierce and Lipcon, 1956 b). The specific learning of the sleepwalking habit has not been studied much, but one observation suggesting the possibility of social imitation is that several patients had one or more family members who were also somnambulists (Sandler, 1945). The somnambulist often has a history of enuresis and nightmares, suggesting that the overall sleep disturbance passed through different symptom phases (Pierce and Lipcon, 1956 b).

Enuresis occurs in about 15% of all children between the ages of 4 and 14 (Baller and Schalock, 1956). As mentioned in the chapter on dreams, enuresis in children occurs at a synchronized level of sleep, often accompanied by an erection, and functions as a dream substitute (Pierce, Whitman, Maas and Gay, personal communication). However, enuresis in young adults may also occur in connection with dreams and the cause is more clearly emotional (Ditman and Blinn, 1955).

The enuretic is usually maladjusted in many areas (Pierce and Lipcon, 1959). It is seen by many clinicians as a symptom of anxiety and conflict (Wiesenhutter, 1954; Decurtins, 1957). Castration fears centering around sexual conflicts are thought to be the main source of anxiety by psychoanalytic observers (Sperling, 1949-1950; Palm, 1953; Grunewald, 1954).

Enuresis appears most often in a passive aggressive personality marked by many indications of immaturity (Wiesenhutter, 1954; Pierce and Lipcon, 1956 b). Male delinquents show a high incidence of enuresis (Bachet, 1951; Michaels, 1955). The basis of the symptom seems to be a feeling of isolation and abandonment stemming from parental rejection (Bostock, 1951; Decurtins, 1957) and especially a disturbed mother-child relationship (Imhof, 1956). The bedwetting symptom is often seen in other family members (Pierce and Lipcon, 1959) and is often dealt with punitively or inconsistently by the parents (Wiesenhutter, 1954).

While this hardly constitutes an adequate review of the specialized topic of enuresis, the literature as a whole strongly suggests that enuresis occurs very frequently on a psychogenic basis. The symptom depends on anxiety, tension, and inhibited anger.

As an addendum, nocturnal orgasms might also be mentioned briefly. Tapia et al. (1958) interviewed normal and neurotic male and female subjects on this point. Fifty-one percent of the normal males and 60% of the neurotic males report this experience; the difference is not significant. On the other hand, 47% of neurotic females report nocturnal orgasms while only 8% of the female controls do. Unfortunately, this last figure is based on only a few cases, so it may be distorted. Nevertheless, Kinsey et al. (1953) found only 22% of a mixed population of females reported this phenomenon. Thus, the possibility exists that, especially in females, nocturnal orgasms represent a neurotic symptom. The orgasms usually accompany dreams and may be part of a general sexual and interpersonal problem.

HYPNOSIS AND SLEEP

The topic of hypnosis is somewhat aside from the main issues in this book and will not be dealt with at length.

It has often been associated with sleep pathology; for example, parallels have been drawn between hypnosis and somnambulism.

For many years, hypnosis was thought to be a specially induced form of sleep. Bernheim, in particular, believed that hypnosis was physiological sleep. The hypnotic induction typically involves suggestions to relax, relax deeply, and fall asleep. The subject may give the outward appearance of being asleep. Nevertheless, objective evidence throws doubt on the equation of hypnosis with sleep.

Physiological measures of various sorts sometimes suggest that the person in the hypnotic trance is asleep but more frequently do not (see Kleitman, 1939, Chapter 32 for a summary). Salivary and gastric secretion changes suggest sleep; but tendon reflexes, PGR, BMR, and other measures are not different from the waking state. Circulatory and respiratory changes in both directions have been reported in hypnosis; it has been suggested that some investigators actually let the subject slip into natural sleep.

Most of the controversy has revolved around the EEG measure of sleep (see Gill and Brenman, 1961, Chapter 6 for a summary). The general finding seems to be that most hypnotic states are clearly different from natural sleep. Under certain circumstances, sleep may be suggested to the subject with an appropriate EEG resulting. However, highly synchronized sleep is rarely found under any circumstances.

Recently, Becker, Bachman, and Friedman (1962) were able to induce changes hypnotically in d.c. potentials similar to those of sleep. According to a personal report from Friedman, the hypnotist, highly synchronized sleep was not obtainable. Furthermore, the general sleep effect was never as dramatic as the induction of local analgesia, using d.c. potentials as the criterion.

The general conclusion that can be drawn from the physiological evidence is that hypnosis is not equivalent to sleep. Still, as Gill and Brenman point out, this does not preclude the possibility of a state of drowsiness, possibly a dream-like condition. Many technical problems remain unsolved. For instance, drugs, light sleep, or relaxation may make the person more suggestible but not be the critical feature of hypnosis. Then, too, the suggestion to go to sleep may be a complicating factor; subjects hypnotized with nonsleep suggestions may be showing analgesia, amnesia, etc., but no signs of sleep.

On the psychological level there is another important difference between sleep and hypnosis. Most investigators are aware of the great importance of the relationship between the hypnotist and the subject. It is a special, intense sort of dependency condition. By definition, hypnotism is the situation in which one person has an unusual degree of control over another. Thus, an essential part of hypnosis is the control by an external person. In sleep, on the other hand, all relationships with the external environment are minimized (Gill and Brenman, 1961).

Similarly, hypnosis differs from sleep in that it involves continued control of behavior by the person. Under the influence of the hypnotist, the person can do things, remember material, and so on. The only naturally occurring analog is somnambulism. Gill and Brenman suggest that the relationship between hypnotism and somnambulism is worthy of study. Recall that the typical sleepwalker is immature, dependent, and especially, overconforming (Pierce and Lipcon, 1956 b).

Finally, there is the possibility—suggested by the EEG studies—that hypnosis is a dream-like state. According to the review by Gill and Brenman, the general level of thought of the hypnotized subject is not like that of the dreamer—it is not concrete or pictorialized, too much verbal content is present. But dreams can be induced very easily during hypnosis. While much of the dream content revolves around the transference to the hypnotist, unconscious impulses are also aroused and represented in the dream. Gill and Brenman believe that this is due to the regression in hypnosis which is comparable to the decrease in cognitive functions during sleep.

SUMMARY

The purpose of this chapter was to examine the pathology of sleep to see if they are consistent with a motivational analysis of sleep. Other physiological motives, particularly hunger, defecation, and sex are involved in psychopathology in many complex ways. This may be on an organic or psychological basis. Important psychological factors are emotional involvement, personality conflict, and personality structure.

Most of the symptoms of sleep disturbance can be caused by organic pathology. Neural injury or inherited defect can be seen in cases of excessive sleep and insomnia. These seem to depend on actual interference with the known mechanisms for synchronized sleep, aroused sleep, and wakefulness. Conditions interfering with brain metabolism also produce disturbances of the sleep function. General brain pathology, such as epilepsy, may be involved in night terrors, sleepwalking, and bedwetting, possibly by upsetting the neural mechanisms for dream behavior. All of this can be explained on the basis of interference with the physiological substrate of the sleep motive. Nevertheless, not all sleep disturbances are on an organic basis, and thus psychological influence is not precluded.

Excessive sleeping can develop as a neurotic symptom. It serves to avoid the perception of internal or external sources of anxiety. While many motives may be involved, hostile feelings are prominent. When in a situation that arouses hostility the person becomes anxious, but by falling asleep he reduces the anxiety. Thus it is a symptom, or response, reinforced by anxiety reduction. Prolonged sleep has been used as a psychotherapy. To the extent that it is effective at all, it seems to work best in excited, anxious states, thus illustrating the tendency of sleep to inhibit anxiety.

On the other hand, anxiety, depression, mania, and similar affective states that arouse the person may produce insomnia. The conditions under which anxiety produces sleeplessness or under which sleep is used to narcotize anxiety are not well known. Nevertheless, in this regard, sleep is like other physiological motives: overeating or hypersexuality may reduce anxiety, but eating and sexual performance may also be inhibited by anxiety. While this may be one weak reed supporting another, it shows the similarity in the pathology of sleep and that of hunger, sex, and other motives.

Anxiety also plays an important role in behavioral anomalies such as night terrors, nightmares, sleepwalking, and enuresis. Both night terrors and nightmares have been produced experimentally by fear-arousing methods. However, there seems to be a strong maturational factor in symptom choice—night terrors are most frequent in preschoolers, nightmares in lower school grade children, with sleepwalking typically appearing around puberty. Innate tendencies toward visual or motor dominance may also partly determine the specific symptom. There is even some question as to whether these sleep disturbances occur any more frequently in a neurotic population. Still, the role of emotional factors—whether on a neurotic level or not—seems clear.

The data relating sleep disturbances to specific psychological conflicts seem hopelessly confused at the present time. Sexual, aggressive, dependence, independence, achievement, competitive, and numerous other motives have been described. The discovery of a particular conflict seems to depend on the theoretical bias of the clinician. One can simply conclude that the data are inadequate. However, the very multiplicity of motives described suggests, to some extent, that the presence of anxiety from any source may produce sleep disturbances. Thus if an individual is concerned about any problem that poses a threat to the personality—for example, an impulse to masturbate that conflicts with social mores, a loss of social status—anxiety will be produced and defended against. Most defenses involve cognitive activity or bodily tension, so sleep is disturbed. The exception is where sleep is the defense against anxiety.

The incidence of sleep disturbances in various diagnostic categories is a bit clearer. Excessive sleeping, in its clearest form, is a neurotic disturbance. Chronic schizophrenia may involve a great deal of time spent in bed as part of the general withdrawal and regression, but this appears to be a drowsy or dreamy state rather than profound sleep. Insomnia is seen in all diagnostic groups involving emotional arousal—anxious neurotics, schizophrenics in the acute stage, depressives, manics, maladjusted geriatric patients, and those suffering from situational anxiety. Behavioral disturbances have not been related often to diagnostic categories, but seem to be most prevalent in neuroses and character disorders. In general, the critical element appears to be the emotional disturbance rather than the specific diagnostic category.

Personality structure may be a more relevant variable. While the information is far from complete, case histories of excessive sleepers, sleepwalkers, enuretics, and sufferers from night terrors or nightmares show a trend that at least suggests a testable hypothesis. The pattern is that of an immature, dependent, suggestible, and outwardly passive individual with inner tensions revolving around suppressed hostility. Many of the symptoms function as a passive-aggressive weapon. Insomnia seems to be more widespread, but even here the most severe insomnia is associated with depression, which has often been related to dependency and inhibited hostility. The impression one gets is that the sleep-disturbed individual is too inhibited to deal with problems during the day in a direct manner, so he takes them to bed with him—narcotizing them, wrestling with them, or acting them out in various ways.

How do sleep disturbances develop? Neuropathology, maturation, and genetic predisposition probably are involved. Nevertheless, social learning in the early family situation appears as an important influence. This may be a direct kind of teaching, as in the case of the excessive sleeper who was always told to sleep when angry or the insomniac who was sent to bed as a form of isolation punishment. Through association, sleep can become equivalent to a masturbation temptation, the eruption of hostile impulses, or the individual's concept of death. In general, the disruption of sleep by anxiety probably requires less specific learning than the other symptoms because of the innate incompatibility between sleep and anxiety.

The relationship between the mother and child is a key learning experience in childhood. Sleep disturbances seem to be related to this. Anxiety about separation from the mother is seen in childhood insomnia and sleep phobia, sleepwalking, enuresis, and other sleep disturbances. The child's security is dependent on the mother, so if she is disturbed he will be too. In this connection, the mothers of insomniacs have been described as "neurotic"; the mothers of sleepwalkers as anxious, domineering, and punitive; and the mothers of sleep-disturbed children as anxious and phobic. The fears of sleep-disturbed children and their mothers tend to be correlated. The frequent mention of a family history of sleep disturbances in those with sleep symptoms, while possibly indicating heredity, raises the chance of imitative learning.

The psychopathology of sleep, as a whole, can be understood as an anxiety phenomenon. Anxiety originating in the social relationships upon which the person's security depends, constitutes the basic motivation involved in sleep disturbance. Along with physiological factors, specific learning situations in childhood determine whether sleep will be the function implicated and, if so, what particular symptom will be acquired. This combination of basic anxiety, physiological influence, and specific learning is comparable to the psychopathologies involved in hunger, sex, and other motives. The next chapter will deal with the development of the sleep motive in more detail.

Hypnotism often involves the induction of a state resembling sleep, but physiological and psychological evidence shows that it is not the same as synchronized sleep. It may have some of the characteristics of drowsiness, dreams, somnambulism, and other states involving a concentration of attention.

The entire area of sleep pathology is ripe for systematic research. We have learned about as much as we can from case studies and casual observation. The clinical material suggests hypotheses that can now be tested with the EEG-REM techniques, objective personality tests, and well-designed field and laboratory experiments. The few investigations along these lines have already toppled several myths and suggested new formulations.

The available data on the pathology of sleep—inadequate as they are—are consistent with a motivational analysis of the sleep function. Neuropathology depends on the malfunctioning of the physiological mechanisms for sleep and wakefulness. Psychopathology depends on anxiety and early social learning, as do other forms of motivational pathology. The basic antagonism between sleep and arousal, discussed earlier, is supported by the data on pathology. In brief, then, the pathology of sleep supports an interpretation of sleep as a motive.

CHAPTER 9

The Socialization of Sleep

In earlier chapters, it was shown that responses relevant to the sleep motive may be learned. The way the person behaves during sleep deprivation may also reflect various kinds of learning. Finally, the different types of psychopathology mentioned in the last chapter may come about through learning in early childhood. The purpose of this chapter is to examine the learning that society imposes on the individual with respect to sleeping behavior.

General psychology, and learning theory in particular, is not ordinarily concerned with *what* is learned. The general laws of learning are concerned with the process of attaching responses to stimuli in any organism. This is why general psychological theories appear so abstract and unrelated to human beings as we know them. To understand a given social phenomenon, it is necessary to add information about the content of the learned material to the general laws of behavior.

The study of the content of psychological processes depends on other fields—particularly developmental psychology, anthropology, and sociology. These fields tell us what the conditions of learning are in a given culture, community, or family The process by which an individual learns the responses to a given situation, with a given motive, in accordance with the customs of a given society, is called socialization.

In this chapter, we will first describe the socialization of physiological motives. Then there will be a discussion of developmental patterns in sleep behavior as they have been studied in our culture. Following this, we will examine cross-cultural variations in sleep customs and present an empirical study of the attitudes of American college students toward sleep behavior. Techniques of training children in the area of sleep will be examined. Finally, we will see if sleep is comparable to other basic motives in terms of the socialization process.

SOCIALIZATION OF PHYSIOLOGICAL MOTIVES

All human beings have the basic physiological motives of hunger, thirst, elimination, sex, and so forth. At birth, the demands of babies are the same the whole world over. Yet when the same babies reach adulthood they have vastly different ways of meeting their needs. One person will only eat a tasteless paste made from roots, another is happy only with beluga caviar. One eats only with a large, happy group, another turns his back and eats in a suspicious silence. One eats four or five times a day, another but once. The intervening variable here, of course, is cultural learning.

Every viable culture makes provision for the satisfaction of basic needs, but each one does it in its own way, based on environmental and economic realities, historically derived adaptive customs, and irrational beliefs and values. The hunger and thirst motives are satisfied with certain foodstuffs, at certain times and places, and under certain conditions. Likewise, eliminative, sexual, and other motives are nearly always gratified eventually but under prescribed conditions.

The control of basic motives is mediated through internalized custom and taboo. In our culture everyone eats with a knife and fork, in another no one eats the totem animal. One does not defecate in the street in modern Western civilization. Marrying one's sister is unthinkable in most societies. Violation of a cultural prescription for motivational satisfaction usually leads to a feeling of guilt or dread, as well as a sense of isolation from one's fellows.

The process goes further. The very customs and institutions set up to mediate the gratification of physiological motives become valued and venerated. A Frenchman will die defending the honor of the wine from his neighborhood vineyards. The noble institutions of marriage, motherhood, and Thanksgiving turkey bolster morale on the battlefront. The loyalty to a given economic system—even by those benefiting least—defies the imagination.

How does this all come about? The primary situation in which socialization takes place in all cultures is the family. Here, in the context of loving care, the development of the child is molded to fit the customs of the society. Several aspects of motivation come under social control.

First, the timing of motive satisfaction is determined by custom. For example, American children at birth require seven or eight feedings a day but by four weeks this has been reduced to five or six, and by maturity to three main meals a day (Gesell et al., 1940). This is not entirely a maturational phenomenon, as any parent attempting to do away with the 2:00 a.m. feeding has learned. There is no physiological reason why adults should not eat seven or eight times a day—in fact, the American tradition of coffee-breaks and midnight snacks represents a tendency in this direction. But it would be very hard to keep a society organized, and production flowing smoothly, if everyone ate on an *ad lib* schedule.

The second area of control is the place for the gratification of motives. We eat in dining rooms, kitchens, and restaurants—not ordinarily in the bedroom. Sexual gratification, on the other hand, is usually left for the bedroom. Eliminative needs are even more highly restricted in most cultures as to the place of execution.

Another area in which the influence of culture is seen, is in the proper dress for particular motivated behavior. We dress well to go out to dinner. In some sub-cultures a certain degree of dress is necessary even for sexual relations. Other conditions may become customary—candlelight at dinner, no light during marital relations, and others.

Finally, the object that is to be used for motivational gratification is frequently prescribed by culture. Thus, we eat the meat of cattle but not that of dogs. We acquire tastes for sweet and sour pork, *pâté de foie gras,* snails, or chocolate-covered ants. In addition, appropriate food objects may change throughout development. At first, breast milk is given the child, then he is weaned and required to use a cup, eat solids, etc. The situation is even clearer in the case of sexual objects where society prescribes the economic status, race, religion, national background, sex, appearance, and degree of relationship of an appropriate sex object.

This all comes about through the social training the child is given in the family, particularly by the mother. The mother may use many training techniques to accomplish the socialization of the physiological motives—ranging from corporal punishment to threats of loss of love. In general, the psychoanalytic thinkers have felt that the harsher training methods—early weaning, rigid toilet training, and punitive attitudes toward sex play—lead to difficulties in these areas. By and large, empirical evidence supports this (Child, 1954).

There is evidence, however, that overindulgence and overpermissiveness also leads to training difficulties. The overindulged boys in Levy's (1943) study tended to be immature, demanding, and dependent. In addition to their evidence for the fixational effect of punitive socialization techniques, Whiting and Child (1953) suggest that continued positive satisfaction at late ages may also lead to fixation of behavior patterns.

The general consensus seems to be that extremes of child-training methods—either in the direction of too strict or too permissive an approach—leads to socially undesirable behavioral consequences. The ideal approach seems to be democratic, flexible, and love-oriented (Mussen and Conger, 1956).

The statements made so far refer to the relatively short-range effects of various training methods in specific areas, e.g., the effect of early weaning on eating behavior. Actually, most of the interest in socialization has been in the possible effects of these early learning events in the development of basic personality characteristics and social motives. The psychoanalytic writers, in particular, believe that the degree of frustration, gratification, and fixation of oral, anal, and sexual drives determine adult personality. Through the blocking of infantile sexual needs and the mechanism of sublimation, the individual develops motives for affection, power, competition, religion, art, and so forth. Objective evidence is much less convincing in this regard (Child, 1954; Murray, 1964 b).

Similarly, learning theorists have used the concept of acquired motivation to explain how social motives are learned on the basis of hunger, thirst, sex, and pain (Dollard and Miller, 1950). The basic idea is that through association a neutral stimulus paired with the increase of a motive comes to have motivating properties. Similarly, a stimulus associated with the reduction of a motive acquires reinforcing properties. Thus, there may be acquired motives and acquired rewards. The acquired-motive paradigm has been demonstrated many times with aversive motives such as pain. But the difficulty in showing a similar phenomenon with, for example, hunger or thirst has led Miller (1959) to question its usefulness with appetitive motives.

Instead, Miller has introduced the concept of motive channelization. This is similar to Freud's (1949) cathexis and Murphy's (1947) canalization. Primary motives are directed by cultural learning into specific channels—particular types of food, etc. The concept of acquired reward is more generally applicable. That is, stimuli associated with a chain of events leading to a primary goal object become secondarily reinforcing. This is contingent upon the stimulus continuing to lead to a primary reward. As Murphy (1947) points out, the animal in the conditioning experiment does not try to *eat* the bell, but prepares for food by salivating. The secondary reward may elicit a fractional anticipatory goal response (Hull, 1943). Perhaps a good term for acquired reward is "sub-goal."

There is an increasing body of evidence that many of the motives once thought to be acquired through learning—such as affection, curiosity, competition—actually have an innate biological basis. Affection, in particular, appears to be an innate need in the face of anxiety for the young of many species, including man (see Murray, 1964 b, for a review). It may be that affection supplies most of the motivating power for the socialization of the other physiological motives. The loss of the mother's approval and love are so threatening to the child that he learns to eat and toilet himself properly, as well as to inhibit sexual, aggressive, and other tendencies. Higher order acquired rewards may be based on this fundamental affectional motive more than on hunger, pain, or sex.

This line of reasoning also suggests that the personality and adjustment of the mother is critical in the socialization process. The child's anxiety appears to be influenced strongly by the mother's feelings. The anxiety the mother feels about sexual matters or the genuine relief she feels when the child is toilet trained may be more critical than the specific techniques used, or at least, may determine the choice and use of those techniques. The mother's need for the continued affection of the child may lead her to prolong training for the independent gratification of hunger and other motives. Thus, the socialization process must be seen as a complex human interaction.

DEVELOPMENT OF SLEEP PATTERNS

Before birth, the fetus shows cycles of activity that appear to be innate and without regard to night or day. They may be influenced by the mother's diurnal rhythm of activity but there does not seem to be an innate diurnal pattern. Direct observations on the fetus are difficult, but Gesell and Amatruda (1945) report observations on prematurely born infants that probably hold true for intra-uterine behavior. A fetal infant born after seven months of pregnancy was observed to have a ten-minute cycle of activity. This began with a drowsy torpor; progressed to a time of slow eye movements, hand extension, and munching movements; and returned to the drowsy torpor. It is difficult, however, to actually distinguish sleeping and wakeful states.

After full-term birth, the neonate wakes up at least 5 or 6 times during the 24-hour period for a brief time to eat and defecate. According to Kleitman (1939), the time awake totals only about 2 hours. By three months of age the time spent awake may be extended to 4 or 6 hours all told. All during the lifespan, the time devoted to wakefulness increases at the expense of sleep. The change is accelerated negatively with the greatest shifts during early childhood and an asymptote of about 7 to 8 hours sleep a night attained at about college age. Some authors believe that sleep needs increase during the growth spurt at puberty, but we have not seen this consistently in many studies. It is possible that the phenomenon is masked by the fact that children reach puberty at different ages. During most of the adult life, changes are small, although in old age the sleeping time may again decrease.

An attempt to draw a curve for sleeping time as a function of age is presented in Fig. 19. This must be viewed as approx-

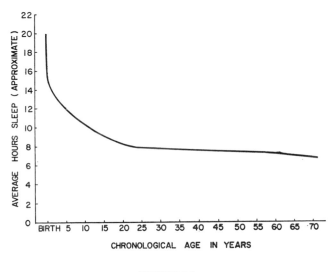

FIGURE 19

imate because it is based on data drawn from diverse sources differing greatly in method of measurement, size of sample, and type of population. However, it was observational, not theoretical, sources that were consulted. In many cases it was impossible to combine findings in a statistically satisfactory manner so a midpoint was arbitrarily chosen between the figures given by various authorities.

The initial point at birth is based on Kleitman's (1939) figure of 22 hours of sleep and somewhat lower figures given by Pratt, Nelson, and Sun (1930), Gesell and Amatruda (1945), and Best and Taylor (1950). The difficulty in determining when a neonate is awake and the rapid day-to-day changes make this point ambiguous. The decrease in sleeping time is very marked during the first year (Gesell and Ilg, 1943). The part of the curve from one year of age to about college level is based on the best evidence (Anderson, 1936; Kleitman, 1939; Louttit's Summary of Six Studies, 1947; Despert, 1949-50; and Faegre, Anderson, and Harris, 1958). The middle years have not been studied as intensively but the available evidence (Kleitman et al., 1937; Kleitman, 1939) suggests that the average adult sleeps about 7.5 to 8 hours a night with relatively little change over a number of decades.

There is some dispute about the duration of sleep in old age. Most authorities suggest that the duration of sleep in elderly patients decreases to an average of about six hours a night (Liberson, 1945; Best and Taylor, 1950; Thewlis, 1950; Thewlis, 1954; Ginzburg, 1955). Actually, the decrease may be compensated by catnaps during the day (May and Ebaugh, 1953). Furthermore, Tiller (1964) reported a systematic survey of 83 elderly office patients aged 60 to 90 years. These patients reported an average of a little more than seven hours of sleep a night, with those over 70 sleeping somewhat more. Tiller's data are the best reported and may be more representative than the earlier reports that were based mostly on hospitalized patients. Tiller doubts that there is any dramatic decrease in the duration of sleep with normal aging. We would judge that the decline, if there be any at all, is slight.

A point of considerable importance, made by nearly all observers, is that the duration of sleep in all age groups shows large individual differences. For example, in a sample of nine-year olds, Terman (1925) found a range of 7.5 to 12 hours of sleep. In the adults studied by Kleitman et al. (1937), some individuals usually slept about 6 hours while others exceeded 9 hours. There are also day-to-day variations in the sleeping time of the same child, with some showing fair constancy but others widely fluctuating, although each child has a fairly stable average over a several-week period (Despert, 1949-50). The duration of sleep is also related to seasonal changes, intelligence, time of going to bed, sex, and a host of other factors that add to the variability.

The empirically determined duration of sleep is not what has traditionally guided our child-rearing procedures. Since the well-known table of children's sleep needs published by Dukes in 1899, various physicians, child-care experts, and others have been prescribing certain "normal" amounts of sleep required for healthy child development. In comparison with direct observations, however, these theoretical expectations turn out to be too high. Louttit (1947) brought together theoretical estimates by five authorities, including Dukes, and the results of six observational studies. Table VII is a summary of Louttit's figures for the ages

TABLE VII

PRESCRIBED VERSUS OBSERVED HOURS OF SLEEP DURATION IN CHILDREN

AGE	PRESCRIBED	OBSERVED	DIFFERENCE
1	14.1	13.5	−0.6
2	13.5	12.8	−0.7
3	13.8	12.2	−1.6
4	12.5	11.8	−0.7
5	12.5	11.2	−1.3
6	12.9	11.0	−1.9
7	12.2	10.8	−1.4
8	11.8	10.5	−1.3
9	11.8	10.2	−1.6
10	10.8	10.0	−0.8

Adapted from Louttit, 1947.

1 to 10. The first year has been omitted, although it shows a similar difference, because the rapid changes during this time makes either prescribed or observational figures meaningless unless a monthly or weekly breakdown is employed.

The comparisons in the table show clearly that the theoretical expectations of the experts are too high, if we assume that the children are getting enough rest—an assumption that all indications suggest is correct. On the average, the experts would have the children sleeping a little more than an extra hour. In addition, the experts do not take the large individual differences into account to the extent that they should. We may be dealing with a cultural bias here, one that is expressed by the experts but may find a highly receptive audience in parents. As a parent, this author can well sympathize with a desire to see the children off to bed before the evening activities without having them spring into action at the crack of dawn. But the attitude may become rigid. Despert (1949-50) mentions cases in which parents use all sorts of techniques to see that the child attains a rigid standard of hours of sleep that may be more than is needed.

More important than the change in the duration of sleep over the lifespan is a shift in the distribution of sleeping time. The 5 or 6 periods of waking at birth have been reduced to 4 or 5 within a month and to 3 or 4 by 6 months of age. This is accomplished mainly by dropping out the night feeding (Kleitman, 1939; Gesell, 1943). Night waking, between midnight and 5:00 a.m., has ceased in 70 percent of American children by age 3 months, 83 percent by 6 months, and 90 percent by a year. However, 50 percent start in again briefly (Moore and Ucko, 1957). This does not appear to be simply an innate maturational change but one actively taught and eagerly sought by the parents for obvious reasons.

By the end of the first year the child in our culture usually has consolidated his sleeping time into one long 12- to 14-hour nocturnal sleep often beginning around 7:00 p.m. and a 1- to 2-hour nap, most frequently in the late morning. The consolidation of sleep periods has been illustrated by Gesell and Amatruda (1945) by having a mother observe her child. At birth the sleep-wakeful pattern is fragmented, with a day-to-day consolidation evident. The data on this infant actually shows about 20 awakenings during the day but this includes very brief stirrings. Taking only substantial wakenings, the number is closer to Kleitman's figure of 5 or 6. The long periods of sleep may be attained during the day as well as the night. Thus consolidation may be purely maturational, but the culture operates to "tilt" the pattern into a desirable preponderance of night sleeping.

Gesell and Amatruda present graphic records of the sleep-wakeful pattern of this child from age 2 weeks to 4 years. This is shown in Fig. 20. The black area of the clock at each age represents sleep, and the white, wakefulness. The child was on a self-

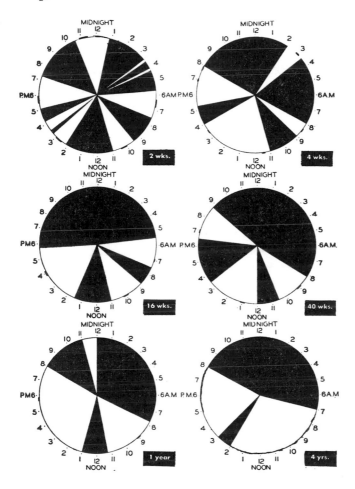

FIGURE 20

demand sleep schedule so that one could argue that the emerging pattern was entirely maturational. However, while the basic consolidation principle may be partly maturational, the greater environmental stimulation during the day obviously plays a role in tilting the cycle. The mother's responsiveness may also vary. Gesell and Amatruda believe that the night sleep records may overestimate the continuity of the sleep. This suggests that—science or no science—the mother just could not keep getting up at night. If the child did awaken at night, he soon found out that mother was much better company in the daytime. The sleep period from 2:00 to 3:00 p.m. at age 4 is actually a wakeful rest period—again suggesting the cultural influence.

By age 4, and sometimes as early as 2, the child has "given up" his nap. The parents may not be quite so eager to "give it up" so the child is put to bed anyway. In this situation the child does not go to sleep, but has what is called a "play nap." The child has now attained a single block of sleep and this pattern will continue throughout most of his lifespan (Gesell, 1943).

With aging, the pattern may reverse itself. The forerunner of this is the after-dinner or after-lunch nap of the middle-aged person. The elderly person may catnap frequently during the day and sleep for a shorter time at night. In the sixties as much as 20 percent of the day is spent in "micro-sleeps" (Liberson, 1945). Thewlis (1954) says that geriatric patients are frequently observed sleeping in their chairs during the day. It is possible that to some extent the polyphasic pattern is enhanced by the permissiveness and apathy in geriatric hospitals.

The overall developmental trend can be viewed as a shift from a polyphasic to a monophasic pattern, with a tendency to return to the polyphasic pattern with advancing age. Kleitman (1963) has described this schematically and his conception is shown in Fig. 21. Kleitman (1939) in his earlier evolutionary theory characterized the polyphasic-monophasic shift as a change from the cyclical "wakefulness of necessity" to a "wakefulness of choice." The wakefulness of necessity is the primary pattern of lower animals, children, and de-corticated dogs. It is a simple response to the demands of hunger and other basic biological

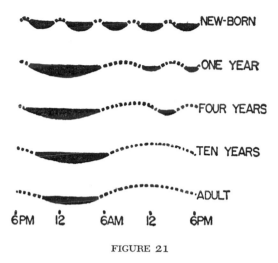

FIGURE 21

urges. Wakefulness of choice depends on a developed cortex and is determined by environmental stimuli and, in the human being, by culture.

The monophasic pattern of adult life, then, appears to be partly maturational and partly determined by the physical environment and cultural custom. Situations in which these later factors are reduced would be expected to facilitate a return to a polyphasic pattern. The environmental supports are reduced radically in the sensory-deprivation studies mentioned in Chapter 4, and some individuals revert to a polyphasic pattern. Schizophrenia involves social withdrawal and schizophrenics sometimes adopt unusual sleep patterns. This author recalls the story of the somewhat odd character who decided to sleep 15 minutes of each hour, carrying an alarm clock to class with him.

Arctic life is a situation in which a polyphasic pattern might be expected to emerge. In the temperate or tropical zones, a completely asocial man might still adopt a monophasic pattern because of the natural advantages of hunting, climbing, and so forth during daylight in a highly visual organism. But in the endless daylight or blackness of the arctic seasons this biological advantage would not hold. The extent to which a diurnal, monophasic cycle continues seems to be dependent on cultural pressures. The civilized Norwegian community studied by Kleitman and Kleitman (1953) maintained a more or less normal diurnal pattern because of the mores of a civilized community. Without these cultural supports a different pattern may emerge.

Studies of polar expeditions offer a better source of information about this problem (Lewis, 1961). These expeditions vary greatly in the degree of social pressure to maintain a civilized pattern. In some expeditions a fixed schedule of duties determined the hours of sleep. On the other hand, some of the situations involved a self-determined schedule of activities. In these cases, during the winter and summer, men used any and all of the hours of the day for sleeping. The total amount slept was not changed but many of the men took naps and interrupted their long periods of sleep. There were large individual differences in this but in many cases it would appear that a polyphasic pattern emerged.

The fact that on these Arctic expeditions the total duration of sleep did not differ from that of men in ordinary civilization suggests that the 7.5 to 8 hours sleep is what is needed biologically. Nevertheless, even this is affected by cultural factors. In one case involving an isolated base, the average sleeping time increased significantly while the leader was away temporarily.

The emergence of a polyphasic sleep pattern in elderly persons may also reflect the removal of social pressures as much as a maturational process. The elderly person in an institution, especially, has little reason to maintain a monophasic pattern. Much of the day may be spent in sitting and rocking with sources of stimulation reduced by sensory deterioration, arthritic impairment of activity, and lack of purpose. Such a situation would be conducive to frequent naps. It would be interesting to see the effects of planned activities. Similarly, it would be interesting to see if individuals retiring from work had a pattern that differed from those continuing some sort of meaningful activity.

Finally, the several stages of sleep itself show a maturational change from birth to old age. Aserinsky and Kleitman (1955 b) observed a cycle of activity and quiescence of about an hour during the sleep of neonates in the first two weeks of life. The quiescent phase lasts about 20 to 25 minutes. The active phase is ushered in by about ten minutes of muscular movement and then Rapid Eye Movements commence with a reduction of gross movements. Sucking is frequently seen during REM periods. Although the neonatal EEG is usually described as flat (Lindsley, 1960), Roffwarg et al. (1964) report finding fast activity during REM periods and slower activity at other times. Clear indications of highly synchronized sleep do not appear until three or four months of age and are more definite by about nine months (Lindsley, 1960; Thompson, 1962).

Roffwarg, Dement, and Fisher (1964) systematically studied the stages of sleep from birth to old age. REM periods account for about 60% of the sleeping time in the neonate and about 40% in young infants. During these early years the REM periods appear at fairly regular intervals throughout the night. At about age three or four, the pattern changes with REM time dropping to about 20% and shifting towards the later half of the night. There is no consistent change in the pattern from age four until old age when the percent of REM time shows some decrease.

Kleitman (1963) believes that a basic rest-activity cycle is involved. This is about an hour in length in infants and lengthens to about an hour and a half in adults. This basic rest-activity cycle is superimposed on the polyphasic sleep and wakefulness cycle shown in Fig. 21. During the night the basic cycle is shown in the alternation between synchronized sleep and dream sleep. During the day the cycle is shown by periods of efficiency and inefficiency. Kleitman has changed his evolutionary theory of sleep to take into account the maturational changes in sleep as well as in wakefulness. He now speaks of primitive sleep and advanced sleep, as well as primitive wakefulness and advanced wakefulness.

In general, there are developmental changes in the duration, distribution, and stages of sleep. While these changes are largely maturational, cultural factors are important in the maintenance of monophasic sleep and the diurnal pattern.

SLEEP AND CULTURAL VALUES

Superficially, it would not appear logical to expect that so simple a physiological function as sleep would become involved in complex social and cultural processes. This is the view of Allport (1940) when he says that "It is obvious . . . that sneezing, sleep, elimination and like bodily functions persist throughout life with relatively little personalizing." Here, sleep is assumed to be too reflexive, too impersonal to be greatly influenced by cultural learning.

We have seen, however, that the basic diurnal monophasic sleeping pattern is partly determined by culture. Society has a strong interest in regulating sleeping behavior. In fact, if sleep were not regulated it might have a more disruptive effect on the organized economic life of the community than if members ate, defecated, or copulated at will. A society in which there was complete "sleep freedom" would have to keep trains and buses running continuously; have restaurants and recreational facilities open all night; provide extra power for nighttime heat and light; and arrange for frequent and uncoordinated naps on the assembly line. We are neither for nor against societal regulation of sleep, but are simply pointing out that it exists. Aubert and White (1959) have taken the position that "Human sleep is an important social event."

In surveying the customs of a large number of primitive cultures, Ford (1939) reports evidence of some kind of social control over sleeping behavior in 76 percent of the sample. This ranges from the prohibition of yawning, sleepwalking, and sleep-talking in the Ingalik tribe to the control of dreaming by many American Indian groups. The Ashanti prohibit dreaming completely.

Many examples of the social control of sleeping behavior can be found in anthropological reports (see Aubert and White, 1959; Naegele, personal communication). The examples given below were obtained from the Human Relations Area Files compiled by C. S. Ford and other Yale anthropologists and on file at the University of Michigan, by Mr. Raleigh J. Huizinga, a student of the writer. There is enough data in the Files to suggest a large-scale systematic study, but for the moment we just want to illustrate some cultural variations.

First of all, the basic sleeping pattern varies from culture to culture. The Arab Bedouin have essentially a polyphasic pattern because of fear of, and participation in, night raiding. Hindus tend to slip into a dozing state at will, especially when idle or hungry. The pattern may be related to the chronic hunger of the Indian peasant and is institutionalized in the Hindu proverb, "He who sleeps, dines." The South American siesta tradition seems to be an adaptation of the sleep pattern to the tropical heat. Possibly as a result of this, dinner parties and theatrical entertainment start very late in many Latin countries—often around midnight. On the other hand, the day may begin early. People on the Yucatan peninsula waken at 3:00 a.m. and consider it appropriate to go visiting at that hour. Other cultures, like ours, negatively sanction daytime sleeping. There is a Navaho proverb that "A man lying down in the daytime is a lazy man." The Tibetans believe that daytime sleep may induce a fever. The patterns not only vary but seem to be related to the economic and environmental conditions of living.

Even as simple a thing as the body position during sleep may be culturally modified. In contrast to American children, Navaho children never sleep with a hand under the face. This is probably due to their always being placed on their backs to sleep. Tibetans and Aleuts usually sleep in a knee-elbow position, possibly to reduce heat loss. The great individual variation in sleeping positions in American subjects may also reflect different family training procedures (Johnson et al., 1930). In a few societies the direction of the body is important. Easter Islanders sleep parallel to the long axis of the house, with heads toward the door. Wind direction is important in the Marshall Islands. Indian tribesmen of New Mexico will not sleep toward the east, because the dead are commonly buried in that direction.

The whole idea of sleep must be at least as mysterious to primitive tribesmen as it is to Western scientists. We react in our characteristic fashion by doing experiments and writing books about sleep. The primitive people turn to religion. For example, in some cultures the sleeping place is sanctified. Thus the Brahmin in India purifies the place in which he sleeps by rubbing it with cow dung. In some cultures sleep becomes involved in black magic. With the aid of dust from dead bones and other apparatus, a burglar can put his victim into a sound sleep (Gaster, 1961).

The great Frazer (Gaster, 1961) gives many examples of the primitive terror of sleep. Among South American Indians, African, Asian, and South Sea tribesmen, and backward European peasants there is a belief that the soul leaves the body during sleep. It wanders, visits places, sees people, and performs the actions contained in dreams. The great danger is that the soul may not be able to get back into the body. This is why some people will not awaken a sleeper abruptly—the soul may not have enough time to get back. In some tribes there is a fear that a wizard will capture the soul while it is wandering. Wizards do this with an earthenware pot, in the Karen tribe, and transfer the soul to a dead man with the rightful owner dying. Friends may hire another wizard to try to recapture the stolen soul. All of this may be a tribute to the fear of the helplessness and vulnerability of the sleeping person.

The religious significance of sleep brings up the question of how this area might fit in with the religious tradition in the West. The dominant religious ideology of Northern Europe and the United States has been called the "Protestant Ethic" by Weber (Bendix, 1962). The basic idea is that work is good in the eyes of God. Hard work is the best defense against religious doubts, feelings of unworthiness, or sexual desires. The Puritan abhorrence of the weaknesses of the flesh is part of this. Thus sexual pleasure, overeating, idle talk, sociability, and similar activities are frowned upon. Time must be spent wisely, productively. According to Weber (1930, pp. 157-158) this attitude applies to sleep: "Waste of time is thus the first and in principle the deadliest of sins. The span of human life is infinitely short and precious to make sure of one's own election. Loss of time through sociability, idle talk, luxury, even more sleep than is necessary for health, six to at most eight hours, is worthy of absolute moral condemnation."

We are using the term "Protestant Ethic" in a general sense

here to refer to the religious tradition of asceticism and control of impulses. As McClelland (1962) has pointed out, this attitude can be found within many formal religions. Whenever it is found, we would expect a negative attitude toward sleep as well as toward other impulses. One form the ascetic attitude takes is to view sleep as an unnecessary habit which can be eliminated. This was attempted by the Catholic ascetics, St. Francis of Assisi and St. Teresa, as well as the Methodists, Fletcher and Wesley. They all abandoned the attempt as unsuccessful (Johnson and Swan, 1930). Some of this attitude can be seen in Hollingworth's (1927) theory of sleep as a habit, showing that there is an ascetic tradition in scientific psychology, as well as in formal religion.

In order to get an idea of the cultural values placed on sleep in our civilization, an Opinionaire was constructed and administered to three undergraduate classes in psychology. The instrument consisted of 40 samples of behavior related to sleep, to which the students had to indicate strong approval, approval, neutrality, disapproval, or strong disapproval on a five-point scale. The items used were examples of behavior that had little or no physiological justification one way or the other. Thus, deviations from neutrality represent cultural values attached to the behavior.

The sample consisted of 162 undergraduates. Most were of college age, but there were perhaps a dozen older people in the one evening class. There were 61 males and 101 females. Religious affiliation included 66 Protestant, 36 Catholic, and 38 Jewish, with the remainder unaffiliated or unclear. About half considered themselves devout and the rest nondevout. In terms of Hollingshead and Redlich's (1958) social class levels, 36 were in Class I, 64 in Class II, 36 in Class III and 23 in Classes IV and V. Thus, the sample is not representative of the entire American culture, but is representative of college populations.

The individual items were evaluated statistically by a chi square technique. The determination of the expected frequencies presents something of a problem. One could assume that, if no cultural values were operative, all respondents should be in the neutral category and none in the other four. One could also assume that there is a tendency for respondents to scatter around the neutral category and then employ a normal distribution for the expected frequencies. Finally, one could assume that a chance result would place an equal number of respondents in each category and thus use an expected rectangular distribution. Actually, the results were compared with all three types of distributions with no difference in the essential pattern of results. In the results presented below, the rectangular distribution was used because it is the most conservative assumption to make. It was assumed that 32.4 respondents would appear in each of the five response categories. For a few items, the total number of respondents was 161 and the expected frequency 32.2 in each category.

The results showed that the answers to each of the forty items on the attitude questionnaire deviated significantly from chance expectations ($p < .001$ for each item). Of the forty, eight deviated significantly in the direction of approval and seventeen in the direction of disapproval, while only five were clearly neutral. The remaining ten items showed a mixture of opinion but were still significantly different from chance. The overall conclusion is that these American students have strong opinions about the matter of sleep.

The results were also analyzed by a chi square technique for the effects of the several background variables—social class, sex, religious affiliation, and devoutness of religious feelings. Each of the forty items was compared on the basis of these four variables. The striking finding was that only eight of the 160 comparisons were significant at the .05 level or better. These included one for social class, two for sex, three for religious affiliation, and two for devoutness of religious feelings. These could easily have occurred by chance. While we will mention the significant relationships as we go along it should be kept in mind that the attitudes of the subjects are basically independent of background variables.

The data are presented below in a series of tables. Items dealing with the same specific topic are grouped together for ease of description, although they may not have appeared in that order in the booklet given to the students.

Items dealing with attitudes about the proper duration of sleep have been grouped together in Table VIII. The frequency

TABLE VIII

ATTITUDES OF COLLEGE STUDENTS TOWARD
DURATION OF SLEEP

ITEM	STRONGLY APPROVE	APPROVE	NEUTRAL	DIS- APPROVE	STRONGLY DIS- APPROVE
1. A person regularly sleeps 6 hours a night	17	53	43	46	3
2. A person regularly sleeps 8 hours a night	44	70	39	8	1
3. A person regularly sleeps 10 hours a night	5	34	47	58	17
4. A person regularly sleeps 12 hours a night	2	11	40	49	60
5. A man believes that it is not proper to sleep any more than the physiological requirements of the body demands	5	29	60	56	12

of students responding in each one of the five categories is presented in the body of the table. The data indicate that the students, as a group, approve shorter sleeping times and disapprove longer ones. Eight hours gets the strongest approbation, but attitudes about deviations from this norm are asymetrical: it is all right to sleep less, but not acceptable to sleep longer. The Puritan Ethic! It is interesting to note that the one item in this table that was significantly related to a background variable was No. 1—devout people approve sleeping six hours a night.

However, Item 5 is a curious result. The respondents tend to be either neutral or disapproving. Why? It sounds like a good statement of the Puritan Ethic. Perhaps this is the reason—it sounds too moralistic. Students are notoriously resistant to moralistic pronouncements—even if they harbor the same moralistic attitude themselves.

In any case, the students' attitudes about the duration of sleep are not in accord with the observations about the great individual variation in sleep needs. It makes little physiological

TABLE IX

ATTITUDES OF COLLEGE STUDENTS TOWARD
SLEEPING WITH WINDOWS OPEN OR CLOSED

ITEM	STRONGLY APPROVE	APPROVE	NEUTRAL	DIS-APPROVE	STRONGLY DIS-APPROVE
1. A person sleeps with all the windows tightly closed	2	4	30	88	38
2. A person sleeps with the windows open a crack	18	89	45	8	2
3. A person sleeps with the windows wide open	15	65	43	31	7

sense to assume that everyone should sleep for eight hours. People ordinarily need from 6 to 10 hours and some people with sluggish endocrine systems need as much as 14 hours. It is also clear that the disapproval is only for longer sleep periods—probably because it appears slothful and lazy. A Spartan regime of six hours wins some approval probably because it seems to denote self-control and instinctual renunciation.

This attitude can be compared with the indulgent feelings of other civilizations. In Japan, for example, while the individual is

Table X

ATTITUDES OF COLLEGE STUDENTS TOWARD
ANTI-SOCIAL ASPECTS OF SLEEP BEHAVIOR

Item	Strongly Approve	Approve	Neutral	Disapprove	Strongly disapprove
1. A student frequently falls asleep in class after class	5	6	19	78	53
2. A student relies entirely on his roommate to get him up for class on time	3	17	26	71	45
3. A man has trouble keeping a job because of constant oversleeping	7	17	14	64	59
4. A student frequently returns to the dormitory late at night making enough noise to wake up other students	4	8	10	52	88
5. A man snores loudly while sleeping	1	7	69	61	24
6. A woman snores loudly while sleeping	1	4	56	59	42

restricted in many of his activities and ridden with feelings of shame if he does not perform as expected, there are relatively few taboos about sensual pleasures such as food and sex. Sleep is treated in the same way—it is a luxury, a sensual delight, to be enjoyed whenever it does not interfere with one's work (Queener, 1951).

Another Spartan attitude is that it is good to sleep with the window open. Table IX shows the students' attitudes about this issue. Closed windows are disapproved, windows open a crack are preferred, but wide-open windows also win approval. According to Kleitman (1939) some authorities are in favor of open windows and others just as strongly say they should be closed. It is not physiology but the cultural tradition that dictates open windows.

Individuals vary greatly in their sleep behavior. Sometimes the sleep behavior has clearly anti-social effects, in that it genuinely disturbs the social order. We would expect negative sanctions in these cases. Table X shows that the students do react with clear disapproval to four examples of such behavior. The two snoring items have a different quality, in that snoring is involuntary. Nevertheless, the students are either neutral or disapproving of snoring. The disapproval is somewhat stronger for snoring by a woman.

The items in Table XI are also idiosyncratic but this time they do not have the anti-social effects. They are expressions of unusual modes of dealing with one's sleep needs and they really concern no one but the person himself. Nevertheless, the students disapprove the first three of these items. On the fourth they are either neutral or disapproving. The behavior is different, non-conforming and society does not approve of this. On the other hand, society sometimes permits an idiosyncratic response if there are other indications that the person is performing adequately. This may be the explanation of the distribution of respondents on Items 5 and 6. The housewife and the writer are presumably making a contribution to society. Society does not approve of their idiosyncratic sleep behavior but at least does not impose negative sanctions. Item 6 was the only one in the questionnaire related to social class—Classes I and II disapprove of the writer's sleeping habits, Class III approves, and Classes IV and V are indifferent. The young housewife in Item 5 is disapproved by the Jewish group but not by the Protestant and Catholic ones.

The next three tables contain items that not only involve

TABLE XI

ATTITUDES OF COLLEGE STUDENTS TOWARD
IDIOSYNCRATIC SLEEP PATTERNS

ITEM	STRONGLY APPROVE	APPROVE	NEUTRAL	DIS-APPROVE	STRONGLY DIS-APPROVE
1. A student rarely goes to bed before 1:00 a.m. regardless of activities scheduled in the morning	9	38	38	51	26
2. A college student arranges his classes so that he can sleep until noon every day	11	17	26	65	42
3. A man trained himself to sleep for 15 minutes each hour during the day and night	4	11	30	50	66
4. On hot nights a man sleeps on his lawn	8	30	52	47	25
5. A young housewife sleeps for 2 hours in the afternoon	6	42	63	41	9
6. A writer works all night and sleeps all day	7	41	55	40	18

sleep patterns but sexual elements as well. The first, Table XII, has to do with proper sleeping apparel. This table is unique in that the observed frequency in the neutral category was higher than the chance level one would expect for all six items. In

TABLE XII

ATTITUDES OF COLLEGE STUDENTS TOWARD
TYPES OF SLEEPING APPAREL

ITEM	STRONGLY APPROVE	APPROVE	NEUTRAL	DIS-APPROVE	STRONGLY DIS-APPROVE
1. A man sleeps in pajamas	8	67	76	10	1
2. A woman sleeps in a nightgown	11	73	70	6	2
3. A woman sleeps in pajamas	4	66	69	14	9
4. A man sleeps in an old-fashioned nightshirt	1	25	104	20	12
5. A man sleeps in the altogether	13	41	87	17	4
6. A woman sleeps in the altogether	23	34	79	21	4

general, pajamas for men and women, and nightgowns for women
—the cultural norm—are mildly approved. Does all this mean
that this area has little affect or value attached to it? Possibly so,
but it is also possible that the sexual theme raised some anxiety
and the neutral category was selected because it was safest.
During the administration, several coeds asked what "altogether"
meant, so perhaps these were simply poor items. On the other
hand, Item 6 was approved by the non-devout and disapproved
by the devout. In addition, the item most significantly related to a
background variable was No. 4—females approve and males
disapprove the man in the old-fashioned nightshirt.

Table XIII deals specifically with the sexual theme in marriage but here the reactions were strong and direct. Separate
rooms for marital partners were strongly disapproved. The reaction to twin beds was scattered from neutral to strong disapproval.
The students strongly approved the close marital relationship

TABLE XIII

ATTITUDES OF COLLEGE STUDENTS TOWARD
MARITAL SLEEPING ARRANGEMENTS

ITEM	STRONGLY APPROVE	APPROVE	NEUTRAL	DIS-APPROVE	STRONGLY DIS-APPROVE
1. A husband and wife have separate bedrooms	3	2	19	44	94
2. A married couple sleep in twin beds	3	32	43	42	41
3. A married couple sleep in a double bed	68	64	28	2	0

implied in sharing a double bed. Why did they not go further and approve of sleeping in the nude? Perhaps this is too frank. Perhaps also the approval of double beds signifies a high value placed on the institution of marriage and its continuing stability. This would be in line with the Puritan Ethic.

While the college students bless close sleeping arrangements between marital partners, their erotic enthusiasm does not extend to the rest of the family. Table XIV shows a general antipathy to communal sleeping. The distribution on Item 1 shows some difference of opinion on the co-habitation of sisters, but leans more toward disapproval when brothers are involved in Item 2. It was the female subjects who most strongly disapproved of pre-school sisters sharing a bed. Furthermore, it was the Protestant group only that objected to pre-school brothers sharing a bed and there was a trend for a similar disapproval of pre-school sisters doing the same thing.

Disapproval becomes marked when it comes to brothers and sisters sharing a bed. But none of the items in the entire Opinion-aire aroused greater or stronger disapproval than the idea of an entire family sleeping together in a large bed. Finally, separate

TABLE XIV

ATTITUDES OF COLLEGE STUDENTS TOWARD
SIBLING SLEEPING ARRANGEMENTS

ITEM	STRONGLY APPROVE	APPROVE	NEUTRAL	DIS-APPROVE	STRONGLY DIS-APPROVE
1. Pre-school sisters share a bed	4	52	49	51	6
2. Pre-school brothers share a bed	5	44	48	56	8
3. A pre-school brother and sister share a bed	3	19	27	70	43
4. An entire family shares a large bed	4	2	2	32	122
5. Each sibling has a separate bedroom	28	89	31	14	0

bedrooms for siblings is approved—probably with some relief.

These results testify to the dread of incest in middle and upper class American culture. Of course, the incest taboo is universal but apparently not as traumatic because many cultures around the world involve communal sleeping arrangements. In several Manchurian, Korean, and Middle Eastern tribes, the entire family sleeps together by the fire, although the highest status person is usually closest to the fire. In many rural Irish families everyone sleeps in a large bed.

The sons and daughters are usually separated in these cultures at some specified age. For example, at around age 7, the Australian Bushmen girls go to sleep with a grandmother or other female relative, while the boys go to the boy's fire. In rural Ireland a boy is separated from his sisters when he reaches the age of chores. But the American college students reacted negatively to preschool brothers and sisters sleeping together or with the family.

The results indicate that college students, who constitute an influential segment of society in training, hold strong beliefs about what is appropriate sleep behavior. Social norms are evident in simple matters such as the appropriate duration of sleep and sleeping with windows open or closed. While it is not surprising that there are disapproving attitudes toward anti-social behavior associated with sleep, it is noteworthy that this extends to behavior that is merely idiosyncratic but not disturbing to others. The control of individual behavior through social norms, which we see in such complex areas as political belief, marital choice, and religious ritual, appears to extend to even as simple a physiological function as sleep.

More is involved than conformity to a statistical norm. Deviation in one direction is approved but that in another disapproved. Sleeping for six hours or sleeping with the windows wide open receive approval but sleeping for ten hours or with the windows closed is not acceptable. This suggests an ascetic attitude consistent with the Puritan Ethic. Sleep can be a pleasurable self-indulgence and as such conflicts with the values of hard work, conservation of time, and self-denial described by Weber. The motive to sleep is a bodily demand to be controlled and kept in check just like other biological forces. Independence in arranging one's own sleeping schedule is as frowned upon as adopting a personal sexual code or unusual eating habits. It is interesting that the typical Bohemian rebellion includes not only indulgence in alcohol, sexual freedom, and "nonproductive" artistic activities but also unusual sleeping patterns.

The general lack of a relationship between attitudes about the various examples of sleep behavior and background variables like social class, sex, religious affiliations and devoutness of religious feelings is particularly important. The negative findings suggest that attitudes towards sleep are part of a general value system in American culture as a whole. Quite possibly the Puritan Ethic has spread from Protestantism to Catholicism and Judaism in the United States and engulfs the nondevout as well as the devout. So, too, the Puritan Ethic seems to have influenced the upper and lower social classes as well as the middle ones. There is some variation in this as the handful of significant relationships suggests. These may very well have been due to chance, however, and in any case represent a minimal effect of background variables. It could be argued that the college student population does not represent the total American society. This might well be true and thus generalization is limited. However, one would expect college students to be more openly rebellious and questioning than the general population. Instead, they are remarkably moralistic with respect to sleep behavior.

The topics of sleep and sex are closely associated for various obvious reasons. The results are interesting here. The students seem to be less Puritanical about sexual matters related to sleep than may have been true earlier. In the old tradition a wife sometimes bragged that her husband had never seen her naked. These students are non-committal about sleeping in the nude and favor close marital sleeping arrangements. However, they do recoil strongly from possible sibling sexuality. It is possible that, with Freud and all, there has been a change in conscious attitudes about sex. Nevertheless, the basic Puritanism may still be there but expressed more deviously and in other areas.

SLEEP AND CHILD-REARING PRACTICES

In the last section variations in cultural attitudes and mores with respect to sleeping behavior were discussed. The values of a culture in any area are transmitted to the developing child in the intimate, face to face, primary groups such as the family. The parents, and especially the mother, teach the child what behavior is acceptable and what is not. Both the content of this training and the methods used are thought to be important in general personality development. Within any culture there is a great variation in adherence to the prevailing mores leading to different child-rearing practices.

It would be useful to have cross-cultural data on child-rearing practices in the sleep area and their effect on personality development. Unfortunately, nearly all of the material is limited to the

American and European scenes. This is, of course, the civilization of most interest to us but the generalizations will have to be limited. Within this constriction we will examine the evidence on how families and mothers approach sleep training and what effect various approaches have on behavior.

As perceived by most parents, the training problem in regard to sleep is to see that the child has enough rest so as not to interfere with health and to get him to do it at a convenient and socially desirable time. However, the definition of "enough rest" and "desirable time" varies from family to family. Furthermore, the methods used to achieve these eminently worthy goals also show considerable variation.

The problem of how much sleep a child at a given age needs was discussed in the section on development. Many experts and parents overestimate the needs. The parental motivation for keeping a child in bed longer than he needs may vary from an insecure compliance with accepted medical prescriptions, so as to be a good parent, to the all too human desire to get rid of the kids, for some time during the day, for relaxation and adult activities. As Emerson once said "There never was a child so lovely but his mother was glad to get him asleep."

On the other hand, the parental demand for the child to sleep may become excessively rigid and extensive. Mention has already been made of the parents who feel that the child should have a set number of hours of sleep "at all costs." In view of the overestimate of sleep needs by most authorities and the tremendous individual variation between children, such demands seem unrealistic. It may become pathological when the parent threatens to withdraw love if the child does not comply—as Despert (1949-50) observed. One mother, reported by Despert, always spoke to the teacher, in front of the child, about the child's great need for sleep, although this three-year-old slept 13 hours a day. The mother promised candy as a reward for sleep.

In interviewing parents of children with sleep disturbances, Hirschberg (1957) found a few—but not a majority—of the mothers actually desired a continual state of sleep in the child. They became annoyed when the child awoke demanding to be fed, cared for, and loved. In these cases, the mother seemed to be totally rejecting the child and avoiding a relationship with him. In reacting with disturbances of sleep, the child may have been fighting against this rejection.

For most parents, the main issue in sleep training is not the length of sleep but problems centering around going to bed and staying there. Most children have some reluctance about going to bed. It means separation from the parents on whom their security hinges, leaving their play activities, and missing out on whatever the parents are up to. The parents react to this in a variety of ways. Some play, read stories, and cuddle the child. Others become anxious. Others are annoyed and spank the child or lock him in the room. In turn, the child may become rebellious, anxious, or demanding (Despert, 1949-50).

Once put to bed, the child may make continued attempts to return from banishment by calling to the mother, demanding drinks of water or trips to the potty, or by crying. Here, too, the parent may react in many ways—ignoring all demands or jumping up at the least whimper.

The distribution of maternal behavior in regard to strictness of child's bedtime has been determined by Sears, Maccoby, and Levin (1957) for a sample of 379 lower and middle class families. The results are shown in Table XV. There is considerable variation but there are more mothers on the strict side than the permissive side. Does this represent rejection or hostility? Probably not. Sears et al. present a factor analysis of a wide variety of child-rearing practices. Strictness about bedtime had high loadings on factors that describe mothers who take their child-rearing duties seriously with perhaps a little too much concern about the child's physical well-being. There was no appreciable loading on the factor indicating aggression in the mother.

A method of classifying maternal reactions to the sleeping behavior of the child has been devised—as well as scales in the feeding, toileting, and socialization areas—along a continuum of rigidity and permissiveness by Klatskin and Jackson (1955). The five-point scales begin with rigidity and go through flexibility to permissiveness. The definitions for the sleep scale vary from year to year but can be summarized as follows:

TABLE XV

STRICTNESS ABOUT CHILD'S BEDTIME

STRICTNESS	% OF MOTHERS
1. Not at all strict—no particular rules. Child goes to bed when sleepy, may have lights on and door open if he wishes	2
2. A few limitations. Parents have bedtime in mind, but allow deviations fairly often; consider child's special needs at time	18
3. Some limitations. Child supposed to be in bed at a certain time, but parents allow some leeway. Mild scolding for not conforming	29
4. Fairly strict. Will not stretch bedtime very much or very often; considerable pressure for conformity	34
5. Very strict—no leeway. Child must be in bed on dot, lights out, door closed; no getting up for company. Punishment for deviation	5
Not ascertained	12

After Sears, Maccoby, and Levin 1957.

1) sets rigid bedtime, allows child to "cry it out," forces child to remain in bed, does not recognize individual sleep patterns;

3) sets approximate bed time, does not respond to every whimper, allows child to get up and attends to his needs but leaves him in his own bed;

5) no effort at guidance, responds to every whimper, takes child into her bed when he awakens.

Other scales were used to rate the child's behavior in the four areas along a dimension of degree of problem. In the case of sleep, the following definitions were used:

1) child never slept through by one year, resistant to going to bed, will sleep only with parents;

3) occasional wakeful nights, occasionally resists going to bed, willing to return to own bed if he awakens;

5) never awakens at night, no problems on going to bed.

These scales were used to evaluate information obtained from hospital and office examinations and home visits on 50 mothers and infants. Ratings were made independently on each scale by three judges and only those items on which two judges agreed were used.

The results (Klatskin, Jackson, and Wilkin, 1956) showed that sleep disturbances were related to maternal overpermissiveness in the sleep area. This was significant for ages 1, 2, and 3. This result is somewhat surprising in view of the great emphasis placed on avoiding rigid training in the sleep area by most authorities (e.g., Despert, 1949-50). Klatskin et al. point out that very few extremes of rigidity or overpermissiveness were found in their sample. More extremely rigid mothers might produce more sleep disturbance.

Klatskin, Jackson, and Wilkin go on to show that the mother's overall adjustment to the maternal role is related to sleep disturbances. Those mothers who tend to reject the maternal role adopt the most rigid sleep-training techniques, while those who are too absorbed in this role tend to be overpermissive. Probably these rejecting mothers were not extremely rejecting at their worst, because Hirschberg (1957) did find that totally rejecting mothers were sometimes found in cases of sleep-disturbed children.

Nevertheless, both the Hirschberg and Klatskin et al. data point to overpermissiveness and overabsorption in the maternal role in the large bulk of cases of sleep-disturbed children. This also fits in with the results of Anthony (1959) who found that sleep-disturbed youngsters had spent more time in the parental bedroom and had more anxious phobic mothers than did the neurotic controls. On the other hand, undue parental pressures and other signs of rigidity did not differentiate the groups. This all sounds like the overpermissive, overabsorbed pattern.

The studies on the mother-child relationship in cases of adult sleep pathology, covered in the last chapter, may shed some light on this problem. The mothers of individuals with sleep disturbances are described as maladjusted in various ways. Sometimes this fits the overpermissive pattern as when the mother is said to be anxious or neurotic. But in some cases, particularly sleepwalkers, the mother is described as domineering and punitive. It is not known if these mothers were rigid in specific sleep-training procedures.

Another issue is whether the emphasis should be on short-range disturbances in the specific area or on long-range personality development. Thus strict mothers may have children who show no symptoms of sleep disturbance. However, they may also grow up to be inhibited, overconforming individuals with hidden tensions. It is also conceivable that the children of overpermissive mothers may be more creative or imaginative while continuing to have lifelong sleeping difficulties. Studies on the long-range effects of practices in this area are sorely needed.

At the present time the case for the malevolent effects of extreme rigidity in sleep training remains open. But the evidence is stronger for the idea that overpermissiveness makes for difficulty. What are overpermissive mothers like?

The notion of overpermissive mothers producing some sort of personality disturbance can be found throughout the literature on psychopathology. The overindulgent mothers in Levy's (1943) classic study produced demanding, spoiled, overdependent children. A frequent pattern in the background of male homosexuals is a "close-binding-intimate" mother (Bieber et al., 1962). Many other neurotic and psychotic disturbances may be related to this maternal syndrome (Bell and Vogel, 1960).

The study of these mothers has only just begun. However, some rough idea of their motivations is emerging. They tend to be insecure individuals, frequently unhappy in their marital relationship. They turn toward their children, or one particular child, for love and fulfillment. It is very important for their security that the child need them very much. This sometimes takes the form of feeding and dressing the child beyond the usual time or making it necessary for the child to have the mother close by when entering new social situations. The mother is indispensable and thus does not have to fear losing the affection of the child.

How does this tie in with sleep disturbances? According to Hirschberg (1957) parents are very concerned about their children's sleep. For many mothers, the area of sleep is as important a part of the relationship as holding or feeding the baby. Sleep disturbances during the first year, especially, are apt to be viewed by the mother as a reflection on her maternal ability. She feels the baby is not loved enough or he would sleep peacefully.

Hirschberg believes that the overabsorbed mothers actually encourage the sleep disturbances because it shows that the child cannot get along without them. They welcome the child's need for mother at bedtime, respond to every cry, and eagerly take the child into bed with them—sometimes displacing father. Other factors enter in, of course—such as guilt, anger toward the sleep disturber—but for these overabsorbed mothers the dependence of the child on them for as basic a commodity as sleep is extremely important in their own personal adjustment.

There is also the possibility that a basic maternal attitude toward child rearing in general underlies training in all the physiological and social areas. Sears, Maccoby, and Levin (1957) do report positive correlations between bedtime rules and maternal attitudes toward table manners, neatness, care of house, and standards of obedience. However, these are all low correlations— ranging from .18 to .26—leaving much of the variance unexplained. Then, too, strictness at bedtime had a satisfactory loading on only one of seven factors describing maternal behavior. Training patterns probably vary with both the personality of the mother and the specific area.

Furthermore, the practices in the sleep area that lead to behavioral disturbances may be different from those that lead to disturbances in other areas. Problem behavior in the feeding and socialization areas was associated with rigid training, problems in the toilet area were associated with either rigid or overpermissive training, while, as we have seen, overpermissiveness is most critical with sleeping problems (Klatskin et al., 1956).

This is not to say that the basic personality of the mother and other significant persons is irrelevant. Recall that the mother's way of dealing with sleep is related to her general adjustment to the maternal role. This is also true for the socialization area but not for feeding or toilet training. This suggests that the sleep area is more dynamically significant with these mothers than the much discussed feeding and toileting areas. Hirschberg (1957) perceives a shift in parent's emphasis from feeding to sleeping problems over the last few years.

Innate temperamental characteristics of the child may also influence his reaction to various sleep-training regimes. Chess, Thomas, and Birch (1959) find it possible to classify babies as malleable or tenacious in their response to various experimental situations. Presumably this is constitutionally determined. They observed that most babies awakened and cried in response to teething, respiratory infections, etc. The malleable babies continued to cry after the cause was removed, however, while the tenacious ones did not usually persist. In keeping with their plasticity, the malleable ones were easy to cure by allowing them to cry it out for one or two nights. On the other hand, if for some reason the tenacious babies persisted in crying after the cause was removed, they were hard to change—not responding to the "crying out" therapy quickly.

Therefore, Chess et al. see sleep disturbances as primarily a matter of inherited disposition. But they also report that— regardless of the temperament of the child—the mothers varied in the speed with which they initiated the "crying out" procedure. Here the mother's insecurity and guilt played a role: the less secure mothers could not bring themselves to let the baby cry at length. This fits in with our discussion of the insecure, over-absorbed mother. Thus, it is unlikely that temperament alone determines sleep patterns or disturbances.

An interesting empirical study of the "crying out" treatment in a two-year-old child was done by Williams (1959). The child had been given special care because of prolonged illness. At the time of the study he was well but insisted on having a parent sit with him for one and a half to two hours before falling asleep at naptime or bedtime. If the parent left, the child would scream and fuss. The parents decided to extinguish this tryannical behavior by not returning to the room. The results are shown in Fig. 22. The child cried for 45 minutes the first time but extinguished after seven sessions. A week later the child cried again—probably through spontaneous recovery——and someone picked him up. Thus a second extinction procedure was necessary.

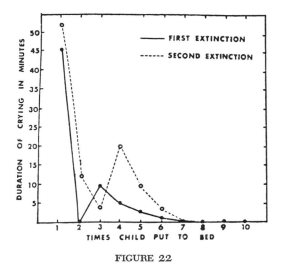

FIGURE 22

Williams observed no ill effects on the general personality of the child of this extinction procedure.

It is of interest to compare prevalent attitudes about child-rearing practices in relation to sleep with the empirical evidence just summarized. In the Opinionaire described in the previous section there were six items relating to maternal behavior in relation to children's sleep. The results on these items are presented in Table XVI.

The first two items suggest highly permissive approaches to putting the child to bed and keeping him there. The college students, as a group, frown upon this approach. The number of students expressing both disapproval and strong disapproval is more than one would expect by chance. On the other hand, the mild permissiveness involved in letting the child come down to a party for a moment wins moderate but not strong approval. For some reason Protestant and Jewish students approve this while Catholics do not. In general, the students do not favor over-permissiveness.

The even-keeled, rational mother who sends the children to bed at a reasonable hour and gets them up respectably seems to be heartily endorsed by the students as is indicated in Item 4.

TABLE XVI

ATTITUDES OF COLLEGE STUDENTS TOWARD
CHILD-REARING PRACTICES RELATED TO
SLEEP

ITEM	STRONGLY APPROVE	APPROVE	NEUTRAL	DIS-APPROVE	STRONGLY DIS-APPROVE
1. A mother permits her pre-school age children to stay up until nine or ten o'clock and lets them get up when they wish	2	26	16	75	43
2. A mother lets her pre-school child get up three or four times after being put to bed to get drinks of water, go to the potty, etc.	3	14	33	80	32
3. A mother permits a child to come down for a mo-ment and see the guests at a late party	5	81	31	31	14
4. A mother sends her pre-school age children to bed at 8:00 p.m. and gets them up at 7 a.m.	20	92	29	17	4
5. A mother is strict about bedtime, not permitting her children to					

TABLE XVI (*Continued*)

ITEM	STRONGLY APPROVE	APPROVE	NEUTRAL	DIS- APPROVE	STRONGLY DIS- APPROVE
stay up more than five minutes beyond	7	31	33	69	22
6. A mother will not pick her child up after he goes to bed even if he cries for an hour	3	7	13	91	48

However, when this becomes rigid—as in Items 5 and 6—the students are disapproving. The child left crying for an hour is the most strongly disapproved behavior in the six items.

As a group these college students adopt a remarkably wise, middle-of-the-road attitude toward the problem of sleep training for children. They oppose both the overpermissive and rigid approaches. In view of the evidence, they are perhaps too frightened of the "crying out" treatment. It is likely that the students have been influenced by the prevalent permissive approach in child psychology. The old form of the Puritan Ethic is not in evidence here, although the desire to conform with the new psychological morality may be its modern equivalent. Still there are sizable minorities. Are these the social rebels or are they the future absorbed mothers?

SUMMARY

Most of the basic physiological human motives are modified and controlled by the customs of the society. The question arises as to whether this is true for the sleep motive. Sleep patterns show a progressive change throughout development with sleep decreasing in duration up to maturity. Estimates of the sleep needs of children tend to be too high, possibly reflecting a cultural bias. Actually, sleep needs show large individual differences at all age levels.

Sleep is initially cyclical but cycles are consolidated into one long period of sleep. This shift from polyphasic to monophasic, while partly maturational or determined by the physical environment, is also strongly supported by cultural custom. Infants spend a large portion of their sleep time in the dream stage of sleep. This declines around age 3 or 4 and declines further in old age.

Many aspects of sleeping behavior are controlled by social customs with a good deal of cross-cultural variation shown in sleeping patterns, sleeping position, and attitudes toward dreams. Religious values influence attitudes about sleep, especially in the Puritan Ethic of northern European and American culture.

An Opinionaire study was done with a sample of American college students. Attitudes consistent with the Protestant Ethic were found in the areas of sleep duration for adults, open windows during sleep, and idiosyncratic sleep patterns. Attitudes about sleeping patterns involving a sexual element were ambivalent. There is some indication that, today, Puritan attitudes are more clearly expressed in the sleep area than with sexual matters.

Child-rearing techniques in the sleep area are varied, ranging from strict to flexible to overpermissive. While most of the theoretical discussion centers around the bad effects of the strict methods, the available evidence shows that sleep disturbances in children are related to overpermissiveness and to mothers overabsorbed in the maternal role.

Does sleep give rise to acquired motivation important in social life as has been postulated for sex, hunger, and pain? The evidence is scanty. There is little reason to believe that social motives can be based on sleep deprivation. On the other hand, there is some indication that the sleep response can be conditioned and that stimuli associated with sleep onset can become sub-goals (see Chapter 4). Concepts of motivational channelizing, canalization, or cathexis seem most appropriate here. There is no indication that higher cultural goals can be based on the sleep motive through sublimation or comparable processes.

In general, the sleep motive seems to go through much the same sort of socialization process as other physiological motives. Society establishes customs and conditions through which the individual satisfies this physiological need while at the same time not disrupting social organization. As with other motives, the customs become values held by the individual and may become rigid. Some people may chafe and rebel against these restrictions. In this context, then, it is meaningful to regard sleep as a motivational process.

CHAPTER 10

Conclusions and Implications

We have now reached the point for summarizing, integrating, and interpreting our facts. First we will discuss sleep motivation in relation to biological functioning. Then we will relate sleep motivation to various concepts in motivation theory—goal-directedness, energization, stimulation, and arousal. Finally, we will draw some implications for the area of social motivation.

SLEEP MOTIVATION, EVOLUTION, AND HOMEOSTASIS

One of the most significant findings is that sleep is not a simple, unitary state. Sleep does not gradually deepen during the early part of the night and gradually lighten towards morning, as was thought earlier. Rather, sleep goes through a number of cycles in level of arousal during the night. The very concept of depth has little meaning because the various measures—auditory threshold, brain potentials, visceral activity, muscle tension—are not well correlated and sometimes suggest diametrically opposite conclusions regarding the depth of sleep.

Aside from quantitative differences, there is a growing body of evidence that there are at least two qualitatively different stages of sleep—the traditional synchronized EEG sleep and

327

sleep showing an aroused EEG. Synchronized sleep is associated with lowered brain and visceral arousal, muscular relaxation, and decreased cognitive activity. Aroused sleep is associated with increased brain and visceral arousal, sudden loss of tonus in certain muscular groups but activity in others, and the special cognitive activity of dreaming. Thresholds appear to be correlated positively with degree of synchronization, except during the aroused or dream stage of sleep in which they are raised, at least in some species.

Sleep onset and offset is controlled by a complex system of brain mechanisms. The sleep system includes influences from the lower brain stem, the limbic system, and the cortex all acting on, and in opposition to, the brain stem activating system. Thus, the sleep system and the activating system are antagonistic. Synchronized sleep appears to be specifically dependent upon the cortex while aroused sleep is specifically dependent on a mechanism in the lower brain stem. The sleep system as a whole acts positively to produce sleep so that the old idea that sleep is simply the result of the inactivity of other systems is not supported.

Sleep and wakefulness appear to have gone through significant evolutionary changes. Cycles of rest and activity are found in all living organisms. This has evolved from the simple "breathing" cycle of the plant, through the polyphasic pattern of lower animals, to the diurnal alternation typical of adult human beings. The primitive polyphasic pattern seems to be dependent on sub-cortical mechanisms and can be seen in lower animals, infants, and de-corticated animals. The prolongation of sleep into one long period appears to be the result of the evolution of the cortex. Furthermore, the attainment of a one-to-two ratio of sleep time to wakeful time seems to be a unique feature of man's highly developed cortex.

Evolutionary changes also involve the two stages of sleep. A great proportion of the sleep time in lower animals consists of aroused sleep, while in man this is reversed. Furthermore, infants and young children spend more time in aroused sleep than synchronized sleep, but this changes with age. Again, the shift from aroused sleep to synchronized sleep is dependent on cortical development.

The aroused stage, then, appears to be a primitive form of sleep. It also appears to be correlated with a primitive form of wakefulness, in that the cognitive level of lower animals and children is not very high. The states of sleep and wakefulness are difficult to distinguish in lower animals and in infants. On the other hand, in the organism with a highly developed cortex the contrast between highly synchronized sleep and alert wakefulness is dramatic. It is intriguing to think that the high level of wakefulness is dependent on the degree of synchronization of sleep. However, there is no evidence to support a causal relation, as yet, so that both highly synchronized sleep and alert wakefulness can be described simply as resulting from the development of the cortex.

The role and function of dreams are difficult to evaluate. However, the dream stage of sleep is a primitive state that appears to have evolved earlier than the traditional synchronized stage. The hypothesis has been advanced that we only sleep in order to dream. The evidence does not support this since it is synchronized sleep that increases after prolonged sleep deprivation. The dream state of sleep may serve some special need. We think it is more reasonable, however, to assume that synchronized sleep is an evolutionary product of the cortex that can not be maintained indefinitely, so that periodically during the night the person slips back into primitive sleep.

The primitive nature of the dream stage and the regularity of its occurrence argues against the theory that dreams are produced by unresolved tension and serve to guard the continuance of sleep. Surely adult human beings and mentally ill individuals have more unresolved tensions than the laboratory cats and tiny infants who appear to dream more. It would seem reasonable to assume that dreams consist of the concrete thought processes that constitute part of the aroused stage of sleep. The content of the dream might very well reflect the unresolved tensions of the day, but the dream does not occur because of them. The possibility that anxiety and other affective states alter the frequency, distribution, duration, and structure of dreams remains to be demonstrated.

What is the biological function of sleep in general? The evolution of rest-activity cycles shows an adaptation to various conditions of existence—tidal patterns, lunar and diurnal cycles, etc. Hibernation—in spite of its peculiarities—can be seen as another form of this adaptation. The adaptation of rest and activity results in a conservation of energy and increases the chances for survival. There is some evidence that metabolic restoration takes place more efficiently during sleep. Prolonged sleep loss results in muscular fatigue and metabolic disruption. Some period of sleep or rest seems essential to continuing life. Thus sleep seems to be important in the general metabolic functioning of the organism.

Does this mean that sleep serves as a homeostatic mechanism for metabolic functioning? In other words, does sleep motivation arise directly out of the tissue needs of the body? The answer appears to be no. The history of this area is filled with accounts of attempts to show that one or another biochemical, endocrinological, physiological, or environmental condition leads to sleep. These attempts have been unsuccessful. There is no single condition leading to sleep and no single condition restored by sleep. Many conditions—monotonous stimulation, muscular fatigue, blood pressure changes, respiration changes, satiety, and blood chemistry—can facilitate sleep but no condition is either necessary or sufficient in an absolute sense.

The role of muscular relaxation highlights the lack of a direct causal relationship between a homeostatic need and sleep. There is no doubt that muscular relaxation is beneficial to a fatigued person and that muscular relaxation favors sleep. However, relaxation does not necessarily produce sleep. People can spend at least one night in bed with a fair degree of relaxation without falling asleep. During prolonged sleep deprivation, there is a considerable amount of involuntary muscular relaxation and yet the subject can fight off sleep for hundreds of hours. Furthermore, sleep is possible while sitting erect on a subway with a fair degree of muscular tension. In his most ingenious contribution to the area of sleep, Hebb (1949) points out that sleep is not simply a de-afferentation but may be viewed as a de-efferentation. Thus, sleep produces relaxation as well as relaxation facilitating sleep.

Hebb suggests that no amount of relaxing in the morning will produce sleep (at least for those who wake up readily).

We would like to suggest that sleep motivation depends primarily on the activity of the neural mechanisms making up the sleep system in the brain. The complex balance between these sleep mechanisms and other parts of the brain determine when sleep will occur and when it will be terminated. This system is sensitive to internal and external conditions facilitating sleep but it is by no means a passive partner reacting automatically to each condition. The brain is no longer thought of as a gigantic switchboard connecting the incoming stimuli with appropriate responses. The work on the reticular activating system has shown that the brain largely determines its own level of arousal, screens stimuli, and selects from a wide range of possible reactions. So, too, the sleep system operates in a positive fashion to determine when fatigue, monotony, or some other condition will lead to sleep and when it will not.

What is being suggested here is that the sleep system in the brain is an active, inherited series of mechanisms that determine the sleep patterns of the organism. There is a built-in sensitivity to various conditions but this may vary between individuals and between species. The lower brain stem mechanism producing aroused sleep appears to operate on an almost endogenous rhythm. This is most clearly seen in the newborn, but as the cortex develops the endogenous rhythm is altered somewhat. The limbic mechanisms seem most sensitive to internal conditions. Here species differences can be seen: the rabbit reacts dramatically to satiety, man much less so. Finally, the cortical mechanism permits the influence of learned habits, social conditioning, and diurnal adaptation. This is most influential in the adult human being, less so in lower animals. These mechanisms and their relative strength are the products of evolution.

This analysis of the sleep motive has implications for the general issue of the relationship between physiological needs and behavioral motives. Traditionally, the physiological motives, hunger, thirst, and so on, are thought to arise directly out of tissue needs. The discovery of brain mechanisms controlling these motives and their satiation has cast doubt on this simple idea.

Sleep motivation is even more clearly dependent on brain mechanisms. Therefore motives can be described as evolved brain mechanisms sensitive to a variety of internal and external stimuli in addition to homeostatic imbalance but resulting in behavior with a certain probability of enhancing survival. In the case of hunger or sleep the favorable consequences are metabolic; in the case of affection, maternal protection; in the case of sex, species reproduction; in the case of curiosity, mastery of the environment.

SLEEP MOTIVATION AND THE ENERGIZING CONCEPT

The energizing concept of motivation was described in the introductory chapter. Briefly, a motivating condition is thought to flood the organism with libido, tension, or general drive. The goal of the organism is simply to eliminate this noxious state. In drive theory, for example, motivation does not steer the organism towards a goal, this is done by learned or unlearned associations. Drive simply energizes all habits, with the selection of habits determined by associational variables.

One of the clearest statements on the nonspecific energizing feature of a motivated state is given by Brown (1961):

A variable is often said to be motivational if it facilitates or energizes a wide variety of responses. This criterion, which is probably more widely accepted than any other, stresses the fact that the presence of certain variables may alter the frequency, latency, or vigor of a number of responses. For example, a moderate degree of muscular tension, produced by squeezing a hand dynamometer, is considered motivational because it facilitates verbal learning, mental arithmetic, the knee jerk, and a variety of other responses (Courts, 1942). Similarly, food deprivation appears to be motivating, especially in animals, since it often intensifies reactions of running, sniffing, exploring, clawing, biting, and even drinking. Thus, it is the nonspecific, broadly generalized effects of certain variables that seem to mark them off as motivational rather than something else (pp. 41-42).

Sleep deprivation does not have the nonspecific, broadly generalized effects on behavior described by Brown. There is either no facilitation or a detrimental effect on performance. Intelligence tests, learning tasks, mental arithmetic, and so on deteriorate with sleep deprivation. The startle response decreases during sleep deprivation. General activity and exploratory behavior show a decline. In general, sleep deprivation has an inhibiting effect on behavior.

On the personality level, sleep deprivation does not have the general alerting effect sometimes associated with motivation. The prevailing mood is apathetic depression. Spontaneity and interest in social interaction are largely lost, with a resulting listlessness. The personality seems drained of energy.

Of course, it is sometimes possible to observe behavioral facilitation during sleep-deprivation experiments. However, these effects are due to the competing and conflicting motives introduced to keep the subject awake. Pain, knowledge of results, and similar motivating conditions have a facilitory effect. Frustration may also produce active behavior but the chief cause of frustration is social. The basic effect of the sleep motive, when these extraneous factors are eliminated, remains inhibitory.

It can be argued that sleep deprivation does in fact have a facilitating effect on behavioral tendencies and multiplies all habits but that this is not seen on the overt behavioral level because the dominant responses during sleep deprivation are incompatible with most active forms of responding. Farber (1954) makes this point when he says that "quiescence or immobility" can be a response so that increasing drive can lead to a diminution of behavior. Sleep deprivation does produce the lapses that may be viewed as a fractional part of the sleep response and sleep tends to be incompatible with other forms of responding. This is an acceptable explanation although it makes it difficult to predict the effect of motivation on performance.

If certain overt responses are masking the energizing effect of sleep deprivation, there should be some indirect indication of this. One indirect indication would be the facilitory effect of an irrelevant motive. According to the general drive theory, all motives contribute to a common pool of energy and should facilitate whatever response is dominant. However, irrelevant motives such as hunger, thirst, heat, and fatigue have not been shown to summate with the sleep motive. For example, an irrelevant hunger motive neither increases nor decreases sleep latency. If the quiescence response is dominant in the hierarchy, the addition of hunger to the drive pool should have acted to produce sleep more quickly. If the hunger motive evoked a more dominant and incompatible response, sleep latency should have decreased. There was no effect. Actually, the summation of various motives other than sleep has been seriously questioned (Bolles, 1958, Estes, 1958). The sleep motive may be a particularly good example of a motive that does not readily summate with other motives.

Another way of determining whether sleep deprivation has an energizing effect not apparent on the overt behavioral level, is to measure internal arousal. During sleep deprivation, muscular tension decreases. Similarly, indicators of autonomic functioning show a decline in visceral tensions. The EEG shows a tendency for the sleep-deprived subject to drift off into drowsy and sleepy states, if not into actual sleep. Here, too, it is important to eliminate extraneous motivational conditions that might produce arousal. Sleep deprivation itself produces a de-arousal rather than an arousal.

Finally, it should be noted that the motivational variables associated with an alert, energized state are mediated by the reticular activating system. The drowsiness and fractional sleep responses found in sleep deprivation are mediated by the sleep system that operates antagonistically to the activating system. Therefore the tendency towards sleep operates on an entirely different neural basis than the tendency towards most other goals.

The presence of an arousal or dream stage of sleep introduces some interesting complexities. This is a very special state. The brain and autonomic nervous system are aroused but certain muscular groups show decreased tension. The arousal is mediated by the limbic system rather than by the reticular activating system. The unique features of this aroused state are strong arguments against the concept of a simple unitary arousal. In any case, the arousal found in the dream stage of sleep is not the same as that found in alerted, motivational states.

Nevertheless, it might be thought that the existence of an aroused stage of sleep offers evidence for the energizing concept of motivation. However, this is not the stage of sleep that seems to be the main goal during sleep deprivation. The lapse periods occurring during sleep loss consist mainly of fractional forms of synchronized sleep. Furthermore, it is synchronized sleep that increases most dramatically during the recovery sleep following sleep deprivation. Aroused sleep may or may not have an important independent function, but the main goal towards which the sleep-deprived subject is directed is synchronized sleep—a de-aroused state.

In general, the sleep motive does not seem to involve a general energization of the organism. Sleep deprivation does not produce a widespread, general facilitation of performance. The sleep motive does not seem to summate with other motives to facilitate the most dominant response. Rather than an internal arousal, sleep deprivation has a strong tendency to lead to a de-arousal. The sleep motive is simply not associated with an active, alert, and tense state.

If this analysis of the sleep motive is taken seriously and if it holds up in the face of future empirical findings, then a fundamental re-evaluation of our basic views of motivation is required. Motivation can no longer be viewed as a simple energizing process. This is not to say that concepts of energization, arousal, activation, and drive can be eliminated. These are valuable conceptual tools for describing certain aspects of behavior. What is being questioned here is the equation of motivation with general energization.

It might be thought that the sleep motive is an oddity, but that in all other respects motivation is still the same as general energization. This would overlook a great many other troublesome features of the energization concept, however, and miss out on an opportunity to make a significant conceptional breakthrough. The fact of the matter is that the drive theory, for example, fails to account for many aspects of learning and performance (Bolles, 1958; Estes, 1958).

The difficulty with the energization concept can also be seen in the area of fear motivation. For example, Miller (1951) observes that during the initial stages of fear conditioning a rat is highly activated. After prolonged avoidance conditioning, however, the animal becomes progressively relaxed and runs off the whole behavior sequence nonchalantly. Similar observations have been made with the dog (Solomon and Wynne, 1954) and the monkey (Galambos and Morgan, 1960). Behavior continues without the usual autonomic, muscular, or brain potential indications of arousal. If arousal is the motivation here, why does the behavior continue long after the arousal drops out? Extinction is going on, but this hardly explains the hundreds of perfectly performed trials without anxiety in the Solomon and Wynne study. Furthermore, Miller also observes that making the escape door inoperable arouses the animal again. Note that this is not reconditioning.

Another reason for questioning the identification of motivation with a general energizing concept like arousal is that arousal is not a simply unitary process (Ax, 1953; Lacey and Lacey, 1958; Hebb, 1958; Arnold, 1960). Arousal patterns vary with the motive involved, individual differences, and many other factors. The dream stage of sleep, with its unique arousal features, also demonstrates this. Finally, some motivation states such as anoxia and fatigue tend to decrease arousal (Bindra, 1959). Naturally, we would add sleep deprivation.

It seems to us that it would be more fruitful to view arousal as part of the response process. Different patterns of arousal and de-arousal depend on the stimulating conditions, the response requirements, the genetic predisposition of the individual and the species, and the learning history. Arousal and de-arousal patterns also seem to depend on the type of motive, the strength of the motive, and speed of onset of the motive. Thus an intense, rapidly developing condition like pain might evoke a very strong arousal response of a particular kind. Hunger, maternal, and curiosity motives might evoke a much milder arousal. Fatigue, heat, and especially sleep deprivation, might produce a de-arousal. Historically, this view might be linked with McDougall's idea that each instinct has a characteristic emotion. In any case, the notion of arousal as part of the response process is an alternative to the view that energization is synonymous with motivation.

SLEEP MOTIVATION AND THE DIRECTIONAL CONCEPT

While sleep motivation does not produce a general energization, it does seem to produce a goal-directed tendency. The goal response of sleep consists of the prone position, muscular relaxation, closing of the eyes, specific EEG and eye movement patterns, and a reversible loss of critical activity. Various fractional forms of this goal response are also possible. The goal response also varies somewhat between species. Nevertheless, all animals, including man, seek this sort of end-state on a regular basis.

The tendency to seek sleep varies with the amount of sleep deprivation, holding diurnal rhythm constant. Sleep latency increases as a function of sleep deprivation. Following prolonged sleep loss, human subjects sleep for the better part of a day and catnap for days afterward. Providing a sufficient amount of sleep will decrease the probability that sleep will be sought as a goal immediately thereafter. Thus the goal-directed tendency varies with the operations of deprivation and satiation.

The directing of behavior toward the goal of sleep is, however, nowhere more dramatically shown than in the lapse phenomenon during prolonged sleep deprivation. These lapses increase in frequency, duration, and degree as sleep deprivation progresses. In these experimental situations, the full goal response is not permitted to occur, but these lapses have the characteristics of fractional goal responses. Physiological measures suggest that the lapses consist of an intermediate level of sleep and eventually the lapses may lead into periods of primitive, aroused sleep. The direction of behavior towards the goal response of sleep is overpowering after prolonged sleep deprivation.

Another characteristic of a goal-directed motive is that it will lead to the learning and performance of responses necessary to perform the goal response itself. Sleep deprivation does lead to the learning of a number of different instrumental or operant responses when these are required to obtain sleep. Stated another way, sleep serves as a reward for a sleep-deprived animal. The technical difficulty in demonstrating this effect has been the tendency of subjects to fall asleep under the most adverse circumstances. Actually, this further demonstrates the strength of the goal tendency. The technical difficulty has been overcome in several studies, but more evidence is needed on this point.

The learning of instrumental responses for the attainment of the goal of sleeping can also be shown in social behavior. Anthropological evidence indicates that, as with other basic motives, all cultures provide for sleeping. However, each culture requires that the individual learns where, when, and how to sleep. The monophasic pattern itself is to some extent a product of social learning.

Granted that sleep deprivation produces a goal-directed tendency, can the sleep motive be construed as a drive stimulus? Let us first consider Estes' (1950, 1958, 1959) statistical learning theory in which motivation is viewed as a population of internal stimuli. According to Estes, deprivation of food or water makes a set of internal stimuli available, as does also satiation. Increasing deprivation results in a progressive sequence of partially overlapping stimulus sets. The number of drive stimuli does not change but their probability of occurrence does. Discrete responses are associated with these discrete stimulus elements on the basis of contiguity. Association by contiguity is the only concept used in Estes' theory.

How well does the drive stimulus theory explain the data on sleep deprivation? If one assumes that the response involved is relaxation, and eventually sleep, then the drive stimulus theory handles most of the data well. Sleep deprivation produces internal stimuli that show an increasing probability. The relaxation response occurs with greater frequency and, since it is incompatible with other kinds of responding, non-sleep-relevant tasks deteriorate. Sleep-relevant responses, such as pressing a microswitch to get sleep, are attached to the cues of the experimental situation, as well as the drive stimuli, and their responses have a greater probability of occurrence than relaxation.

There is one observation that is difficult to reconcile with Estes' theory. While simple association theory can explain the diurnal rhythm, it is difficult to see how it accounts for the progressive de-arousal or relaxation that goes on from day to day of sleep deprivation when the diurnal cycle is held constant. Since most people have experienced no more than one or two days of sleep deprivation, and most have been "trained" to sleep after 16 hours of wakefulness, the association theory would have to predict that the relaxation response should increase up to a point and then, because of stimulus generalization, decrease in probability of occurrence. Thus, after a couple of days of sleep loss, the person should be more and more aroused. The data, of course, do not show this.

This problem in Estes' theory is analogous to that raised by Brown (1961) about the difficulty in accounting for drive shift in terms of stimulus generalization. An animal trained on a high drive and shifted to a low one decreases the frequency and vigor of his responding. This can be explained easily by stimulus generalization. The stimulus generalization idea would also suggest, however, that going from a low to a high drive would produce a stimulus generalization decrement. There are clear instances where a shift to a higher drive is clearly energizing.

What seems to be missing in Estes' drive stimulus theory is some idea of stimulus intensity. Estes' theory could be modified by assuming that the *number* of drive stimuli sampled varies with the level of motivation. Miller and Dollard's (1941) concept of motivation as a strong stimulus implies an intensity dimension. Recently, Champion (1961) suggested a modification of Hullian theory in which a stimulus intensity dynamism is assumed for drive stimuli. In this interesting proposal, drive stimuli multiply only the relevant habits. It seems to us that a theory developed along these lines could account most adequately for the sleep motive. Sleep motivation does not have a general energizing effect, but it does energize specific responses in proportion to the degree of sleep deprivation. Thus, something between a general energizer and a purely associational factor is needed— a specific energizer.

Assuming now that sleep motivation is a specific energizer

of responses leading to the goal of sleep, what is the nature of this goal in relation to current concepts of reward and satiation? The known facts about sleep are not inconsistent with the idea that reward and satiation consist of an elimination of drive stimuli. The drive reduction and stimulus reduction theories have been found wanting, however, in accounting for motives for activity and curiosity, as well as for the effects of sensory deprivation (Murray, 1964 b).

Hebb (1958) attempted to account for the fact that organisms sometimes seek to reduce excessive stimulation and at other times seek an increase in stimulation by assuming that the organism seeks an optimal, moderate level of arousal. Hebb sees clearly, however, that the tendency to sleep cannot be fit into this scheme. He says that the theory has ". . . a glaring defect: it makes no provision for sleep" (1958, p. 174). Therefore he modified his theory by saying that the organism will seek a moderate level of arousal until he becomes sleepy. At that point "he begins to seek conditions which minimize arousal."

What other possibilities are there? Tinbergen (1951), along with many others, would simply say that sleep is an innate consummatory response. Tinbergen makes an important distinction between appetitive, or goal-seeking, responses that tend to be variable, plastic, and subject to learning, and consummatory responses that are fixed reactions to internal "directing stimuli." This is perhaps the simplest approach to the problem but it suggests no general principles about reward and satiation.

One other possibility is the newer version of hedonic theory. For example, McClelland defines a motive as ". . . the redintegration by a cue of a change in an affective situation" (McClelland, 1951; McClelland et al., 1953). The situation redintegrated by the cue is an affective arousal elicited on an innate basis by a sensory stimulus. The arousal may be pleasant or unpleasant, with corresponding approach or avoidance behavior. Small discrepancies in stimulation from an existing adaptational level arouse a positive affective response, while large discrepancies arouse a negative one.

To the extent that McClelland's theory depends on an active aroused state it is subject to the same criticisms as the idea of general arousal. However, McClelland et al. clearly recognize that ". . . further exploration of motives based on *decreases* in affective states is definitely called for" (p. 75). Sleep, of course, involves a de-aroused state. Sleep seems to have a positive affective quality, as when we speak of sleeping "peacefully" or "blissfully." The redintegrated form of this by learned cues would be drowsiness. Drowsiness can also be described hedonically as when we speak of a "pleasant drowsiness" after a day at the seashore or when we feel "bushed" after a trying day. Here a mild drowsiness is pleasant but extreme sleepiness is unpleasant.

It is more difficult to relate sleep motivation to discrepancies from an adaptational level. Sleep involves a drastic change from the wakeful level of adaptation and presents the same problem as with Hebb's idea of the organism seeking an optimal level of stimulation. A possible solution has been suggested by Fiske and Maddi (1961). They suggest that for each stage in the sleep-wakefulness cycle there is a characteristic level of activation. Sleep would be greatly discrepant from the normal level of activation in the middle of the morning, and would produce a negative affective state. On the other hand, sleep after a heavy meal or at the end of the day would constitute a small discrepancy from the existing adaptational level and would produce a positive affective state.

In general, the rewarding and satiating characteristics of sleep are not consistent with theories suggesting that the organism always seeks an optimal level of stimulation. The goal towards which the sleep motive directs behavior involves a lessening of stimulation. This is consistent with drive or drive-stimulus reduction theories but it may also be consistent with hedonistic theories.

SLEEP MOTIVATION, SOCIALIZATION, AND PSYCHODYNAMICS

One of the most fascinating results of the present review of the literature on sleep was the discovery that sleep motivation has a good deal of social and dynamic significance.

This was not entirely expected. The sleep motive has played little role in personality theory, except for Freud's reliance on the wish to sleep in connection with dreams. Yet, the sleep motive is as intimately bound up with social living as hunger, fear, or even sexual motivation.

To begin with, society controls and regulates sleeping behavior just as it does other physiological functions. Society determines the time, place, and duration of sleeping. Fairly strong cultural norms and standards, bearing little relation to physiological realities, exist in our own culture and almost surely do in other cultures as well. In our own culture, attitudes about proper sleep behavior have a moralistic tone suggestive of the Puritan Ethic. While social controls on sleep behavior may not be as powerful as those for other physiological motives, one can observe rebelliousness in this area and a certain amount of guilt for a failure to conform.

Sleeping behavior is socialized in about the same way that eating and other basic activities are. Parents use permissive and rigid training procedures, with the permissive methods associated with subsequent difficulty in control and the rigid methods possibly resulting in overconformity. The specific content of dreams may be taught to the child in various ways. The gradual shift from polyphasic sleep to the monophasic pattern, while largely maturational, also shows the influence of socialization. With social controls removed, the polyphasic pattern may return.

The individual seems to use the same sort of adjustment mechanisms in dealing with the sleep motive as with other motives, such as sex and aggression. Besides the spectrum from rebelliousness to overconformity to social norms, the classical defense mechanisms may appear in special situations. Thus there is evidence for a repressive mechanism during sleep-deprivation studies, as well as defensive maneuvers such as apathy, social withdrawal, rationalization, and reality distortion. While sleep deprivation cannot be said to produce a true psychotic state, serious distortions of thinking, perception, and orientation occur.

In the actual world of psychopathology, sleep disturbances are as prevalent as disturbances in any other physiological function. Sleep seems to be disturbed by affective states in general, and depressive states in particular. Excessive sleeping occurs, not only as the result of neuropathology, but also as a defensive maneuver in neurosis. The various sleep disturbances—insomnia, excessive sleep, nightmares, night terrors, enuresis, sleepwalking, —have only begun to be studied.

Dreams have long been thought to be involved in psychopathology. The occurrence of nightmares and the dynamic significance of dream content supports this. Therefore, it is particularly surprising to find little evidence for a relationship between the number, distribution, and structure of dream periods, and psychopathology. Dream recall, of course, varies with personality and psychopathology but differences found between pathological groups in the formal aspects of dreams have been relatively minor. The research has only begun so that more dramatic findings may appear in the future. At the present time, however, there is little evidence for the theory that dynamic factors produce dreams or that dreams serve as the guardian of sleep. The content of dreams may still reflect personal conflicts, of course, as the consequence of the naturally occurring stage of aroused sleep.

The involvement of sleep motivation, in general, with socialization, personality adjustment, and psychopathology raises an interesting question about the significant motives in human behavior. There is a tradition in personality theory of assuming that one or another motive—sex, aggression, power, and so on—is the key to everything else. For example, in the classical Freudian theory, pathologies involving eating, defecating, fornicating, and so on are seen as aspects of sexual development. Nothing is said about the place of sleeping in this developmental scheme, and there is no evidence that the sleep pathologies operate as sexual displacements. In his last book, Freud (1949) conceded that any motive *could* become a source of conflict. The evidence, here, suggests that as simple a thing as the sleep motive can become involved in personal conflict and serve as the base for defensive maneuvers and pathological symptoms.

This raises the question of how any physiological motive becomes involved in personal conflict. The other arm of the conflict seems to be anxiety, but there is little agreement about the nature of anxiety. Originally Freud saw castration threat as the only source of anxiety but later added the threat of the loss of parental love. In another place, we have suggested that the anxiety of most concern in psychopathology stems from basic affectional motives (Murray, 1964 a). What little information we have about the socialization of sleep would support this. For example, the over-absorbed mother uses the child's need for affection to generate sleep disturbances and thus bind the child closer to her.

In reviewing the material on sleep, we have also kept close watch for evidence of social motives that may have been derived from sleep motivation. Theories of sublimation, acquired motives, and functional autonomy suggest that the more complex social motives are derived in one way or another from simple physiological motives (Murray, 1964 b). We have been unable to find any evidence for this in the case of the sleep motive.

An alternative idea suggested by several theorists is that society operates by channelizing, canalizing, or cathecting physiological motives (Murray, 1964 b). There is evidence that this occurs with the sleep motive. All societies provide for sleeping but control the time, place, and so on. After a time one is strongly motivated to sleep only in a bed in one culture but on the ground in another, and so on. It is possible that there are no social motives in the traditional, derived sense but only physiological motives for affection, effectance, and similar complex goals as well as for food, water, and sex. All these motives may be channelized by society and thus socialized just as the sleep motive is.

CONCLUDING REMARKS

The main thesis of this book was that a motive to sleep can be assumed. The sleep motive hypothesis appears to be useful in integrating and organizing findings from widely scattered sources. This simple theoretical framework also points to areas where further research is needed. For example, the work on the neurophysiological mechanisms of sleep has made great progress in recent years, but relatively little is known about the metabolic effects of sleep and sleep deprivation. Then, too, there have been many studies on the learning and performance of non-relevant responses during sleep deprivation, but relatively few on behavior leading to sleep as a goal or reward. Finally, the research on dreams is in an exciting stage of development but sleep pathology and sleep socialization are nearly virgin fields. Perhaps the hypothesis of a sleep motive will stimulate systematic research or, better yet, the formulation of alternative hypotheses.

Another purpose in writing this book was to add to the list of motives entering the theoretical discourse on the nature of motivation. The relationship between the sleep motive and homeostatic balance provides additional evidence for the idea that motives are based on evolved neural mechanisms partially correlated with bodily needs rather than simple reflexes growing out of tissue deficiencies. The discovery of a unique stage of sleep involving arousal and dreams has raised a number of important theoretical issues. Among other things, the evidence does not support the idea that dreams are produced by unresolved tensions or serve to guard sleep. The material on learning, performance, and arousal suggests that, while the sleep motive has directional properties, it does not function as a general energizer. The analysis suggests a closer examination of the relationship between motivation and arousal. The nature of the goal response in the sleep motive runs contrary to the assumption that the organism always seeks an optimal level of stimulation. The involvement of sleep in personality adjustment and psychopathology suggests that special motives such as sex and aggression are not necessarily the basis of psychological disturbance. There was no evidence that social motives are derived from the sleep motive but the sleep motive does seem to be socialized through channelization. Thus, the phenomena under discussion here do bear on a number of important theoretical issues.

The comprehensive analysis of a motivational variable is an enormously complex task. Nevertheless, we would like to see similar analyses made of a great variety of motivational variables. Perhaps, then, we would be ready for a really meaningful theory of motivation.

REFERENCES

ABSE, D. W. Hysteria. In S. Arieti (Ed.), *American handbook of psychiatry*, Vol. I. New York: Basic Books, 1959.

ADEY, W. R., KADO, R. T., & RHODES, J. M. Sleep: Cortical and subcortical recordings in the chimpanzee. *Science*, 1963, *141*, 932-933..

ADRIAN, E. D. The physiology of sleep. *Irish J. med. Sci.*, 1937, *6*, 237-248.

AKERT, K., KOELLA, W. P., & HESS, R. Sleep produced by electrical stimulation of the thalamus. *Amer. J. Physiol.*, 1952, *168*, 260-267.

AKIMOTO, H., YAMAGUCHI, N., OKABE, K., NAKAGAWA, T., NAKAMURA, I., ABE, K., TORII, H., & MASAHASHI, K. On the sleep induced through electrical stimulation on the dog thalamus. *Folia Psychiat. Neurol. Jap.*, 1956, 10, 117-146.

ALEXANDER, F. *Fundamentals of psychoanalysis*. New York: Norton, 1948.

ALEXANDER, F., & WILSON, G. W. Quantitative dream studies. *Psychoanal. Quart.*, 1935, *4*, 371-407.

ALLEE, W. C. *The social life of animals*. Boston: Beacon, 1958.

ALLPORT, G. W. The trend in motivation theory. *Amer. J. Orthopsychiat.*, 1953, *23*, 107-119.

ALLPORT, G. W. *Pattern and growth in personality*. New York: Holt, Rinehart & Winston, 1937, 1961.

ALPERS, B. J. *Clinical neurology*. Philadelphia: F. A. Davis, 1958.

ALTMAN, J. W., SMITH, R. W., MEYERS, R. L., McKENNA, F. S., & BRYSON, S. *Psychological and social adjustment in a simulated shelter: A research report*. Pittsburgh: Amer. Inst. Research, 1960.

AMSEL, A. Selective association and the anticipatory goal response mechanism as explanatory concepts in learning theory. *J. exp. Psychol.*, 1949, *39*, 785-799.

AMSEL, A., & COLE, K. F. Generalization of fear-motivated interference with water intake. *J. exp. Psychol.*, 1953, *46*, 243-247.

AMSEL, A., & MALTZMAN, I. The effect upon generalized drive strength of emotionality as inferred from the level of consummatory response. *J. exp. Psychol.*, 1950, *40*, 563-569.

ANDERSON, A. An inquiry into the hours of rest (sleep) of 1,600 school children. *Med. Officer*, 1936, *55*, 147-148.

ANDERSON, O. W. The management of "infantile insomnia." *J. Pediat.*, 1951, *38*, 394-401.

ANDERSSON, B., & McCANN, S. M. A further study of polydipsia evoked by hypothalamic stimulation in the goat. *Acta Physiol., Scand.*, 1955, *33*, 333-346.

ANDERSSON, B., & McCANN, S. M. The effect of hypothalamic lesions on the water intake of the dog. *Acta Psysiol., Scand.*, 1956, *35*, 312-320.

ANDREEV, B. V. *Sleep therapy in the neuroses.* New York: Consultants Bureau, 1960.

ANTHONY, J. An experimental approach to the psychopathology of childhood: Sleep disturbances. *Brit. J. med. Psychol.*, 1959, *32*, 19-37.

ANTROBUS, J. S., DEMENT, W., & FISHER, C. Patterns of dreaming and dream recall: An EEG study. *J. abnorm. soc. Psychol.*, 1964, *69*, 341-344.

ARIETI, S. Manic-depressive psychosis. In S. Arieti (Ed.), *American handbook of psychiatry*, Vol. I. New York: Basic Books, 1959.

ARMINGTON, J. D., & MITNICK, L. L. Electroencephalogram and sleep deprivation. *J. appl. Physiol.*, 1959, *14*, 247-250.

ARNOLD, M. B. *Emotion and personality.* Vol. II. *Neurological and physiological aspects.* New York: Columbia Univer., 1960.

ASERINSKY, E., & KLEITMAN, N. Two types of ocular motility during sleep. *J. appl. Physiol.*, 1955, *8*, 1-10. (a)

ASERINSKY, E., & KLEITMAN, N. A motility cycle in sleeping infants as manifested by ocular and gross bodily activity. *J. appl. Physiol.*, 1955, *8*, 11-18. (b)

ATKINSON, J. W. Explorations using imaginative thought to assess the strength of human motives. In M. R. Jones (Ed.), *Nebraska symposium on motivation.* Lincoln: Univer. Nebraska, 1954.

ATKINSON, J. W. (Ed.) *Motives in fantasy, action, and society.* Princeton: Van Nostrand, 1958.

ATKINSON, J. W. Discussion of Dr. Lazarus' paper. In J. Kagan & G. S. Lesser (Eds.), *Contemporary issues in Thematic Apperceptive methods.* Springfield, Ill.: C. C. Thomas, 1961.

ATKINSON, J. W., & MCCLELLAND, D. C. The projective expression of needs: II The effect of different intensities of the hunger drive on thematic apperception. *J. exp. Psychol.*, 1948, *38*, 643-658.

AUBERT, V., & WHITE, H. Sleep: A sociological interpretation. *Acta Sociol.*, 1959, *4*, 1-16, 46-54.

AX, A. F. The physiological differentiation between fear and anger in humans. *Psychosom. Med.*, 1953, *15*, 433-442.

AX, A. F., FORDYCE, W., LOOVAS, I., MEREDITH, W., PIROJNIKOFF, L., SHMAVONION, B., & WENDALH, R. Quantitative effects of sleep deprivation. *U.S.A. Qr. Res. Develpm. Res. Rep.*, 1957.

AX, A. F., & LUBY, E. D. Autonomic responses to sleep deprivation. *Arch. gen. Psychiat.*, 1961, *4*, 55-59.

AZIMA, H. Prolonged sleep treatment in mental disorders (some new psychopharmacological considerations). *J. ment. Sci.*, 1955, *101*, 593-603.

AZIMA, H. Sleep treatment in mental disorders; results of four years of trial. *Dis. nerv. Syst.*, 1958, *19*, 523.

BACHET, M. The concept of criminal encephalosis. *Amer. J. Orthopsychiat.*, 1951, *21*, 794-799.

BAKIS, E. The so-called DP-apathy in Germany's DP camps. *Trans. Kansas Acad. Sci.*, 1952, *55*, 62-86.

BALLER, W., & SCHALOCK, H. Conditioned response treatment of enuresis. *Except. Child*, 1956, *22*, 233-236, 247-248.

BARBER, T. X. Comparison of suggestibility during "light sleep" and hypnosis. *Science*, 1956, *124*, 405.

BARD, P. Central nervous mechanisms for the expression of anger in animals. In M. L. Reymert (Ed.), *Feelings and emotions.* New York: McGraw-Hill, 1950.

BARKER, W. Studies in epilepsy: Personality pattern, situational stress, and the symptoms of narcolepsy. *Psychosom. Med.*, 1948, *10*, 193-202.

BARRY, J., & BOUSFIELD, W. A. A quantitative determination of euphoria and its relation to sleep. *J. abnorm. soc. Psychol.*, 1935, *29*, 385-389.

BARTLETT, F. C. The measurement of human skill. *Occup. Psychol.*, 1948, *22*, 31-38.

BARTLEY, S. H., & CHUTE, E. *Fatigue and impairment in man.* New York: McGraw-Hill, 1947.

BATINI, C., MORUZZI, G., PALESTRINI, M., ROSSI, G. F., & ZAN-CHETTI, A. Persistent patterns of wakefulness in the pretrigeminal midpontine preparation. *Science,* 1958, *128,* 30-32.

BATSEL, A. L. Electroencephalographic synchronization and de-synchronization in the chronic "cerveau isolé" of the dog, *EEG clin. Neurophysiol.,* 1960, *12,* 421-430.

BEACH, F. A. Analysis of factors involved in the arousal, maintenance, and manifestation of sexual excitement in male animals. *Psychosom. Med.* 1942, *4,* 173-198.

BEACH, F. A. *Hormones and behavior.* New York: Hoeber, 1949.

BEACH, F. A. Characteristics of masculine "sex drive." In M. R. Jones (Ed.), *Nebraska symposium on motivation.* Lincoln: Univer. Nebraska, 1956.

BEAN, W. B., HODGES, R. E., & DAUM, K. Pantothenic acid deficiency induced in human subjects. *J. clin. Invest.,* 1955, *34,* 1073-1084.

BECK, A. T., & HURVICH, M. S. Psychological correlates of depression. *Psychosom. Med.,* 1959, *21,* 50-55.

BECKER, R. O., BACHMAN, C. H., & FRIEDMAN, H. The direct current control system: A link between environment and organism. *N.Y. State J. Med.,* 1962, *62,* 1169-1176.

BEHANAN, K. T. *Yoga: A scientific evaluation.* New York: Dover, 1960.

BÉLANGER, D., & FELDMAN, S. M. Effects of water deprivation upon heart rate and instrumental activity in the rat. *J. comp. physiol. Psychol.,* 1962, *55,* 220-225.

BÉLANGER, D., & TÉTREAU, B. L'influence d'une motivation inappro-priée dur le compartment du rat et sa frequence cardiaque. *Canad. J. Psychol.,* 1961, *15,* 6-14.

BELL, N. W., & VOGEL, E. F. (Eds.). *The family.* New York: Free Press, 1960.

BENEDEK, T. F. Sexual functions in women and their disturbance. In S. Arieti (Ed.), *American handbook of psychiatry,* Vol. I. New York: Basic Books, 1959.

BERGER, R. J. Tonus of extrinsic laryngeal muscles during sleep and dreaming. *Science,* 1961, *34,* 840.

BERGER, R. J. Experimental modification of dream content. Mimeo-graphed paper, Dept. of Psychological Medicine, Univer. of Edinburgh, 1963.

BERGER, R. J., OLLEY, P., & OSWALD, I. The EEG, eye-movements and dreams of the blind. *Quart. J. exp. Psychol.,* 1962, *14,* 183-186.

BERGER, R. J., & OSWALD, I. Eye movements during active and passive dreams. *Science,* 1962, *137,* 601.

BERGER, R. J., & OSWALD, I. Effects of sleep deprivation on behaviour, subsequent sleep and dreaming. *EEG clin. Neurophysiol.*, 1962, *14*, 297.

BERLYNE, D. E. *Conflict, arousal and curiosity*. New York: McGraw-Hill, 1960.

BEST, C. H., & TAYLOR, N. B. *Physiological basis of medical practice*. Baltimore: Williams and Wilkins, 1950.

BEXTON, W. H., HERON, W., & SCOTT, T. H. Effects of decreased variation in the sensory environment. *Canad. Psychol.*, 1954, *8*, 70-76.

BIEBER, I., and associates. *Homosexuality*. New York: Basic Books, 1962.

BILLS, A. G. Blocking: A new principle in mental fatigue. *Amer. J. Psychol.*, 1931, *43*, 230-245.

BILLS, A. G. Some causal factors in mental blocking. *J. exp. Psychol.*, 1935, *18*, 172-185.

BINDRA, D. *Motivation*. New York: Ronald, 1959.

BIRD, B. Pathological sleep. *Int. J. Psychoanal.*, 1954, *35*, 20-29.

BIZZI, E., & BROOKS, D. C. Pontine reticular formation: Relation to lateral geniculate nucleus during deep sleep. *Science*, 1963, *141*, 270-272.

BJERK, E. M., & HORNISHER, J. J. Narcolepsy: A case report and a rebuttal. *EEG clin. Neurophysiol.*, 1958, *10*, 550-552.

BJERNER, B. Alpha depression and lowered pulse rate during delayed actions in a serial reaction test. *Acta Physiol., Scand.*, 1949, *19*, Supp. 65, 93 p.

BLAIR, J. R., URBUSH, F. W., & REED, I. T. Preliminary observations on physiological, nutritional, and psychological problems in extreme cold. *Army Medical Research Lab., Ft. Knox, Ky.*, 1947. Report No. 8.

BLISS, E. L., CLARK, L. D., & WEST, C. D. Studies of sleep deprivation: Relationship to schizophrenia. *A.M.A. Arch. Neurol. Psychiat.*, 1959, *81*, 348-359.

BOLLES, R. C. The usefulness of the drive concept. In M. R. Jones (Ed.), *Nebraska symposium on motivation*. Lincoln: Univer. Nebraska, 1958.

BOREN, J. J. Decrement in performance during prolonged avoidance sessions, *J. exp. Anal. Behav.*, 1960, *3*, 201-206.

BOSTOCK, J. Enuresis and toilet training. *Med. J. Australia*, 1951, *2*, 110-113.

BOUSFIELD, W. A. Further evidence of the relation of the euphoric attitude to sleep and exercise. *Psychol. Rec.*, 1938, *2*, 334-344.

BOUSFIELD, W. A. Relation of euphoric attitude to quality of sleep. *J. Psychol.*, 1940, *9*, 393-401.

BOWEN, J. H., ROSS, S., & ANDREWS, T. G. A note on the interaction of conditioned and reactive inhibition in pursuit tracking. *J. gen. Psychol.*, 1956, *55*, 153-162.

BOWLING, G., & RICHARDS, N. G. Diagnosis and treatment of the norcolepsy syndrome: Analysis of 75 case records. *Cleveland Clinic Quart.*, 1961, *28*, 38-45.

BRADY, J. V. Extinction of a conditioned "fear" response as a function of reinforcement schedules for competing behavior. *J. Psychol.*, 1955, *40*, 25-34.

BRADY, J. V. Emotional behavior. In *Handbook of physiology, Sect. I Neurophysiology*, Vol. III. Washington: Amer. Physiol. Soc., 1960.

BRADY, J. V., & NAUTA, W. J. H. Subcortical mechanisms in emotional behavior: Affective changes following septal forebrain lesions in the albino rat. *J. comp. physiol. Psychol.*, 1953, *46*, 339-346.

BRAITHWAITE, J. Enuresis in childhood. *Practitioner*, 1950, *165*, 273-281.

BRAUCHI, J. T., & WEST, L. J. Sleep deprivation. *J.A.M.A.*, 1959, *171*, 11-14.

BRAZIER, M. A. B. *The electrical activity of the nervous system.* London: Pitman, 1960.

BREMER, F. The neurophysiological problem of sleep. In *Brain mechanisms and consciousness.* Oxford: Blackwell, 1954.

BREMER, F. Neurophysiological mechanisms in cerebral arousal. In CIBA Foundation, *The nature of sleep.* Boston: Little, Brown, 1961.

BROADBENT, D. E. *Perception and communication.* New York: Pergamon Press, 1958.

BRODY, S. *Bioenergetics and growth.* New York: Reinhold, 1945.

BROWMAN, L. G. Light in its relation to activity and estrous rhythms in the albino rat. *J. exp. Zool.*, 1937, *75*, 375-388.

BROWN, F. A. Biological chronometry. *Amer. Nat.*, 1957, *91*, 129-133.

BROWN, J. S. Problems presented by the concept of acquired drives. In *Current theory and research in motivation: A symposium.* Lincoln: Univer. Nebraska, 1953.

BROWN, J. S. Pleasure-seeking behavior and the drive reduction hypothesis. *Psychol. Rev.*, 1955, *62*, 169-179.

BROWN, J. S. *The motivation of behavior.* New York: McGraw-Hill, 1961.

BROWNLOW, C. F., & STAFF (Eds.). *Gould's medical dictionary*. Philadelphia: Blakiston, 1941.

BROZEK, J. Nutrition and behavior: Psychologic changes in acute starvation with hard physical work. *J. Amer. Dietetic Ass.*, 1955, *31*, 703-707.

BROZEK, J. Psychological effects of thiamine restriction and deprivation in normal young men. *Amer. J. clin. Nutrition*, 1957, 5, 109-120.

BROZEK, J., & TAYLOR, H. L. Psychological effects of maintenance on survival rations. *Amer. J. Psychol.*, 1958, *71*, 517-528.

BRUNER, J. S., GOODNOW, JACQUELINE J., & AUSTIN, G. A. *A study of thinking*. New York: Wiley, 1956.

BUENDIA, N., GOODE, M., & SIERRA, G. Behavioral and EEG study of pitch discrimination in naturally sleeping cats. *Fed. Proc.*, 1962, *21*, No. 2, 347.

BUNCH, M. E., COLE, A., & FRERICHS, J. The influence of twenty-four hours of wakefulness upon the learning and retention of a maze problem in white rats. *J. comp. Psychol.*, 1937, *23*, 1-11.

BUNCH, M. E., FRERICHS, J. B., & LICKLIDER, J. R. An experimental study of maze learning ability after varying periods of wakefulness. *J. comp. Psychol.*, 1938, *26*, 499-514.

BURNS, N. M. Apparent sleep produced by cortical stimulation, *Canad. J. Psychol.*, 1957, *11*, 171-181.

BUROS, O. K. *The third mental measurements yearbook*. New Brunswick: Rutgers Univer., 1949.

BURTON, A., & HARRIS, R. E. *Clinical studies of personality*. New York: Harper & Row, 1955.

BUSSE, E. W., DAVENMUEHLE, R. H., & BROWN, R. G. Psychoneurotic reactions of the aged. *Geriatrics*, 1960, *15*, 97-105.

BYCK, R., & HEARST, E. Adjustment of monkeys to five continuous days of work. *Science*, 1962, *138*, 43-44.

CADILHAC, J., PASSOUNT-FONTAINE, T., & PASSOUANT, P. Modifications in the activity of the hippocampus during the various stages of spontaneous sleep in cats. *EEG clin. Neurophysiol.*, 1962, *14*, 138.

CAMERON, N. *The psychology of behavior disorders*. Boston: Houghton Mifflin, 1947.

CAMP, C. D. Morbid sleepiness: With a report of a case of narcolepsy and a review of some recent theories of sleep. *J. abnorm. Psychol.*, 1907, *2*, 9-21.

CANNON, W. B. *Bodily changes in pain, hunger, fear and rage*. New York: Appleton, 1929.

CANNON, W. B. Hunger and thirst. In C. Murchison (Ed.), *A hand-*

book of general experimental psychology. Worcester: Clark Univer., 1934.

CAPPON, D., & BANKS, R. Studies in perceptual distortion: Opportunistic observations on sleep deprivation during a talkathon. *A.M.A. Arch. gen. Psychiat.*, 1960, *2*, 346-349.

CAPRIO, F. S. Bisexual conflicts and insomnia. *J. clin. Psychopath.*, 1949, *4*, 376-379.

CARLI, G. ARMENGOL, V., & ZANCHETTI, A. Electroencephalographic desynchronization during deep sleep after destruction of midbrain-limbic pathways in the cat. *Science*, 1963, *140*, 677-679.

CARMICHAEL, L. KENNEDY, J. L., & MEAD, L. Some recent approaches to the experimental study of human fatigue. *Proc. Nat. Acad. Sci.*, 1949, *35*, 691-696.

CASON, H. The nightmare dream. *Psychol. Monogr.*, 1935, *46*, (Whole No. 209).

CASPERS, H. Changes of cortical D.C. potentials in the sleep-wakefulness cycle. In CIBA Foundation, *The nature of sleep.* Boston: Little, Brown, 1961.

CAVE, H. A. Narcolepsy. *A.M.A. Arch. Neurol. Psychiat.*, 1931, *26*, 50-101.

CHAMPION, R. A. Motivational effects in approach-avoidance conflict. *Psychol. Rev.*, 1961, *68*, 354-358.

CHAPANIS, A., GARNER, W. R., & MORGAN, C. T. *Applied experimental psychology.* New York: Wiley, 1949.

CHATFIELD, P. O., & LYMAN, C. P. Subcortical electrical activity in the golden hamster during arousal from hibernation. *EEG clin. Neurophysiol.*, 1954, *6*, 403-408.

CHESS, S., THOMAS, A., & BIRCH, H. Characteristics of the individual child's behavioral responses to the environment. *Amer. J. Orthopsychiat.*, 1959, *29*, 791-802.

CHILD, I. L., & WATERHOUSE, I. K. Frustration and quality of performance: II. A theoretical statement. *Psychol. Rev.*, 1953, *60*, 127-139.

CHILES, W. D. The effects of sleep deprivation on performance of a complex mental task. *Air Force Hum. Eng., Personnel and Train. Res.*, ARDC Tech. Rep. No. S6-8, 1956, pp. 74-81.

CHILES, W. D. Effects of elevated temperatures on performance of a complex mental task. *Ergonomics*, 1958, *2*, 89-96.

CHRZANOWSKI, G. Neurasthenia and hypochondriasis. In S. Arieti (Ed.), *American handbook of psychiatry*, Vol. I. New York: Basic Books, 1959.

CLAPARÈDE, E. Théorie biologique du sommeil. *Arch. Psychol.*, 1905, *4*. (not seen)

CLAPARÈDE, E. *Experimental pedagogy and the psychology of the child.* New York: Longmans, Green, 1911.

CLARDY, E. R., & HILL, B. C. Emotional sleep disturbances in childhood. *Nerv. Child*, 1949-1950, *8*, 47-49.

CLARK, R. A. The projective measurement of experimentally induced levels of sexual motivation. *J. exp. Psychol.*, 1952, *44*, 391-399.

COHEN, M. B. Countertransference and anxiety. *Psychiatry*, 1952, *15*, 231-243.

COLEMAN, P. D., GRAY, F. E., & WATANABE, K. EEG Amplitude and reaction time during sleep, *J. appl. Physiol.*, 1959, *14*, 397-400.

CONN, J. H. Psychogenesis and psychotherapy of insomnias. *J. clin. exp. Psychopath.*, 1950, *11*, 85-91.

CORCORAN, D. W. J. Noise and loss of sleep. *Quart. J. exp. Psychol.*, 1962, *14*, 178-182.

CORIAT, I. H. The nature of sleep. *J. abnorm. soc. Psychol.*, 1911-12, *6*, 329-367.

CORWIN, W., & BARRY, H. Respiratory plateaux in "day dreaming" and in schizophrenia. *Amer. J. Psychiat.*, 1940, *97*, 308-317.

COURTS, F. A. Relations between muscular tension and performance. *Psychol. Bull.*, 1942, *39*, 347-367.

CREUTZFELDT, O., & JUNG, R. Neuronal discharge in the cat's motor cortex during sleep and arousal. In CIBA Foundation, *The nature of sleep.* Boston: Little, Brown, 1961.

DALY, D. D., & YOSS, R. Electroencephalogram in narcolepsy. *EEG clin. Neurophysiol.*, 1957, *9*, 109-119.

DANIELS, L. E. Narcolepsy. *Medicine*, 1934, *13*, 1-17.

DAVIS, H. Homeostasis of cerebral excitability. *EEG clin. Neurophysiol.*, 1950, *2*, 243-247.

DAVISON, C. Physiological and psychodynamic aspects of disturbances in the sleep mechanism. *Psychoanal. Quart.*, 1945, *14*, 478-497.

DAVISON, C., & DEMUTH, C. L. Disturbances in sleep mechanisms: A clinicopathologic study. *A.M.A. Arch. Neurol. Psychiat.*, 1945, *53*, 399-406.

DAVISON, C., & DEMUTH, C. L. Disturbances in sleep mechanisms: A clinicopathologic study. *A.M.A. Arch. Neurol. Psychiat.*, 1946, *55*, 364-381.

DECURTINS, F. Bedwetting from the psychiatric point of view. *Heilpadaq. Werkbl.*, 1957, *26*, 197-201.

DEESE, J. *The psychology of learning.* New York: McGraw-Hill, 1958.

DEGLIN, V. A study of sleep disturbances in schizophrenia. *Psychol. Abstr.*, 1958, *32*, 393 (Abstr. 4373).

DELGADO, J. M. R., ROBERTS, W. W., & MILLER, N. E. Learning motivated by electrical stimulation of the brain. *Amer. J. Physiol.*, 1954, *179*, 587-593.

DELL, P. C. Humoral effects on the brain stem reticular formations. In *Reticular formation of the brain.* Boston: Little, Brown, 1958.

DELL, P., BONVALLET, M., & HUGELIN, A. Mechanisms of reticular deactivation. In CIBA Foundation, *The nature of sleep.* Boston: Little, Brown, 1961.

DEMENT, W. Dream recall and eye movements during sleep in schizophrenics and normals. *J. nerv. ment. Dis.*, 1955, *122*, 263-269.

DEMENT, W. The occurrence of low voltage, fast electroencephalogram patterns during behavioral sleep in the cat. *EEG clin. Neurophysiol.*, 1958, *10*, 291-296.

DEMENT, W. The effect of dream deprivation. *Science*, 1960, *131*, 1705-1707.

DEMENT, W. Experimental interference with the sleep cycle. *Canad. Psychiat. Ass. J.*, 1961. (a)

DEMENT, W. Eye movements during sleep. *U.S.P.H.S. Symposium on the Oculomotor System*, 1961. (b)

DEMENT, W., & KLEITMAN, N. The relation of eye movements during sleep to dream activity: An objective method for the study of dreaming. *J. exp. Psychol.*, 1957, *53*, 339-346. (a)

DEMENT, W., & KLEITMAN, N. Cyclic variations in EEG during sleep and their relation to eye movements, body motility, and dreaming. *EEG clin. Neurophysiol.*, 1957, *9*, 673-690. (b)

DEMENT, W., & WOLPERT, E. A. The relation of eye movements, body motility, and external stimuli to dream content. *J. exp. Psychol.*, 1958, *55*, 543-553.

DERI, S. K. A problem in obesity. In A. Burton & R. E. Harris (Eds.), *Clinical studies of personality*, Vol. II. New York: Harper & Row, 1955.

DESPERT, J. L. Sleep in pre-school children: A preliminary study. *Nerv. Child.*, 1949-1950, *8*, 8-27.

DEUTSCH, F., & MURPHY, W. F. *The clinical interview:* Vol. I. *Diagnosis.* New York: Int. Univer. Press, 1955.

DIAZ-GUERRERO, R. GOTTLIEB, J., & KNOTT, J. The sleep of patients with manic-depressive psychoses, depressive type. *Psychosom. Med.*, 1946, *8*, 399-404.

DITMAN, K. S., & BLINN, K. A. Sleep levels in enuresis. *Amer. J. Psychiat.* 1955, *111*, 913-920.

DOLLARD, J., DOOB, L. W., MILLER, N. E., MOWRER, O. H., & SEARS, R. R. *Frustration and aggression.* New Haven: Yale Univer. Press, 1939.

DOLLARD, J., & MILLER, N. E. *Personality and psychotherapy.* New York: McGraw-Hill, 1950.

DRAKE, F. R. Narcolepsy: Brief review and report of cases. *Amer. J. med. Sci.,* 1949, *218*, 101-114.

DUCHARME, R., & BÉLANGER, D. Influence d'une stimulation électrique sur le niveau d'activation et la performance. *Canad. J. Psychol.* 1961, *15*, 61-68.

DUFFY, E. The concept of energy mobilization. *Psychol. Rev.,* 1951, *58*, 30-40.

DUFFY, E. The psychological significance of the concept of "arousal" or "activation." *Psychol. Rev.,* 1957, *64*, 265-275.

DUSEK, E. R. Effect of temperature on manual performance. In F. R. Fisher (Ed.), *Protection and functioning of the hands in cold climates.* Washington: Nat. Acad. Sci., 1957.

EAGLES, J. B., HALLIDAY, A. M., & REDFEARN, J. W. T. The effects of fatigue on tremor. In W. F. Floyd & A. T. Welford (Eds.), *Symposium on fatigue.* London: Lewis, 1953.

VON ECONOMO, C. Sleep as a problem of localization. *J. nerv. ment. Dis.,* 1930, *71*, 249-267.

EDWARDS, A. S. Effects of the loss of one hundred hours of sleep. *Amer. J. Psychol.,* 1941, *54*, 80-91.

ELLINGSON, R. J. Brain waves and problems of psychology. *Psychol. Bull.,* 1956, *53*, 1-34.

ELLINGSON, R. J. Comments on Schmidt's "The reticular formation and behavioral wakefulness." *Psychol. Bull.,* 1957, *54*, 76-78. (a)

ELLINGSON, R. J. Comment on Kleitman's note. *Psychol. Bull.,* 1957, *54*, 360. (b)

ELLIS, F. P. Tropical fatigue. In W. F. FLOYD & A. T. WELFORD (Eds.), *Symposium on fatigue.* London: Lewis, 1953.

EMMONS, W. H., & SIMON, C. W. The non-recall of material presented during sleep. *Amer. J. Psychol.,* 1956, *69*, 76-81.

EPSTEIN, S. The measurement of drive and conflict in humans: Theory and experiment. In M. R. Jones (Ed.), *Nebraska symposium on motivation.* Lincoln: Univer. Nebraska, 1962.

EPSTEIN, S., & SMITH, R. Thematic apperception as a measure of the hunger drive. *J. proj. Tech.,* 1956, *20*, 372-384.

ERIKSEN, C. W., & BROWNE, C. T. An experimental and theoretical analysis of perceptual defense. *J. abnorm. soc. Psychol.*, 1956, *52*, 224-230.

ESTES, W. K. Toward a statistical theory of learning. *Psychol. Rev.*, 1950, *57*, 94-107.

ESTES, W. K. Stimulus-response theory of drive. In M. R. Jones (Ed.), *Nebraska symposium on motivation*. Lincoln: Univer. Nebraska, 1958.

ESTES, W. K. The statistical approach to learning theory. In S. Koch (Ed.), *Psychology: A study of a science, Study 1. Conceptual and systematic*. Vol. 2. *General systematic formulations, learning, and special processes*. New York: McGraw-Hill, 1959.

EVARTS, E. V. Effects of sleep and waking on spontaneous and evoked discharge of single units in visual cortex. *Fed. Proc.*, 1960, *19*, 828-837.

EVARTS, E. V. Effects of sleep and waking on activity of single units in the unrestrained cat. In CIBA Foundation, *The nature of sleep*. Boston: Little, Brown, 1961.

EVARTS, E. V. Activity of neurons in visual cortex of cat during sleep with low voltage fast EEG activity. *J. Neurophysiol.*, 1962, *25*, 812-816.

EVARTS, E. V. Photically evoked responses in visual cortex units during sleep and waking. *J. Neurophysiol.* 1963, *26*, 229-248.

EWEN, J. Sleep and its relationship to schizophrenia. *J. neurol. Psychopath.*, 1934, *14*, 247-251.

FAEGRE, M. L., ANDERSON, J. E., & HARRIS, D. B. *Child care and training*. Minneapolis: Univer. Minnesota, 1958.

FALK, J. L. The behavioral regulation of water-electrolyte balance. In M. R. Jones (Ed.), *Nebraska symposium on motivation*. Lincoln: Univer. Nebraska, 1961.

FARBER, I. E. Anxiety as a drive state. In M. R. Jones (Ed.), *Nebraska symposium on motivation*. Lincoln: Univer. Nebraska, 1954.

FEATHERSTONE, R. M., & SIMON, A. *A pharmacologic approach to the study of the mind*. Springfield, Ill.: C. C. Thomas, 1959.

FEDERN, P. The awakening of the ego in dreams. *Int. J. Psycho-Anal.*, 1934, *15*, 296-301.

FEIFEL, H. Death: Relevant variable in psychology. In R. May (Ed.), *Existential psychology*. New York: Random House, 1961.

FELDMAN, M. Research study on nightmares. Unpublished data, Dept. of Psychol., Buffalo Univer.

FENICHEL, O. *The psychoanalytic theory of neurosis.* New York: Norton, 1945.

FERENCZI, S. On falling asleep during analysis. In *Further contributions to the theory and technique of psychoanalysis.* London: Hogarth, 1950.

FERNBERGER, S. W. Unlearned behavior of the white rat. *Amer. J. Psychol.,* 1929, *41,* 343-344.

FESTINGER, L. Motivation leading to social behavior. In M. R. Jones (Ed.), *Nebraska symposium on motivation.* Lincoln: Univer. Nebraska, 1954.

FINE, B. J., & GAYDOS, H. F. Relationship between individual personality variables and body temperature response patterns in the cold. *Psychol. Rep.,* 1959, *5,* 71-78.

FINGERMAN, M. Lunar rhythmicity in marine organisms. *Amer. Nat.,* 1957, *91,* 167-177.

FISCHGOLD, H., & SCHWARTZ, BETTY A. A clinical, electroencephalographic and polygraphic study of sleep in the human adult. In CIBA Foundation, *The nature of sleep.* Boston: Little, Brown, 1961.

FISHER, C. (Ed.) *Preconscious stimulation in dreams, associations and images.* New York: Int. Univer. Press, 1960.

FISHER, C., GROSS, J., & ZUCH, J. A cycle of penile erections synchronous with dreaming (REM) sleep. *Arch. gen. Psychiat.,* 1965, *12,* 29-45.

FISKE, D. W., & MADDI, S. R. *Functions of varied experience.* Homewood, Ill.: Dorsey, 1961.

FOLK, G. E. Twenty-four hour rhythms of mammals in a cold environment. *Amer. Nat.,* 1957, *91,* 153-166.

FORD, C. S. Society, culture, and the human organism. *J. gen. Psychol.,* 1939, *20,* 135-179.

FOULKES, W. P. Dream reports from different stages of sleep. *J. abnorm. soc. Psychol.,* 1962, *65,* 14-25.

FRAIBERG, S. On sleep disturbances of early childhood. *Psychoanal. Study Child.,* 1950, *5,* 285-309.

FRANKL, V. E. Group therapeutic experiences in a concentration camp. *Grp. Psychother.,* 1954, *7,* 81-90.

FREEDMAN, S. J., & GREENBLATT, M. Studies in human isolation. I. Perceptual findings. II. Hallucinations and other cognitive findings. *U. S. Arm. Forc. Med. J.,* 1960, *11,* 1330-1497.

FREEDMAN, S. J., GRUNEBAUM, H. U., & GREENBLATT, M. Perceptual and cognitive changes in sensory deprivation. In P. Solomon, et al. (Eds.), *Sensory deprivation.* Cambridge: Harvard Univer., 1961.

FREEMAN, G. L. Compensatory reinforcements of muscular tension subsequent to sleep loss. *J. exp. Psychol.,* 1932, *15,* 267-283.

FREEMAN, G. L. *The energetics of human behavior.* Ithaca: Cornell Univer., 1948.

FREEMAN, W., & WATTS, J. W. *Psychosurgery.* Baltimore: Thomas, 1942.

FRENCH, J. D., VERZEANO, M., & MAGOUN, H. W. A neural basis of the anesthetic state. *Arch. Neurol., Psychiat.,* 1953, *69,* 519-529.

FRENCH, T. M. *The integration of behavior.* Vol. I. *Basic postulates.* Chicago: Univer. of Chicago Press, 1952.

FRENCH, T. M. *The integration of behavior.* Vol. I. *The integrative process in dreams.* Chicago: Univer. of Chicago Press, 1954.

FREUD, S. *The problem of anxiety.* New York: Norton, 1936.

FREUD, S. *An outline of psychoanalysis.* New York: Norton, 1949.

FREUD, S. *Beyond the pleasure principle.* New York: Liveright, 1950. (a)

FREUD, S. *Collected papers,* Vol. IV. London: Hogarth, 1950. (b)

FREUD, S. *Three essays on sexuality.* In *Standard Edition.* Vol. VII. London: Hogarth, 1953.

FREUD, S. *A general introduction to psychoanalysis.* New York: Permabooks, 1958.

FREUD, S. *The interpretation of dreams.* New York: Science Editions, 1961.

FUNKENSTEIN, D. H., KING, S. H., & DROLETTE, M. *Mastery of stress.* Cambridge: Harvard Univer., 1957.

GAITE, J., HANNA, T. D., BOWE, R., & GRECO, S. *Environmental effects of sealed cabins for space and orbital flights. Part 3: Performance and habitability aspects of extended confinement.* Philadelphia: Naval Air Material Center, 1958.

GALAMBOS, R., & MORGAN, C. T. The neural basis of learning. In *Handbook of physiology, Sect. 1, Neurophysiology,* Vol. III. Washington: Amer. Physiol. Soc., 1960.

GARDNER, G. E. *Psychiatric problems of adolescence.* In S. Arieti (Ed.), *American handbook of psychiatry.* Vol. I. New York: Basic Books, 1959.

GARRETT, H. E. *Great experiments in psychology,* 3rd. ed. New York: Appleton-Century-Crofts, 1951.

GARVEY, C. R. *The activity of young children during sleep.* Minneapolis: Univer. Minnesota, 1939.

GASTAUT, H., & BERT, J. Electroencephalographic detection of sleep induced by repetitive sensory stimuli. In CIBA Foundation, *The nature of sleep.* Boston: Little, Brown, 1961.

GASTER, T. H. (Ed.) *The new golden bough: A new abridgment of the classic work by Sir James George Frazer.* Garden City, N.Y.: Doubleday, 1961.

GELLHORN, E. *Physiological foundations of neurology and psychiatry.* Minneapolis: Univer. Minnesota, 1953.

GELLHORN, E. *Autonomic imbalance and the hypothalamus.* Minneapolis: Univer. Minnesota, 1957.

GERARD, R. The biological roots of psychiatry. *Amer. J. Psychiat.*, 1955, *112*, 81-90.

GESELL, A., & AMATRUDA, C. S. *The embryology of behavior.* New York: Harper & Row, 1945.

GESELL, A., HALVERSON, H. M., THOMPSON, H., ILG, F. L., COSTNER, B. M., AMES, L. B., & AMATRUDA, C. S. *The first five years of life.* New York: Harper & Row, 1940.

GESELL, A., & ILG, F. L. *Infant and child in the culture of today.* New York: Harper & Row, 1943.

GIBBS, E. L., & GIBBS, F. A. Electroencephalographic changes with age during sleep. *EEG clin. Neurophysiol.*, 1950, *2*, 355. (Abstract)

GILL, M. M., & BRENMAN, M. *Hypnosis and related states.* New York: Int. Univer. Press, 1961.

GILMAN, L. Insomnia in relation to guilt, fear, and masochistic intent. *J. clin. Psychopath.*, 1950, *11*, 63-64.

GINZBERG, R. Sleep and sleep disturbances in geriatric psychiatry. *J. Amer. geriat. Soc.*, 1955, *3*, 493-511.

GOLDBERGER, L., & HOLT, R. R. Experimental interference with reality contact (perceptual isolation): Method and group results. *J. nerv. ment. Dis.*, 1958, *127*, 99-112.

GOLDBERGER, L., & HOLT, R. R. Experimental interference with reality contact: Individual differences. In P. Solomon et al. (Eds.), *Sensory deprivation.* Cambridge: Harvard Univer., 1961.

GOLDSTEIN, N. P., & GIFFIN, M. E. Psychogenic hypersomnia. *Amer. J. Psychiat.*, 1959, *115*, 922-928.

GOODENOUGH, D. R., LEWIS, H. B., SHAPIRO, A., JARET, L., & SLESER, I. Dream reporting following abrupt and gradual awakenings from different sleep stages. Mimeographed paper, Downstate Medical Center, Brooklyn, N. Y., 1963.

GOODENOUGH, D. R., SHAPIRO, A., HOLDEN, M., & STEINSCHRIBER, L.

A comparison of "dreamers" and "non-dreamers" eye movements, electroencephalograms, and the recall of dreams. *J. abnorm. soc. Psychol.*, 1959, 59, 295-302.

GRANDA, A. M., & HAMMACK, J. T. Operant behavior during sleep. *Science*, 1961, *133*, 1485-1486. (Plus personal communication)

GRASTYAN, E. The hippocampus and higher nervous activity. *Sec. Conf. on Central Nervous System and Behavior*. New York: Josiah Macy Found., 1959.

GREEN, J. D., & ARDUINI, A. A. Hippocampal activity in arousal. *J. Neurophysiol.*, 1954, *17*, 533-557.

GRESHAM, S. C., WEBB, W. B., & WILLIAMS, R. L. Alcohol and caffeine: Effect on inferred dreaming. *Science*, 1963, *140*, 1226-1227.

GRINKER, R. R., MILLER, J., SABSHIN, M., NUNN, R., & NUNNALLY, J. C. *The phenomena of depressions*. New York: Hoeber, 1961.

GRINKER, R. R., & SPIEGEL, J. P. *Men under stress*. Philadelphia: Blakiston, 1945.

GROTJAHN, M. The process of awakening: Contribution to ego psychology and the problem of sleep and dreams. *Psychoanal. Rev.*, 1942, *29*, 1-19.

GRUNEWALD, E. Castration threat and bed-wetting. *J. Psychol. Psychother.*, 1954, *2*, 364-367.

GUNNARSON, S., & MELIN, K. The EEG in enuresis. *Acta Paediatr. Stockh.*, 1951, *40*, 496-501.

GUTHEIL, E. A. Reactive depressions. In S. Arieti (Ed.), *American handbook of psychiatry*, Vol. I. New York: Basic Books, 1959. (a)

GUTHEIL, E. A. Sexual dysfunctions in men. In S. Arieti (Ed.), *American handbook of psychiatry*, Vol. I. New York: Basic Books, 1959. (b)

GUTHEIL, E. *The handbook of dream analysis*. New York: Grove, 1960.

GUTHRIE, E. R. *The psychology of learning*. New York: Harper & Row, 1952.

GUTHRIE, E. R., & EDWARDS, A. L. *Psychology*. New York: Harper & Row, 1949.

HALL, C. S. Temperament: A survey of animal studies. *Psychol. Bull.*, 1941, *38*, 909-943.

HALL, C. S. What people dream about. *Scient. Amer.*, 1951, *184*, No. 5, 60-63.

HALL, C. S. A cognitive theory of dreams. *J. gen. Psychol.*, 1953, *49*, 273-282. (a)

HALL, C. S. A cognitive theory of dream symbols. *J. gen. Psychol.*, 1953, *48*, 169-186. (b)

HALL, C. S. Current trends in dream research. In D. Brower & L. E. Abt (Eds.), *Progress in clinical psychology.* New York: Grune & Stratton, 1956.

HALL, C. S. *The meaning of dreams.* New York: Dell, 1959.

HALL, J. F. The relationship between external stimulation, food deprivation, and activity. *J. comp. physiol. Psychol.*, 1956, *49*, 339-341.

HALLMAN, N. On the ability of enuretic children to hold urine. *Acta Paediatr. Stockh.*, 1950, *39*, 87-93.

HAMILTON, M. The assessment of anxiety states by rating. *Brit. J. med. Psychol.*, 1959, *32*, 50-55.

Handbook of human engineering data (Part 7) Medford, Mass.: Tufts Univer., 1949.

HARDY, J. D., FABIAN, L. W., & TURNER, M. D. Electrical anesthesia for major surgery. *J.A.M.A.*, 1961, *175*, 599-600.

HARLOW, H. F. The nature of love. *Amer. Psychologist*, 1958, *13*, 673-685.

HARLOW, H. F. The heterosexual affectional system in monkeys. *Amer. Psychologist*, 1962, *17*, 1-9.

HEBB, D. O. *The organization of behavior.* New York: Wiley, 1949.

HEBB, D. O. Drives and the C.N.S.: The conceptual nervous system. *Psychol. Rev.*, 1955, *62*, 243-254.

HEBB, D. O. *A textbook of psychology.* Philadelphia: Saunders, 1958.

HEDIGER, H. *Studies of the psychology and behaviour of captive animals in zoos and circuses.* London: Butterworths, 1955.

HEINROTH, O., & HEINROTH, K. *The birds.* Ann Arbor: Univer. of Michigan, 1958.

HERNÁNDEZ-PEÓN, R. Sleep induced by localized electrical or chemical stimulation of the forebrain. *EEG clin. Neurophysiol.*, 1962, *14*, 423-424.

HERNÁNDEZ-PEÓN, R. (Ed.). The physiological basis of mental activity. *EEG clin. Neurophysiol.*, 1963, Supp. 24.

HERNÁNDEZ-PEÓN, R., CHÁVEZ-IBARRA, G., MORGANE, P. J., & TIMO-IARIA, C. Limbic cholinergic pathways involved in sleep and emotional behavior. *Exp. Neurol.*, 1963, *8*, 93-111.

HERON, W. Cognitive and physiological effects of perceptual isolation. In P. Solomon, et al. (Eds.), *Sensory deprivation.* Cambridge: Harvard Univer., 1961.

HESS, R., KOELLA, W. P., & AKERT, K. Cortical and subcortical recordings in natural and artificially induced sleep in cats. *EEG clin. Neurophysiol.*, 1953, 5, 75-90.

HESS, W. R. The diencephalic sleep center. In *Brain mechanisms and consciousness*. Oxford: Blackwell, 1954.

HESS, W. R. *The functional organization of the diencephalon*. New York: Grune & Stratton, 1957.

HINKLE, L. E., & WOLFF, H. C. Communist interrogation and indoctrination of "Enemies of the state." *A.M.A. Arch. Neurol. Psychiat.*, 1956, 76, 115-174.

HIRSCHBERG, J. C. Parental anxieties accompanying sleep disturbance in young children. *Bull. Menninger Clin.*, 1957, 21, 129-139.

HODES, R., HEATH, R., & HENDLEY, C. *Studies in schizophrenia*. Cambridge: Harvard Univer., 1954.

HOEDEMAKER, F. S., KALES, A., JACOBSON, A., & LICHTENSTEIN, E. Dream deprivation: An experimental reappraisal. Mimeographed paper, Neuropsychiatric Institute, Univer. California, Los Angeles, 1963.

HOLLINGSHEAD, A. B., & REDLICH, F. C. *Social class and mental illness*. New York: Wiley, 1958.

HOLLINGWORTH, H. L. *The psychology of thought*. New York: D. Appleton & Co., 1927.

HORNEY, K. *The neurotic personality of our time*. New York: Norton, 1937.

HULL, C. L. Differential habituation to internal stimuli in the albino rat. *J. comp. Psychol.*, 1933, 16, 255-273.

HULL, C. L. Stimulus intensity dynamism (V) and stimulus generalization. *Psychol. Rev.*, 1949, 56, 67-76.

HULL, C. L. *Principles of behavior*. New York: Appleton-Century-Crofts, 1943.

IMBODEN, J., & LASAGNA, L. An evaluation of hypnotic drugs in psychiatric patients. *Bull. Johns Hopkins Hosp.*, 1956, 99, 91-100.

IMHOF, B. Enuretics in child guidance. *Heilpadaq. Werkbl.*, 1956, 25, 122-127.

IMLAB, N. Narcolepsy in identical twins. *J. Neurol. Neurosurg. Psychiat.*, 1961, 24, 158-160.

ISAKOWER, O. A contribution to the psycho-pathology of phenomena associated with falling asleep. *Int. J. Psycho-Anal.*, 1938, 19, 331-345.

JACOBSON, E. *Progressive relaxation*. Chicago: Univer. of Chicago Press, 1929.

JANET, P. *The major symptoms of hysteria.* New York: Macmillan, 1920.

JANET, P. A case of sleep lasting five years; with loss of sense of reality. *Arch. Neurol. Psychiat.*, 1921, *6*, 467-475.

JANIS, I. L. *Air war and emotional stress.* New York: McGraw-Hill, 1951.

JASPER, H. H. Functional properties of the thalamic reticular system. In *Brain mechanisms and consciousness.* Oxford: Blackwell, 1954.

JEKELS, L. A bioanalytical contribution to the problem of sleep and wakefulness. *Psychoanal. Quart.*, 1945, *14*, 169-189.

JENKINS, J. G., & DALLENBACH, K. M. Obliviscence during sleep and waking. *Amer. J. Psychol.*, 1924, *35*, 605-612.

JENNESS, A., & JORGENSEN, A. P. Ratings of vividness of imagery in the waking state compared with reports of somnambulism. *Amer. J. Psychol.*, 1954, *54*, 253-259.

JERVIS, G. A. The mental deficiencies. In S. Arieti (Ed.), *American handbook of psychiatry*, Vol. II, New York: Basic Books, 1959.

JOHNSON, H., & ERIKSEN, C. W. Preconscious perception: A re-examination of the Poetzl phenomenon. *J. abnorm. soc. Psychol.*, 1961, *62*, 497-503.

JOHNSON, H. M., & SWAN, T. H. Sleep. *Psychol. Bull.*, 1930, *27*, 1-39.

JOHNSON, H. M., SWAN, T. H., & WEIGAND, G. E. In what positions do healthy people sleep? *J.A.M.A.*, 1930, *94*, 2058-2062.

JONES, E. *On the nightmare.* New York: Grove, 1959.

JONES, M. S. A case of recurrent attacks of prolonged sleep. *J. neurol. Psychopath.*, 1935, *16*, 130-139.

JOUVET, M. Telencephalic and rhombencephalic sleep in the cat. In CIBA Foundation, *The nature of sleep.* Boston: Little, Brown, 1961.

JOUVET, M., & MOUNIER, D. Neurophysiological mechanisms of dreaming. *EEG clin. Neurophysiol.*, 1962, *14*, 424.

KAGAN. J. The measurement of overt aggression from fantasy. *J. abnorm. soc. Psychol.*, 1956, *53*, 96-99.

KALES, A., HOEDEMAKER, F. S., & JACOBSON, A. Reportable mental activity during sleep. Mimeographed paper, Neuropsychiatric Institute, Univ. of California, Los Angeles, 1963.

KAMIYA, J. Behavioral, subjective, and physiological aspects of drowsiness and sleep. In D. W. Fiske & S. R. Maddi (Eds.), *Functions of varied experience.* Homewood, Ill.: Dorsey, 1961.

KAMMERER, T., ISRAEL, L., & GEISSMANN, P. An objective study of sleep in mental patients. *Canad. J. Psychiat.*, 1957, *8*, 37-50.

KANNER, L. Insomnia in children. *J. clin. Psychopath.*, 1950, *11*, 79-81.

KANNER, L. *Child psychiatry.* Springfield, Ill.: C. C. Thomas, 1957.

KARPMAN, B. Paraphiliac preoccupations and guilt in the etiology of insomnia. *J. clin. Psychopath.*, 1950, *11*, 75-78.

KATZ, S. E., & LANDIS, C. Psychologic and physiologic phenomena during a prolonged vigil. *Arch. Neurol. Psychiat.*, 1935, *34*, 307-317.

KAWAKAMI, M., & SAWYER, C. H. Induction of "paradoxical" sleep by conditional stimulation in the rabbit. *The Physiologist*, 1962, *5*, 165.

KELLOGG, W. N. *Porpoises and sonar.* Chicago: Univer. of Chicago, 1961.

KENNEDY, J. L., & TRAVIS, R. C. Prediction of speed of performance by muscle action potentials. *Science*, 1947, *105*, 410-411.

KENNEDY, J. L., & TRAVIS, R. C. Prediction and control of alertness: II. Continuous tracking. *J. comp. physiol. Psychol.*, 1948, *41*, 203-210.

KETY, S. S. Sleep and the energy metabolism of the brain. In CIBA Foundation, *The nature of sleep.* Boston: Little, Brown, 1961.

KEYS, A., BROZEK, J., HENSCHEL, A., MICHELSON, O., & TAYLOR, H. L. *The biology of human starvation,* Vols. I and II. Minneapolis: Univer. Minnesota Press, 1950.

KING, E. E., NAQUET, R., & MAGOUN, H. W. Alterations in somatic afferent transmission through the thalamus by central mechanisms and barbiturates. *J. Pharmacol. exp. Ther.*, 1957, *119*, 48-63.

KINGMAN, R. The insomniac: A psychological study of sleep and wakefulness. *Psychol. Abstr.*, 1929, *3*, 430 (Abstr. 3130).

KINSEY, A. C., POMEROY, W. B., MARTIN, C. E., & GEBHARD, P. H. *Sexual behavior in the human female.* Philadelphia: Saunders, 1953.

KLATSKIN, E. H., & JACKSON, E. B. Methodology of the Yale rooming-in project on parent-child relationship. *Amer. J. Orthopsychiat.*, 1955, *25*, 81-108, 373-397.

KLATSKIN, E. H., JACKSON, E. B., & WILKIN, L. C. The influence of degree of flexibility in maternal child care practices on early child behavior. *Amer. J. Orthopsychiat.*, 1956, *26*, 79-93.

KLEITMAN, N. Studies on the physiology of sleep. V. Some experiments on puppies. *Amer. J. Physiol.*, 1927, *84*, 386-395.

KLEITMAN, N. *Sleep and wakefulness.* Chicago: Univer. of Chicago Press, 1939, 1963.

KLEITMAN, N. Sleep. *Scient. Amer.,* 1952, *187,* 34-38.

KLEITMAN, N. Sleep, wakefulness, and consciousness. *Psychol. Bull.,* 1957, *54,* 354-359.

KLEITMAN, N. The nature of dreaming. In CIBA Foundation, *The nature of sleep.* Boston: Little, Brown, 1961.

KLEITMAN, N., & CAMILLE, N. Studies on the physiology of sleep. VI. The behavior of decorticated dogs. *Amer. J. Physiol.,* 1932, *100,* 474-480.

KLEITMAN, N., COOPERMAN, N. R., & MULLIN, F. J. Motility and body temperature during sleep. *Amer. J. Physiol.,* 1933, *105,* 574-584.

KLEITMAN, N., & JACKSON, D. P. Body temperature and performance under different routines. *J. appl. Physiol.,* 1950, *3,* 309-328.

KLEITMAN, N., & KLEITMAN, H. The sleep-wakefulness pattern in the Arctic. *Scient. Monthly,* 1953, *76,* 349-356.

KLEITMAN, N., MULLIN, F. J., COOPERMAN, N. R., & TITELBAUM, S. *Sleep characteristics.* Chicago: Univer. of Chicago, 1937.

KLINE, N. S. Pharmacotherapy: Retrospect and prospect. *Ann. Proc. Amer. Pharm. Mfg. Ass.,* 1958.

KLINEBERG, O. *Social psychology.* New York: Holt, Rinehart & Winston, 1940.

KOCH, S. The logical character of the motivation concept. I. *Psychol. Rev.,* 1941, *48,* 15-38.

KORANYI, E. K., & LEHMANN, H. E. Experimental sleep deprivation in schizophrenic patients. *A.M.A. Arch. gen. Psychiat.,* 1960, *2,* 534-544.

KORESKO, R. L., SNYDER, F., & FEINBERG, I. 'Dream time' in hallucinating and non-hallucinating schizophrenic patients. *Nature,* 1963, *199,* 1118-1119.

KRAINES, S. H. *Mental depressions and their treatment.* New York: Macmillan, 1957.

KREMEN, I. Dream reports and rapid eye movements. Unpublished dissertation, Harvard Univer., 1961.

LACEY, J. I., & LACEY, B. C. Verification and extension of the principle of autonomic response-stereotype. *Amer. J. Psychol.,* 1958, *71,* 50-73.

LACHMAN, F. M., LAPKIN, B., & HANDELMAN, N. J. The recall of dreams: its relation to repression and cognitive control, *J. abnorm. soc. Psychol.,* 1962, *64,* 160-162.

LADD, G. Contributions to the psychology of visual dreams. *Mind*, 1892, *1*, 299-304.

LANGWORTHY, O. R., & BETZ, B. J. Narcolepsy as a type of response to emotional conflicts. *Psychosom. Med.*, 1944, *6*, 211-226.

LASHLEY, K. S. Experimental analysis of instinctive behavior. *Psychol. Rev.*, 1938, *45*, 445-471.

LASHLEY, K. S. Dynamic processes in perception. In *Brain mechanisms and consciousness.* Oxford: Blackwell, 1954.

LASLETT, H. R. Experiment on the effects of the loss of sleep. *J. exp. Psychol.*, 1924, *7*, 45-58.

LASLETT, H. R. Experiments on the effects of the loss of sleep. *J. exp. Psychol.*, 1928, *11*, 370-396.

LATIES, V. Modification of affect, social behavior, and performance by sleep deprivation and drugs. *J. psychiat. Res.*, 1961, *1*, 12-25.

LAZARUS, R. S. A substitutive-defensive conception of apperceptive fantasy. In J. Kagan & G. S. Lesser (Eds.), *Contemporary issues in thematic apperceptive methods.* Springfield, Ill.: C. C. Thomas, 1961.

LAZARUS, R. S., YOUSEM, H., & ARENBERG, A. Hunger and perception. *J. Pers.*, 1953, *21*, 312-328.

LEEPER, R. W. The role of motivation in learning: A study of the phenomenon of differential motivational control of the utilization of habits. *J. genet. Psychol.*, 1935, *40*, 3-40.

LEHRMAN, S. R., & WEISS, E. J. Schizophrenia in cryptogenic narcolepsy: Report of a case. *Psychiat. Quart.*, 1943, *17*, 135-143.

LESTER, D. Continuous measurement of the depth of sleep. *Science*, 1958, *127*, 1340-1341.

LESTER, D. A new method for the determination of the effectiveness of sleep-inducing agents in humans. *Compre. Psychiat.*, 1960, *1*, 301-307.

LESTER, B. K., PIERCE, C. M., & MATHIS, J. L. Simultaneous dreaming in a mother and infant child. Unpublished manuscript, Dept. of Psychiatry, Neurology, and Behavioral Sciences, Univer. of Oklahoma.

LEVIN, M. Premature waking and post-dormitial paralysis. *J. nerv. ment. Dis.*, 1957, *125*, 140-141.

LEVINE, S. The role of irrelevant drive stimuli in learning. *J. exp. Psychol.*, 1953, *45*, 410-416.

LEVY, D. M. *Maternal overprotection.* New York: Columbia Univer., 1943.

LEWIN, B. D. Sleep, narcissistic neurosis, and the analytic situation. *Psychoanal. Quart.*, 1954, *23*, 487-510.

LEWIN, K. *The conceptual representation and the measurement of psychological forces.* Durham: Duke Univer., 1938.

LEWIS, H. E. Sleep patterns on polar expeditions. In CIBA Foundation, *The nature of sleep.* Boston: Little, Brown, 1961.

LIBERSON, W. T. The problem of sleep and mental disease. *Dig. Neurol. Psychiat.*, 1945, *13*, 93-108.

LICKLIDER, J. C. R., & BUNCH, M. E. Effects of enforced wakefulness upon the growth and the maze-learning performance of white rats. *J. comp. Psychol.*, 1946, *39*, 339-350.

LIDZ, T., & RUBENSTEIN, R. Psychology of gastrointestinal disorders. In S. Arieti (Ed.), *American handbook of psychiatry.* Vol. I. New York: Basic Books, 1959.

LINDSLEY, D. B. Emotion. In S. S. Stevens (Ed.), *Handbook of experimental psychology.* New York: Wiley, 1951.

LINDSLEY, D. B. Psychological phenomena and the electro-encephalogram. *EEG clin. Neurophysiol.*, 1952, *4*, 443-456.

LINDSLEY, D. B. Physiological psychology. *Annu. Rev. Psychol.*, 1956, *7*, 323-348.

LINDSLEY, D. B. Psychophysiology and motivation. In M. R. Jones (Ed.), *Nebraska symposium on motivation.* Lincoln: Univer. Nebraska, 1957.

LINDSLEY, D. B. Attention, consciousness, sleep, and wakefulness. In *Handbook of physiology. Sect. 1, Neurophysiology,* Vol. III. Washington: Amer. Physiol. Soc., 1960.

LINDSLEY, D. B. Common factors in sensory deprivation, sensory distortion, and sensory overload. In P. Solomon et al. (Eds.), *Sensory deprivation.* Cambridge: Harvard Univer., 1961.

LINDSLEY, O. Operant behavior during sleep: A measure of depth of sleep. *Science,* 1957, *126*, 1290-1291.

LITVIN, P. Tension, organic-disease phobia, guilt, competition, and insomnia. *J. clin. Psychopath.*, 1950, *11*, 72-74.

LIVINGSTON, R. B. Central control of afferent activity. In *Reticular formation of the brain.* Boston: Little, Brown, 1958.

LOGAN, F. A. The Hull-Spence approach. In S. Koch (Ed.), *Psychology: A study of a science. Study 1. Conceptual and systematic,* Vol. 2. *General systematic formulations, learning, and special processes.* New York: McGraw-Hill, 1959.

LONDON, L. S. Unconscious hostility and insomnia. *J. clin. Psychopath.*, 1950, *11*, 70-71.

LOOMIS, A. L., HARVEY, E. N., & HOBART, G. A. Cerebral states during sleep, as studied by human brain potentials. *J. exp. Psychol.*, 1937, *21*, 127-144.

LOUTTIT, C. M. *Clinical psychology of children's behavior problems.* New York: Harper & Row, 1947.

LOVE, E. G. *Subways are for sleeping.* New York: New American Library, 1958.

LOVELAND, N. T., & SINGER, M. T. Projective test assessment of the effects of sleep deprivation. *J. proj. Tech.*, 1959, *23*, 323-334.

LUBIN, A., & WILLIAMS, H. L. Sleep loss, tremor, and the conceptual reticular formation. *Psychol. Rep.*, 1959, 9, 237-238.

LUBY, E. D., FROHMAN, C. E., GRISELL, J. L., AX, A., & LENZO, J. E. Sleep deprivation: A multi-disciplinary study. *Scientific Papers and Discussions, Amer. Psychiat. Ass.*, 1960, *1*, 230-240.

LUBY, E. D., FROHMAN, C. E., GRISELL, J. L., LENZO, J. E., & GOTTLIEB, J. S. Sleep deprivation: Effects on behavior, thinking, motor performance, and biological energy transfer systems. *Psychosom. Med.*, 1960, *22*, 182-192.

LUCE, G. G. *Research on sleep and dreams.* Bethesda, Md.: National Institute of Mental Health, 1965.

LYKETOS, G., BELINSON, L., & GIBBS, F. A. Electroencephalograms of non-epileptic psychotic patients awake and asleep. *A.M.A. Arch. Neurol. Psychiat.*, 1953, *69*, 707-712.

McCLELLAND, D. C. *Personality.* New York: Dryden, 1951.

McCLELLAND, D. C. *The achieving society.* Princeton, N. J.: Van Nostrand, 1961.

McCLELLAND, D. C., ATKINSON, J. W., CLARK, R. A., & LOWELL, E. L. *The achievement motive.* New York: Appleton-Century-Crofts, 1953.

McDOUGALL, W. *An introduction to social psychology.* London: Methuen, 1960.

McFARLAND, R. A. Anoxia: Its effects on the physiology and biochemistry of the brain and on behavior. In Milbank Memorial Fund, *The biology of mental health and disease.* New York: Hoeber, 1952.

McFARLAND, R. A., & BARACH, A. L. The response of psychoneurotics to variations in oxygen tension. *Amer. J. Psychiat.*, 1937, *93*, 1315-1341.

McGEOCH, J. A. *The psychology of human learning.* New York: Longmans, Green, 1942.

McGRAW, R. B., & OLIVEN, J. F. Miscellaneous therapies. In S. Arieti

(Ed.), *American handbook of psychiatry*, Vol. II. New York: Basic Books, 1959.

MACKWORTH, N. H. Effects of heat on wireless telegraph operators hearing and recording Morse messages. *Brit. J. indust. Med.*, 1946, *3*, 143-158.

MACKWORTH, N. H. High incentives versus hot and humid atmospheres in a physical effort task. *Brit. J. Psychol.*, 1947, *38*, 90-102.

MACKWORTH, N. H. The breakdown of vigilance during prolonged visual search. *J. exp. Psychol.*, 1948, *38*, 6-21.

MacLEAN, P. D. Psychosomatics. In *Handbook of physiology, Sect. 1 Neurophysiology*, Vol. III. Washington: Amer. Physiol. Soc., 1960.

MACNISH, R. *The philosophy of sleep.* New York: Appleton, 1834.

MADSEN, K. B. *Theories of motivation.* Cleveland: Allen, 1961.

MAGNES, J., MORUZZI, G., & POMPEIANO, O. Synchronization of the EEG produced by low-frequency electrical stimulation of the region of the solitary tract. *Arch. Ital. Biol.*, 1961, *99*, 33-67. (a)

MAGNES, J., MORUZZI, G., & POMPEIANO, O. Electroencephalogram-synchronizing structures in the lower brain stem. In CIBA Foundation, *The nature of sleep.* Boston: Little, Brown, 1961. (b)

MAGNUSSEN, G. The sleep function and sleep disturbance. *Ment. Hyg.*, 1953, *37*, 89-118.

MAGOUN, H. W. The ascending reticular system and wakefulness. In *Brain mechanisms and consciousness.* Oxford: Blackwell, 1954.

MAGOUN, H. W. *The waking brain.* Springfield, Ill.: C. C. Thomas, 1958.

MAGOUN, H. W. Brain mechanisms for wakefulness. *Brit. J. Anaesth.*, 1961, *33*, 183-193.

MAGOUN, H. W. Central Neural inhibition. In M. R. Jones (Ed.), *Nebraska symposium on motivation.* Lincoln: Univer. Nebraska, 1963.

MALMO, R. B. Measurement of drive: An unsolved problem in psychology. In M. R. Jones (Ed.), *Nebraska symposium on motivation.* Lincoln: Univer. Nebraska, 1958.

MALMO, R. B. Activation: A neuropsychological dimension. *Psychol. Rev.*, 1959, *66*, 367-386.

MALMO, R. B., & SURWILLO, W. W. Sleep deprivation: Changes in performance and physiological indicants of activation. *Psychol. Monogr.*, 1960, *74*, No. 15 (Whole No. 502), 1-24.

MARKOWITZ, I. Psychotherapy of narcolepsy in an adolescent boy: Case presentation. *Psychiat. Quart.*, 1957, *31*, 41-56.

MARRIOTT, H. L. *Water and salt depletion.* Springfield, Ill.: C. C. Thomas, 1950.

MASLOW, A. H. *Motivation and personality.* New York: Harper & Row, 1954.

MASLOW, A. H., & MITTELMANN, B. *Principles of abnormal psychology.* New York: Harper & Row, 1941.

MAY, P. R. A., & EBAUGH, F. G. Use of hypnotics in aging and senile patients. *J.A.M.A.*, 1953, *152*, 801-805.

MAY, R. (Ed.) *Existential psychology.* New York: Random House, 1961.

MENDELSON, J. H., KUBZANSKY, P. E., LEIDERMAN, P. H., WEXLER, D., & SOLOMON, P. Physiological and psychological aspects of sensory deprivation, a case analysis. In P. Solomon et al. (Eds.), *Sensory deprivation.* Cambridge: Harvard Univer., 1961.

MEYER, J. S., & HUNTER, J. Behavior deficits following diencephalic lesions. *EEG clin. Neurophysiol.*, 1952, *2*, 112-130.

MEYERS, R. D. Personal communication, 1961.

MICHAELS, J. *Disorders of character: Persistent enuresis, juvenile delinquency, and psychopathic personality.* Springfield, Ill.: C. C. Thomas, 1955.

MILES, W. R., & LASLETT, H. R. Eye movement and visual fixation during profound sleepiness. *Psychol. Rev.*, 1931, *38*, 1-13.

MILLER, N. E. Experimental studies of conflict. In J. McV. Hunt (Ed.), *Personality and the behavior disorders,* Vol. I. New York: Ronald, 1944. Pp. 431-465.

MILLER, N. E. Theory and experiment relating psychoanalytic displacement to stimulus-response generalization. *J. abnorm. soc. Psychol.*, 1948, *43*, 155-178.

MILLER, N. E. Learnable drives and rewards. In S. S. Stevens (Ed), *Handbook of experimental psychology.* New York: Wiley, 1951.

MILLER, N. E. Experiments on motivation: Studies combining psychological, psysiological, and pharmacological techniques. *Science*, 1957, *126*, 1271-1278.

MILLER, N. E. Liberalization of basic S-R concepts: Extensions to conflict behavior, motivation, and social learning. In S. Koch (Ed.), *Psychology: A study of a science, Study 1. Conceptual and systematic,* Vol. 2. *General systematic formulations, learning, and special processes.* New York: McGraw-Hill, 1959.

MILLER, N. E. Analytical studies of drive and reward. *Amer. Psychologist*, 1961, *16*, 739-754.

MILLER, N. E. Some reflections on the law of effect produce a new alternative to drive reduction. In M. R. Jones (Ed.), *Nebraska symposium on motivation* Lincoln: Univer. Nebraska, 1963.

MILLER, N. E., & DOLLARD, J. *Social learning and imitation.* New Haven: Yale Univer., 1941.

MILLER, N. E., & KRAELING, D. Displacement: Greater generalization of approach than avoidance in a generalized approach-avoidance conflict. *J. exp. Psychol.,* 1952, *43,* 217-221.

MILLER, N. E., & MURRAY, E. J. Displacement and conflict: Learnable drive as a basis for the steeper gradient of avoidance than of approach. *J. exp. Psychol.,* 1952, *43,* 227-231.

MILLER, N. E. (with the collaboration of Sears, R. R., Mowrer, O. H., Doob, L. W., & Dollard, J.) The frustration-aggression hypothesis. *Psychol. Rev.,* 1941, *48,* 337-342.

MILLET, J. A. P. *Insomnia: Its causes and treatment.* New York: Greenberg, 1938.

MIRSKY, A., & CARDON, P. V. A comparison of the behavioral and physiological changes accompanying sleep deprivation and chlorpromazine administration in man. *EEG clin. Neurophysiol.,* 1962, *14,* 1-10.

MOLNAR, G. W., BLAIR, J. R., GOTTSCHALK, C. W., LAYTON, W. M., OSGOOD, L. E., ZIMMERMAN, W. J., & JOHNSON, C. A. Energy expenditure and endurance of men in an arctic bivouac. *Army med. res. Lab., Ft. Knox, Ky.,* 1950, Report No. 39.

MOLNAR, G. W., MAGEE, R. B., & DURRAM, E. L. Observations with AGF task forces Frigid and Williwaw. *Army medical research Laboratory, Ft. Knox, Ky.,* 1948, Report No. 13.

MOLTZ, H. Imprinting: Empirical basis and theoretical significance. *Psychol. Bull.,* 1960, *57,* 291-314.

MONNIER, M., KALBERER, M., & KRUPP, P. Functional antagonism between diffuse reticular and intralaminary recruiting projections in the medial thalamus. *Exp. Neurol.,* 1960, *2,* 271-289.

MONROE, L. J., RECHTSCHAFFEN, A., & FOULKES, D. The discriminability of reports elicited from different stages of sleep. Mimeographed paper, Dept. of Psychiatry, Univer. of Chicago, 1963.

MOORE, T., & UCKO, L. E. Night waking in early infancy. *Arch. dis. Child.,* 1957, *32,* 333-342.

MORGAN, C. T. *Introduction to psychology.* New York: McGraw-Hill, 1956.

MORGAN, C. T. Physiological mechanisms of motivation. In M. R. Jones (Ed.), *Nebraska symposium on motivation.* Lincoln: Univer. Nebraska, 1957.

MORGAN, C. T. Physiological theory of drive. In S. Koch (Ed.), *Psy-*

chology: A study of a science, Study 1. *Conceptual and systematic,* Vol. I. *Sensory, perceptual, and physiological formulations.* New York: McGraw-Hill, 1959.

MORGAN, C. T., & STELLAR, E. *Physiological psychology.* New York: McGraw-Hill, 1950.

MORISON, R. S., DEMPSEY, E. W., & MORISON, B. R. Cortical responses from electrical stimulation of the brain stem. *Amer. J. Physiol.,* 1941, *131,* 732-743.

MORRIS, G. O., & SINGER, M. T. Sleep deprivation: Transactional and subjective observations. *Arch. gen. Psychiat.,* 1961, *5,* 453-461.

MORRIS, G. O., WILLIAMS, H. L., & LUBIN, A. Misperception and disorientation during sleep deprivation. *Arch. gen. Psychiat.,* 1960, *2,* 247-254.

MORUZZI, G. Synchronizing influences of the brain stem and the inhibitory mechanisms underlying the production of sleep by sensory stimulation. *EEG clin. Neurophysiol.,* 1960, Supp. 13, 231-256.

MOSS, F. A., et al. A study of experimental insomnia. *Geo. Wash. Univer. Bull.,* 1925, *1,* 1-24. (not seen)

MOTT, F. Sleep, sleeplessness, and sleepiness. *Lancet,* 1924, *2,* 1161-1165.

MULLIN, F. J., KLEITMAN, N., & COOPERMAN, N. R. Studies on the physiology of sleep changes in irritability to auditory stimuli during sleep. *J. exp. Psychol.,* 1937, *21,* 88-96.

MUNCIE, W. Insomnia in clinical psychiatric practice. *Bull. Johns Hopkins Hosp.,* 1934, *55,* 131-153.

MUNN, N. L. *Psychology.* (3rd. ed.) Boston: Houghton Mifflin, 1956.

MURPHY, G. *Personality: A biosocial approach to origins and structure.* New York: Harper & Row, 1947.

MURPHY, G. Social motivation. In G. Lindzey (Ed.), *Handbook of social psychology.* Cambridge: Addison-Wesley, 1954.

MURRAY, E. J. The effects of hunger and type of manipulandum on spontaneous instrumental responding. *J. comp. physiol. Psychol.,* 1953, *46,* 182-183.

MURRAY, E. J. A case study in a behavioral analysis of psychotherapy. *J. abnorm. soc. Psychol.,* 1954, *49,* 305-310.

MURRAY, E. J. A content-analysis method for studying psychotherapy. *Psychol. Monogr.,* 1956, *70,* No. 13 (Whole No. 420).

MURRAY, E. J. Conflict and repression during sleep deprivation. *J. abnorm. soc. Psychol.,* 1959, *59,* 95-101.

MURRAY, E. J. Adjustment to environmental stress in fallout shelters.

In *Human factors in the utilization of fallout shelters.* Washington: National Academy of Sciences, 1960.

MURRAY, E. J. The integration of clinical and experimental approaches to the science of psychology. *Proc. N. Y. State Psychol. Ass.,* May, 1961.

MURRAY, E. J. Sociotropic-learning approach to psychotherapy. In P. Worchel & D. Byrne (Eds.), *Personality change.* New York: Wiley, 1964.(a)

MURRAY, E. J. *Motivation and emotion.* Englewood Cliffs, N. J.: Prentice-Hall, 1964.(b)

MURRAY, E. J. Sleep and motivation. In *Proceedings XVIIth international congress of psychology.* Amsterdam: North-Holland Pub. Co., 1964.(c)

MURRAY, E. J. Review of N. Kleitman's "Sleep and Wakefulness." *Contemp. Psychol.* 1964, *9,* 388-389.(d)

MURRAY, E. J., AULD, F., & WHITE, A. M. A psychotherapy case showing progress but no decrease in the discomfort relief quotient. *J. consult. Psychol.,* 1954, *18,* 349-353.

MURRAY, E. J., & BERKUN, M. M. Displacement as a function of conflict. *J. abnorm. soc. Psychol.,* 1955, *51,* 47-56.

MURRAY, E. J., & MILLER, N. E. Displacement: Steeper gradient of generalization of avoidance than of approach with age of habit controlled. *J. exp. Psychol.,* 1952, *43,* 222-226.

MURRAY, E. J., SCHEIN, E. H., ERIKSON, K. T., HILL, W. F., & COHEN, M. The effects of sleep deprivation on social behavior. *J. soc. Psychol.,* 1959, *49,* 229-236.

MURRAY, E. J., WILLIAMS, H. L., & LUBIN, A. Body temperature and psychological ratings during sleep deprivation. *J. exp. Psychol.,* 1958, *56,* 271-273.

MURRAY, H. A. The effect of fear upon estimates of the maliciousness of other personalities. *J. soc. Psychol.,* 1933, *4,* 310-329.

MURRAY, H. A. *Exploration in personality.* New York: Oxford Univer. Press, 1938.

MUSSEN, P. H., & CONGER, J. J. *Child development and personality.* New York: Harper & Row, 1956.

MUSSEN, P. H., & NAYLOR, H. K. The relationships between overt and fantasy aggression. *J. abnorm. soc. Psychol.,* 1954, *49,* 235-240.

NAEGELE, K. D. Sociological observations on everyday life (including holidays). I First and further thoughts on sleep. Unpublished manuscript. Dept. of Anthropology and Sociology, Univer. of British Columbia, Vancouver, 8, Canada.

NAKAO, H., BALLIM, H. M., & GELLHORN, E. The role of the sino-aortic receptors in the action of adrenaline, noradrenaline, and acetylcholine on the cerebral cortex. *EEG clin. Neurophysiol.,* 1956, *8,* 413-420.

NAUTA, W. J. H. Hypothalamic regulation of sleep in rats: An experimental study. *J. Neurophysiol.,* 1946, *9,* 285-316.

NAUTA, W. J. H. Hippocampal projections and related neural pathways to the midbrain of the cat. *Brain,* 1958, *81,* 319-340.

NEFF, W. D. Sensory discrimination. In *Handbook of physiology, Sect. 1: Neurophysiology,* Vol. III. Washington: Amer. Physiol. Soc., 1960.

NEWMAN, E. B. Forgetting of meaningful material during sleep and waking. *Amer. J. Psychol.,* 1939, *52,* 65-71.

NICHOLS, R. S. The relationship between chronic anxiety level and response to sleep deprivation and medication with secobarbital-amphetamine. Unpublished doctoral dissertation, Dept. of Psychology, Univer. of Rochester, 1956.

NOTKIN, J., & JELLIFFE, S. E. The narcolepsies. *A. M. A. Arch. Neurol. Psychiat.,* 1934, *31,* 615-634.

NOWLIS, V. The development and modification of motivational systems in personality. In *Current theory and research in motivation: A Symposium.* Lincoln: Univer. Nebraska, 1953.

O'CONNOR, W. A. A case of periodic hypersomnia. *Brit. J. Med. Psychol.,* 1951, *24,* 296-300.

OFFENKRANTZ, W., & WOLPERT, E. The detection of dreaming in a congenitally blind subject. *J. nerv. ment. Dis.* 1963, *136,* 88-90.

OLDS, J., & MILNER, P. Positive reinforcement produced by electrical stimulation of septal area and other regions of rat brain. *J. comp. physiol. Psychol.,* 1954, *47,* 419-427.

OLSZEWSKI, J. The cytoarchitecture of the human reticular formation. In *Brain mechanisms and consciousness.* Oxford: Blackwell, 1954.

OSWALD, I. Falling asleep open-eyed during intense rhythmic stimulation. *Brit. Med. J.* 1960, *1,* 1450-1455.

OSWALD, I. *Sleeping and waking: Physiology and psychology.* New York: Elsevier, 1962.

OSWALD, I., BERGER, R. J., JARAMILLO, R. A., KEDDIE, K. M. G., OLLEY, P. C., & PLUNKETT, G. B. Melancholia and barbiturates: A controlled EEG, body, and eye movement study of sleep. *Brit. J. Psychol.,* 1963, *109,* 66-78.

OSWALD, I., TAYLOR, ANNE M., & TREISMAN, M. Cortical function during human sleep. In CIBA Foundation, *The nature of sleep.* Boston: Little, Brown, 1961.

OSWALD, I., & THACORE, V. R. Amphetamine and phenmetrazine addiction: Physiological abnormalities in the abstinence syndrome. *Brit. Med. J.,* 1963, 2, 427-431.

PAGE, J. An experimental study of the day and night motility of normal and psychotic individuals. *Arch. Psychiat.,* 1935, 28, 1-39.

PAI, M. N. Somnambulism. *J. ment. Sci.,* 1946, 92, 756-765.

PAI, M. N. Hypersomnia syndromes. *Brit. Med. J.,* 1950, 1, 522-524.

PALM, R. The psychodynamics of enuresis. *Amer. Imago,* 1953, 10, 167-180.

PARFITT, D. N. A comparison of prolonged narcosis and convulsion therapy in mental disorder. *J. ment. Sci.,* 1946, 92, 128-137.

PARKIN, A. Emergence of sleep during psycho-analysis: A clinical note. *Int. J. Psycho-Anal.,* 1955, 36, 1-3.

PATRICK, G. T. W., & GILBERT, J. A. On the effects of loss of sleep. *Iowa Univer. Stud. Psychol.,* 1897, 1, 40-61.

PAVLOV, I. P. *Experimental psychology and other essays.* New York: Philosophical Library, 1957.

PEPLER, R. D. Warmth and lack of sleep: Accuracy or activity reduced. *J. comp. physiol. Psychol.,* 1959, 52, 446-450.

PIAGET, J. *The child's conception of the world.* Paterson, N. J.: Littlefield, Adams, 1960.

PIERCE, C. M., LESTER, B. K., & MATHIS, J. L. Food and dreams. Unpublished manuscript, Department of Psychiatry, Univer. of Oklahoma.

PIERCE, C. M., & LIPCON, H. H. Somnambulism: Electroencephalographic studies and related findings. *U.S. Armed Forces Med. J.,* 1956, 7, 1419-1426.(a)

PIERCE, C. M., & LIPCON, H. H. Somnambulism: Psychiatric interview studies. *U.S. Armed Forces Med. J.,* 1956, 7, 1143-1153.(b)

PIERCE, C. M., & LIPCON, H. H. A survey study of bedwetting. *South Med. J.,* 1959, 52, 1520-1524.

PIERCE, C. M., WHITMAN, R. M., MAAS, J. W., & GAY, M. L. Experimental studies in enuresis and dreaming. Unpublished manuscript, Department of Psychiatry, Univer. of Cincinnati.

PLUTCHIK, R. The effects of high intensity intermittent sound on performance, feeling, and physiology. *Psychol. Bull.,* 1959, 56, 133-151.

PODOLSKY, E. Somnambulistic homicide. *Dis. nerv. Syst.,* 1959, 20, 1-3.

POND, D. A. Narcolepsy: A brief critical review and study of eight cases. *J. ment. Sci.*, 1952, 98, 595-604.

PORTNOY, I. The anxiety states. In S. Arieti (Ed.), *American handbook of psychiatry.* Vol. I. New York: Basic Books, 1959.

POSTMAN, L. J. Comments on papers by Professors Brown and Harlow. *Current theory and research in motivation: A symposium.* Lincoln: Univer. Nebraska, 1953.

POSTMAN, L., & CRUTCHFIELD, R. S. The interaction of need, set, and stimulus-structure in a cognitive task. *Amer. J. Psychol.*, 1952, 65, 196-217.

PRATT, K. C., NELSON, A. K., & SUN, K. H. *The behavior of the newborn infant.* Columbus: Ohio State Univer., 1930.

QUEENER, E. L. *Introduction to social psychology.* New York: Dryden, 1951.

RANSON, S. W. Somnolence caused by hypothalamus lesions in the monkey. *Arch. Neurol. Psychiat.*, 1939, 41, 1-23.

RAPAPORT, D. *Organization and pathology of thought.* New York: Columbia Univer., 1951.

RECHTSCHAFFEN, A., GOODENOUGH, D. R., & SHAPIRO, A. Patterns of sleep talking. *Arch. gen. Psychiat.*, 1962, 7, 418-426.

RECHTSCHAFFEN, A., & MARON, L. The effect of amphetamine on the sleep cycle. *EEG and clin. Neurophysiol.*, 1964, 16, 438-445.

RECHTSCHAFFEN, A., SCHULSINGER, F., & MEDNICK, S. A. Schizophrenia and physiological indices of dreaming. *Arch. gen. Psychiat.*, 1964, 10, 89-93.

RECHTSCHAFFEN, A., VERDONE, P., & WHEATON, J. Reports of mental activity during sleep. *Canad. Psychiat. Ass. J.*, 1963, 8, 409-414.

RECHTSCHAFFEN, A., VOGEL, G., & SHAIKON, G. The interrelatedness of mental activity during sleep. *Arch. gen. Psychiat.*, 1963, 9, 536-547.

RECHTSCHAFFEN, A., WOLPERT, E. A., DEMENT, W. C., MITCHELL, S. A., & FISHER, C. Nocturnal sleep of narcoleptics. *EEG clin. Neurophysiol.*, 1963, 15, 599-609.

REED, A. C. Tropical neurasthenia. *Amer. J. trop. Med.*, 1942, 22, 127-130.

REED, J. D. Spontaneous activity of animals. *Psychol. Bull.*, 1947, 44, 393-412.

RENSHAW, S., MILLER, V. I., & MARQUIS, D. P. *Children's sleep.* New York: Macmillan, 1933.

RICHTER, C. P. A behavioristic study of the activity of the rat. *Comp. psychol. Monogr.*, 1922-23, 1, No. 2, 1-55.

RICHTER, C. P. On the phenomenon of sudden death in animals and man. *Psychosom. Med.*, 1957, *19*, 191-198.

RIESENMAN, R. R. Anxiety and tension in pathogenesis of sleep disturbances. *J. clin. Psychopath.*, 1950, *11*, 82-84.

ROBIN, E. D. Some interrelations between sleep and disease. *A.M.A. Arch. int. Med.*, 1958, *102*, 669-675.

ROBINSON, E. S., & HERRMANN, S. O. Effects of loss of sleep. *J. exp. Psychol.*, 1922, *5*, 19-32.

ROBINSON, E. S., & ROBINSON, F. Effects of sleep loss, II. *J. exp. Psychol.*, 1922, *5*, 93-100.

ROFFWARG, H. P., DEMENT, W. C., & FISHER, C. Preliminary observations of the sleep-dream pattern in neonates, infants, children, and adults. In Harms, E. (Ed.) *Monographs on child psychiatry No. 2.* New York: Pergamon, 1964.

ROSEN, J. *Direct analysis: Selected papers.* New York: Grune & Stratton, 1953.

ROSSI, G. F. Sleep-inducing mechanisms in the brain stem. *EEG clin. Neurophysiol.*, 1962, *14*, 428.

ROSVOLD, H. E., & DELGADO, J. M. R. The effect of delayed-alternation test performance of stimulating or destroying electrically structures within the frontal lobes of the monkey's brain. *J. comp. physiol. Psychol.*, 1956, *49*, 365-372.

ROTHENBERG, S. Psychoanalytic insight into insomnia. *Psychoanal. Rev.*, 1947, *34*, 141-169.

ROWLAND, V. Differential electroencephalographic response to conditioned auditory stimuli in arousal from sleep. *EEG clin. Neurophysiol.*, 1957, *9*, 585-594.

ROWLAND, V. Electrographic responses in sleeping conditioned animal. In CIBA Foundation, *The nature of sleep.* Boston: Little, Brown, 1961.

RUCH, F. L. *Psychology and life.* (4th ed.) Chicago: Scott, Foresman, 1953.

RUFF, G. E., LEVY, E. Z., & THALER, V. H. Factors influencing reactions to reduced sensory input. In P. Solomon et al. (Eds.), *Sensory deprivation.* Cambridge: Harvard Univer., 1961.

RUST, L. Changes in bar-pressing performance and heart rate in sleep-deprived rats. *J. comp. physiol. Psychol.*, 1962, *55*, 621-625.

SAGAL, Z. Insomnia in the aged. *Geriatrics*, 1958, *13*, 463-466.

SAMUELS, I. Reticular mechanisms and behavior. *Psychol. Bull.*, 1959, *56*, 1-25.

SANDLER, S. Somnambulism in the armed forces. *Ment. Hyg.*, 1945, April, 236-247.

SARGANT, W. *Battle for the mind.* Baltimore: Penguin, 1961.

SARMA, R. N. Psychology of insomnia. *Psychol. Abstr.*, 1933, 7, 130 (Abstr. 934).

SAWYER, C. N., & KAWAKAMI, M. Interactions between the central nervous system and hormones influencing ovulation. In C. A. Villee (Ed.), *Control of ovulation.* New York: Pergamon, 1961.

SCHEIN, E. H. The effects of sleep deprivation on performance in a simulated communication task. *J. appl. Psychol.*, 1957, 41, 247-252.

SCHMIDEBERG, M. The borderline patient. In S. Arieti (Ed.), *American handbook of psychiatry*, Vol. I. New York: Basic Books, 1959.

SCHMIDT, H. The reticular formation and behavioral wakefulness. *Psychol. Bull.* 1957, 54, 75.

SCHNECK, J. M. Sleep paralysis. *Amer. J. Psychiat.*, 1952, 108, 921-923.

SCHNEDORF, J. G., & IVY, A. C. An examination of the hynotoxin theory of sleep. *Amer. J. Physiol.*, 1939, 125, 491-505.

SCHNEIRLA, T. C. An evolutionary and developmental theory of biphasic processes underlying approach and withdrawal. In M. R. Jones (Ed.), *Nebraska symposium on motivation.* Lincoln: Univer. Nebraska, 1959.

SCHONBAR, R. A. Some manifest characteristics of recallers and non-recallers of dreams. *J. consult. Psychol.*, 1959, 23, 414-418.

SCHREINER, L., RIOCH, D. McK., PECHTEL, C., & MASSERMAN, J. H. Behavioral changes following thalamic injury in cat. *J. Neurophysiol.*, 1953, 16, 234-246.

SCHULTE, W. Sleep in epileptic, schizophrenic, and manic-depressive patients. *Excerpt. Med., Neurol., Psychiat.*, 1957, 10, 984 (Abstr., 4618).

SCOTT, J. P., & CHARLES, M. S. Genetic differences in dogs: A case of magnification by thresholds and by habit formation. *J. genet. Psychol.*, 1954, 84, 175-188.

SCOTT, W. C. M. Patients who sleep or look at the psycho-analyst during treatment—technical considerations. *Int. J. Psycho-Anal.*, 1952, 33, 1-5.

SEARS, R. R., HOVLAND, C. I., & MILLER, N. E. Minor studies of aggression. I. Measurement of aggressive behavior. *J. Psychol.*, 1940, 9, 277-281.

SEARS, R. R., MACCOBY, E. E., & LEVIN, H. *Patterns of child rearing.* Evanston, Ill.: Row, Peterson, 1957.

SEGUNDO, J. P. Sleep and learning. *EEG clin. Neurophysiol.*, 1962, *14*, 419-430.

SEGUNDO, J. P., ARANA, R., & FRENCH, J. D. Behavioral arousal by stimulation of the brain in the monkey. *J. Neurosurg.*, 1955, *12*, 601-613.

SEGUNDO, J. P., NAQUET, R., & BUSER, P. Effects of cortical stimulation on electrocortical activity in monkeys. *J. Neurophysiol.*, 1955, *18*, 236-245.

SELYE, H. *The stress of life.* New York: McGraw-Hill, 1956.

SHAFFER, L. F., & SHOBEN, E. J. *The psychology of adjustment.* (2nd ed.) Boston: Houghton Mifflin, 1956.

SHEFFIELD, F. A., & CAMPBELL, B. A. The role of experience in the "spontaneous" activity of hungry rats. *J. comp. physiol. Psychol.*, 1954, *47*, 97-100.

SHERRINGTON, C. S. *Man on his nature.* London: Cambridge Univer., 1940.

SHEVRIN, H., & LUBORSKY, L. The measurement of preconscious perception in dreams and images: An investigation of the Poetzl phenomenon. *J. abnorm. soc. Psychol.*, 1958, *56*, 285-294.

SHNEIDMAN, E. S. Suicide, sleep, and death. *J. consult. Psychol.*, 1964, *28*, 95-106.

SIMON, C. W. Some immediate effects of drowsiness and sleep on normal human performance. *Human Factors*, 1961, *3*, 1-17.

SIMON, C. W., & EMMONS, W. H. Learning during sleep? *Psychol. Bull.*, 1955, *52*, 328-343.

SIMON, C. W., & EMMONS, W. H. Responses to material presented during various levels of sleep. *J. exp. Psychol.*, 1956, *51*, 89-97.

SKINNER, B. F. *The behavior of organisms.* New York: Appleton-Century-Crofts, 1938.

SKINNER, B. F. *Science and human behavior.* New York: Macmillan, 1953.

SLIGHT, D. Hypnogogic phenomena. *J. abnorm. soc. Psychol.*, 1924, *19*, 274-282.

SMITH, C. M. Psychosomatic aspects of narcolepsy. *J. ment. Sci.*, 1958, *104*, 593-607.

SMITH, C. M., & HAMILTON, J. Psychological factors in the narcolepsy-cataplexy syndrome. *Psychosom. Med.*, 1959, *21*, 40-49.

SMITH, K. U., & SMITH, W. M. *The behavior of man: Introduction to psychology.* New York: Holt, Rinehart & Winston, 1958.

SMITH, M. A contribution to the study of fatigue. *Brit. J. Psychol.*, 1915-17, *8*, 327-350.

SNYDER, F. The new biology of dreaming. *Arch. gen. Psychiat.*, 1963, *8*, 381-391.

SNYDER, F., HOBSON, J. A., MORRISON, D. F., & GOLDFRANK, F. Changes in respiration, heart rate, and systolic blood pressure in human sleep. *J. appl. Physiol.*, 1963.

SNYDER, F., HOBSON, J. A., & GOLDFRANK, F. Blood pressure changes during human sleep. *Science*, 1963, *142*, 1313-1314.

SOKOLOFF, L. Relation of cerebral circulation and metabolism to mental activity. In S. R. Korey & J. I. Nurnberger (Eds.), *Progress in neurobiology*. Vol. I. *Neurochemistry*. New York: Hoeber, 1956.

SOLOMON, P., KUBZANSKY, P. E., LEIDERMAN, P. H., MENDELSON, J. H., TRUMBULL, R., & WEXLER, D. (Eds.) *Sensory deprivation*. Cambridge: Harvard Univer., 1961.

SOLOMON, R. L., & WYNNE, L. C. Traumatic avoidance learning: The principles of anxiety conservation and partial irreversibility. *Psychol. Rev.*, 1954, *61*, 353-385.

SPENCE, K. W. *Behavior theory and conditioning*. New Haven: Yale Univer., 1956.

SPERLING, M. Neurotic sleep disturbances in children. *Nerv. Child*, 1949-1950, *8*, 28-46.

SPERLING, M. Etiology and treatment of sleep disturbances in children. *Psychoanal. Quart.*, 1955, *24*, 358-368.

SPERLING, M. Pavor nocturnus. *J. Amer. Psychoanal. Ass.*, 1958, *6*, 79-94.

SPERLING, M. Equivalents of depression in children. *J. Hillside Hosp.*, 1959, *8*, 138-148.

SPIEGEL, L. A., & OBERNDORF, C. P. Narcolepsy as a psychogenic symptom. *Psychosom. Med.*, 1946, *8*, 28-35.

STACEY, C. L., & DEMARTINO, M. F. *Understanding human motivation*. Cleveland: Allen, 1958.

STELLAR, E. The physiology of motivation. *Psychol. Rev.*, 1954, *61*, 5-22.

STELLAR, E. Drive and motivation. In *Handbook of physiology Sect. 1. Neurophysiology*, Vol. III. Washington: Amer. Physiol. Soc., 1960.

STENNETT, R. G. The relationship of performance level to level of arousal. *J. exp. Psychol.*, 1957, *54*, 54-61.

STEPHENS, G. C. Twenty-four hour cycles in marine organisms. *Amer. Nat.*, 1957, *91*, 135-151.

STERMAN, M. B., WYRWICKE, W., & CLEMENTE, C. D. The basal forebrain synchronizing system in the cat. *The Physiologist*, 1962, *5*, 217.

Stevens, S. S. The science of noise. *Atlantic Mon.*, 1946, *178*, 96-102.

Stone, L. Transference sleep in a neurosis with duodenal ulcer. *Int. J. Psycho-Anal.*, 1947, *28*, 18-32.

Strassman, H. D., Thaler, M. B., & Schein, E. H. A prisoner of war syndrome: Apathy as a reaction to severe stress. *Amer. J. Psychiat.*, 1956, *112*, 990-1003.

Sullivan, H. S. *The interpersonal theory of psychiatry.* New York: Norton, 1953.

Sullivan, H. S. *Clinical cases in psychiatry.* New York: Norton, 1956.

Suomalainen, P. Hibernation and sleep. In CIBA Foundation, *The nature of sleep.* Boston: Little, Brown, 1961.

Switzer, R. E., & Berman, A. O. Comments and observations on the nature of narcolepsy. *Ann. intern. Med.*, 1956, *44*, 938-957.

Tapia, F., Werboff, J., & Winokur, G. Recall of some phenomena of sleep. *J. nerv. ment. Dis.*, 1958, *127*, 119-123.

Tart, C. T. Frequency of dream recall and some personality measures. *J. consult. Psychol.*, 1962, *26*, 467-470.

Teichner, W. H., & Kobrick, J. L. Effects of prolonged exposure to low temperature on visual-motor performance. *J. exp. Psychol.*, 1955, *49*, 122-126.

Teichner, W. H., & Wehrkamp, R. F. Visual-motor performance as a function of short-duration ambient temperature. *J. exp. Psychol.*, 1954, *47*, 447-450.

Temmes, Y., & Towakka, E. EEG findings in enuresis. *Acta Paediatr. Stockh.*, 1954, *43*, 259-263.

Terman, L. M. *Genetic studies of genius: Mental and physical traits of 1000 gifted children.* Berkeley: Stanford Univer., 1925.

Thewlis, M. W. *The care of the aged (geriatrics).* St. Louis: Mosby, 1954.

Thorpe, W. H. *Learning and instinct in animals.* London: Methuen, 1956.

Tiller, P. M. Bed rest, sleep, and symptoms. *Ann. int. Med.*, 1964, *61*, 98-105.

Tinbergen, N. *The study of instinct.* Oxford: Clarendon Press, 1951.

Tinker, M. A. Lighting and color. In Panel on psychology and physiology, *Human factors in undersea warfare.* Washington: National Research Council, Committee on Undersea Warfare, 1949.

Tolman, E. C. *Purposive behavior in animals and men.* New York: Appleton-Century-Crofts, 1932.

Tolman, E. C. A stimulus-expectancy need-cathexis psychology. *Science*, 1945, *101*, 160-166.

TOMAN, W. *Psychoanalytic theory of motivation.* New York: Pergamon, 1960.

TORRANCE, E. P., & MASON, R. Psychologic and sociologic aspects of survival ration acceptability. *Amer. J. clin. Nutr.,* 1957, 5, 176-179.

TRAVIS, R. C., & KENNEDY, J. L. Prediction and automatic control of alertness, I. Control of lookout alertness. *J. comp. physiol. Psychol.,* 1947, 40, 457-461.

TRAVIS, R. C., & KENNEDY, J. L. Prediction and control of alertness, III. Calibration of the alertness indicator and further results. *J. comp. physiol. Psychol.,* 1949, 42, 45-57.

TROSMAN, A. Dream research and the psychoanalytic theory of dreams. *Arch. gen. Psychiat.,* 1963, 9, 9-18.

TWENTE, E. W. Patterns of awakening. *Clin. Counsel.,* 1964, 1, 2-12.

TYLER, D. B. The effect of amphetamine sulfate and some barbiturates on the fatigue produced by prolonged wakefulness. *Amer. J. Physiol.,* 1947, 150, 253-262.

TYLER, D. B. Psychological changes during experimental sleep deprivation. *Dis. nerv. Syst.,* 1955, 16, 2-8.

UJHELY, V. A. Oedipal jealousy and passive dependency states in insomnia. *J. clin. Psychopath.,* 1950, 11, 65-69.

ULLMAN, M. Dreams and arousal. *Amer. J. Psychother.,* 1958, 12, 222-242.(a)

ULLMAN, M. Hypotheses on the biological roots of the dream. *J. clin. exp. Psychopath.,* 1958, 19, 128-133.(b)

VELLUTI, R., & HERNÁNDEZ-PEÓN, R. Atropine blockade within a cholinergic hypnogenic circuit. *Exp. Neurol.,* 1963, 8, 20-29.

VERNON, H. M. *Accidents and their prevention.* Cambridge: Cambridge Univer., 1936.

VERNON, J. A., McGILL, T. E., GULICK, W. L., & CANDLAND, D. K. The effect of human isolation upon some perceptual and motor skills. In P. Solomon et al., (Eds.), *Sensory deprivation.* Cambridge: Harvard Univer., 1961.

VERZEANO, M., & NEGISHI, K. Neuronal activity in wakefulness and in sleep. In CIBA Foundation, *The nature of sleep.* Boston: Little, Brown, 1961.

WADA, T. An experimental study of hunger in its relation to activity. *Arch. Psychol.,* 1922, 8, No. 57.

WALSH, E. G. *Physiology of the nervous system.* New York: Longmans, Green, 1957.

WANG, G. H. The relation between "spontaneous" activity and oestrous cycle in the white rat. *Comp. psychol. Monogr.*, 1923, *2*, No. 6.

WARREN, N., & CLARK, B. Blocking in mental and motor tasks during a 65-hour vigil. *J. exp. Psychol.*, 1937, *21*, 247-266.

WEBB, W. B. Antecedents of sleep. *J. exp. Psychol.*, 1957, *53*, 162-166.

WEBB, W. B. Some effects of prolonged sleep deprivation on the hooded rat. *J. comp. physiol. Psychol.*, 1962, *55*, 791-793.

WEBB, W. B., & AGNEW, H. W. Sleep deprivation, age, and exhaustion time in the rat. *Science*, 1962, *136*, 1122.

WEBER, M. *The Protestant ethic and the spirit of capitalism.* New York: Scribner's Sons, 1930.

WEISKOTTEN, T. F. On the effects of loss of sleep. *J. exp. Psychol.*, 1925, *8*, 363-380.

WEISKOTTEN, T. F., & FERGUSON, J. E. A further study of the effects of loss of sleep. *J. exp. Psychol.*, 1930, *13*, 247-266.

WEISS, E., & ENGLISH, O. S. *Psychosomatic medicine.* Philadelphia: Saunders, 1950.

WEISS, H. R., KASINOFF, B. H., & BAILEY, M. A. An exploration of reported sleep disturbance. *J. nerv. ment. Dis.*, 1962, *134*, 528-534.

WEITZMANN, E. D. A note on the EEG and eye movements during behavioral sleep in monkeys. *EEG clin. Neurophysiol.*, 1961, *5*, 790-795.

WENDT, G. R. An interpretation of inhibition of conditioned reflexes as competition between reaction systems. *Psychol. Rev.*, 1936, *43*, 258-281.

WENDT, H. Comparative examination of children with pavor nocturnus and enuresis nocturna. *Prax. Kinderpsychol. Kinderpsychiat.*, 1952, *1*, 106-109. (not seen)

WENGER, M. A., JONES, F. N., & JONES, M. H. *Physiological psychology.* New York: Holt, Rinehart & Winston, 1956.

WEXBERG, L. E. Insomnia as related to anxiety and ambition. *J. clin. Psychopath.*, 1949, *10*, 373-375.

WHITE, R. W. Motivation reconsidered: The concept of competence. *Psychol. Rev.*, 1959, *66*, 297-333.

WHITING, J. W. M., & CHILD, I. L. *Child training and personality.* New Haven: Yale Univer., 1953.

WHITMAN, R. M., PIERCE, C. M., & MAAS, J. Drugs and dreams. Unpublished manuscript, Dept. of Psychiat., Univer. of Oklahoma.

WIESENHUTTER, E. Bed-wetting. *J. psychol. Psychother.*, 1954, *2*, 205-213.

WIKLER, A. *The relation of psychiatry to pharmacology.* Baltimore: Williams & Wilkins, 1957.

WILDER, R. M. Experimental induction of psychoneuroses through restriction of intake of thiamine. In Milbank Memorial Fund, *The biology of mental health and disease.* New York: Hoeber, 1952.

WILKINSON, R. T. The effects of sleep loss on performance. *Medical Research Council's Applied Psychology Research Unit Report,* No. APU 323/58, 1958.

WILKINSON, R. T. Rest pauses in a task affected by lack of sleep. *Ergonomics,* 1959, *2,* 373-380.

WILKINSON, R. T. Effects of sleep deprivation on performance and muscle tension. In CIBA Foundation, *The nature of sleep.* Boston: Little, Brown, 1961. (a)

WILKINSON, R. T. Interaction of lack of sleep with knowledge of results, repeated testing, and individual differences. *J. exp. Psychol.,* 1961, *62,* 263-271. (b)

WILKINSON, R. T. Muscle tension during mental work under sleep deprivation. *J. exp. Psychol.,* 1962, *64,* 565-571.

WILKINSON, R. T. Interaction of noise with knowledge of results and sleep deprivation. *J. exp. Psychol.,* 1963, *66,* 332-337. (a)

WILKINSON, R. T. Aftereffect of sleep deprivation. *J. exp. Psychol.,* 1963, *66,* 439-442. (b)

WILLEY, M. M. Sleep as an escape mechanism. *Psychoanal. Rev.,* 1924, *11,* 181-183.

WILLEY, M. M., & RICE, S. A. The psychic utility of sleep. *J. abnorm. soc. Psychol.,* 1924, *19,* 174-178.

WILLIAMS, C. D. The elimination of tantrum behavior by extinction procedures. *J. abnorm. soc. Psychol.,* 1959, *59,* 269.

WILLIAMS, H. L. Report of current research. *Association for the Psychophysiological Study of Sleep,* 1961.

WILLIAMS, H. L., GRANDA, A. M., JONES, P. C., LUBIN, A., & ARMINGTON, J. C. EEG frequency and finger pulse volume as predictors of reaction time during sleep loss. *EEG clin. Neurophysiol.,* 1962, *14,* 64-70.

WILLIAMS, H. J., HAMMACK, J. T., DALY, R. T., DEMENT, W. C., & LUBIN, A. Responses to auditory stimulation, sleep loss, and the EEG stages of sleep. *EEG clin. Neurophysiol.,* 1964, *16,* 269-279.

WILLIAMS, H. L., & LUBIN, A. Impaired performance in a case of prolonged sleep loss. Mimeographed paper. Walter Reed Army Institute of Research, Washington, D.C., 1959.

WILLIAMS, H. L., LUBIN, A., & GOODNOW, JACQUELINE, J. Impaired performance with acute sleep loss. *Psychol. Monogr.*, 1959, *73*, No. 14 (Whole No. 484).

WILLIAMS, R. L., AGNEW, H. W., & WEBB, W. B. Sleep patterns in young adults: An EEG study. *EEG clin. Neurophysiol.*, in press.

WINDHOLZ, E. Symposium on neurotic disturbances of Sleep, I. *Int. J. Psycho-Anal.*, 1942, *23*, 49-52.

WISPE, L. G. Physiological need, verbal frequency and word association. *J. abnorm. soc. Psychol.*, 1957, *54*, 1-8.

WOHL, M. G., & GOODHART, R. S. (Eds.) *Modern nutrition in health and disease.* Philadelphia: Lee & Febiger, 1955.

WOLF, A. V. Thirst. *Scient. Amer.*, 1956, *194*, 70-76.

WOLPERT, E. A., & TROSMAN, H. Studies in psychophysiology of dreams. I. Experimental evocation of sequential dream episodes. *A. M. A. Arch. Neurol. Psychiat.*, 1958, *79*, 603-606.

WOODSON, W. E. *Human engineering guide for equipment designers.* Berkeley: Univer. Calif., 1956.

WOODWORTH, R. S. *Dynamic psychology.* New York: Columbia Univer., 1918.

WOODWORTH, R. S. *Experimental psychology.* New York: Holt, Rinehart & Winston, 1938.

WYRWICKA, W., STERMAN, M. B., & CLEMENTE, C. O. Conditioning of induced electroencephalographic sleep patterns in the cat. *Science*, 1962, *137*, 616-618.

YARROW, L. J. Maternal deprivation: Toward an empirical and conceptual reevaluation. *Psychol. Bull.*, 1961, *58*, 459-490.

YOSS, R. E., & DALY, D. D. Hereditary aspects of narcolepsy. *Trans. Amer. Neurol. Ass.*, 1960, 239-240. (a)

YOSS, R. E., & DALY, D. D. Narcolepsy. *A. M. A. Arch. int. Med.*, 1960, *106*, 168-171. (b)

YOSS, R. E., & DALY, D. D. Narcolepsy in children. *Pediatrics*, 1960, *25*, 1025-1033. (c)

YOUNG, K. *Social psychology.* (3rd ed.) New York: Appleton-Century-Crofts, 1956.

YOUNG, P. T. *Motivation of behavior.* New York: Wiley, 1936.

YOUNG, P. T. *Motivation and emotion.* New York: Wiley, 1961.

ZUNG, W. K., & WILSON, W. P. Response to auditory stimulation during sleep. *Arch. gen. Psychiat.*, 1961, *4*, 348-352.

Author Index

389

Subject Index